Basic Neuroanatomy

1

Introduction

The nervous system is the *communication system* of the body. It conveys excitation from the sense organs, the listening posts of the body, to the effectors, muscles, and glands. When several sense organs are excited simultaneously, the nervous system has the additional job of processing the data obtained and selecting the particular effectors that will ensure an appropriate response. The processing of data is done in the brain and spinal cord, axial portions of the nervous system, called the *central nervous system*. In addition, the central nervous system provides the substrate for a person's conscious experience.

The cable-like structures that connect the central nervous system with (1) the sense organs and (2) the effectors comprise the sensory and motor nerves, respectively. Those nerves make up the *peripheral nervous system*.

Parts of the Central Nervous System

The parts of the central nervous system may be classified by tracing their development. By examining the derivation of each part, the relationships between parts of the nervous system will become clear.

The nervous system begins to develop at an early stage of intrauterine life, when the embryo consists of only three layers of cells. The outermost of those layers, the primordial skin, is called the *ectoderm*. During the fourth week of gestation, the cells of the ectoderm, which are developing into nerve cells, form the floor and walls of a midline dorsal furrow, called the *neural groove*. That groove becomes progressively deeper until, eventually, the elevated borders come together, enclosing a part of the external surface to form the *neural*

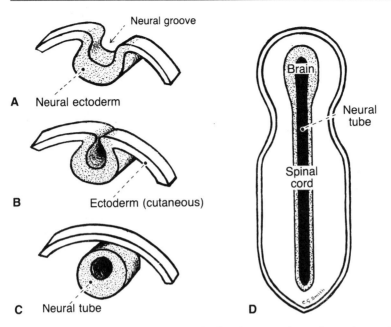

Figure 1-1. (A, B, C) Cross sections of the dorsal portion of an embryo, showing the derivation of the neural tube. (D) A longitudinal section of an embryo in a plane through the neural tube.

tube. The neural tube soon separates from the rest of the ectoderm, as shown in Figure 1-1. The basic tubular form of the central nervous system is retained throughout its future development. Cross sections at all levels contain a more-or-less central lumen.

Differentiation of the neural tube begins with an enlargement of its rostral portion to form the brain. As the brain enlarges, it acquires constrictions that demarcate three primary subdivisions: the *forebrain, midbrain,* and *hindbrain* (Fig. 1-2A). Soon after, secondary constrictions mark the division of the forebrain and the hindbrain into rostral and caudal segments.

The rostral part of the forebrain is called the *telencephalon* (far brain); the caudal part is called the *diencephalon* (between brain) (Fig. 1-2B). The lateral walls of the cavity of the telencephalon evaginate to form the right and left cerebral hemispheres (Fig. 1-2C). As the hemispheres enlarge to form the major part of the brain, they extend their attachment onto the entire lateral surface of the diencephalon, as illustrated in Figure 1-1D. The portion of the telencephalon that forms the rostral wall of the neural tube remains thin and is called appropriately the *lamina terminalis.*

The rostral part of the hindbrain is the *pons segment;* the caudal part is the *medulla oblongata,* which tapers and becomes continuous with the *spinal cord.*

The *cerebellum* does not develop as an evagination, but as a thickening of the membranous dorsal wall of the cavity of the pons segment (Fig. 1-3) and enlarges to form a dumbbell-shaped mass set across the back of the hindbrain. As the cerebellum develops on the dorsal aspect of the pons segment, a transverse band of nervous tissue, called the *pons,* develops on its ventral surface (Fig. 1-3C). The pons extends across the front of

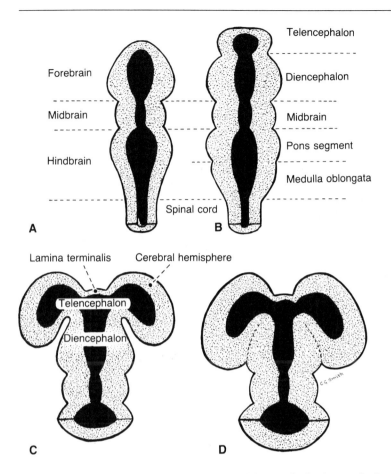

Figure 1-2. The ventral half of the rostral portion of the neural tube showing the development of the brain. (A) Primary subdivisions. (B) Secondary subdivisions. (C) Evaginations of the lateral portion of the telencephalon to form the cerebral hemisphere. (D) Enlargement of the attachment of the cerebral hemisphere.

the pons segment, connecting the right and left cerebellar hemispheres. It is likened to a bridge (*pons*, "a bridge") and gives the pons segment its name.

With the development of the cerebral hemispheres and the cerebellum, the midline portion of the brain comes to be known as the *brain stem*. It is applied to the floor of the cranial cavity, that is, the base of the skull, and is bent sharply at the junction of the midbrain and the diencephalon to extend forward as far as the anterior border of the sella turcica (Fig. 1-4). The *sella turcica* is a hollow portion in the floor of the cranial cavity that accommodates the pituitary gland. Part of that gland is formed by a funnel-like evagination of the floor of the cavity of the diencephalon.

In the fully developed brain, the cerebral hemispheres and the cerebellum occupy most of the cranial cavity. They expand laterally and posteriorly to enclose and conceal all of the brain stem except its anterior surface (Fig. 1-5).

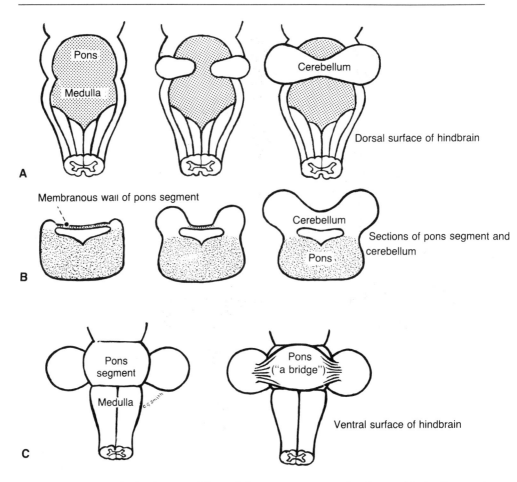

Figure 1-3. Stages in the development of the cerebellum as seen in (A) a dorsal view of the hindbrain and (B) cross sections through the pons segment. In the lower two drawings (C), the ventral surface of the embryonic hindbrain is shown before and after the acquisition of the pons.

Cavity of the Central Nervous System: The Ventricular System

The cavity of the neural tube acquires a right and a left pocket–like extension into each of the developing cerebral hemispheres. There is no comparable extension into the cerebellum because, as previously explained, it develops as a thickening of the dorsal wall of the pons segment. As nerve cells accumulate in the walls of the neural tube and in the walls of the cavity of the hemisphere, some portions of the wall get thick and other portions remain thin. The resulting variable encroachment on the central cavity of the brain and spinal cord leaves some parts large and chamber-like, called *ventricles,* and others reduced to small-bored tubular passages. The ultimate form of the central cavity is shown diagrammatically in Figure 1-6, which is a midsagittal section of the brain.

The cavity of the spinal cord is a central canal less than 1 mm in diameter. The canal

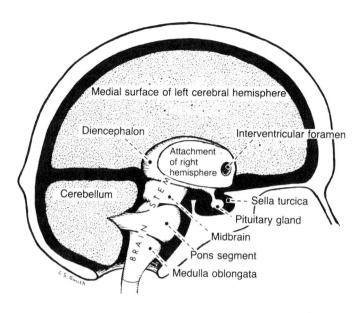

Figure 1-4. Midsagittal section of the skull, showing the position of each part of the brain. The right cerebral hemisphere has been removed.

extends upward a short distance into the hindbrain, where it enlarges to form the fourth ventricle, the large cavity in the upper half of the medulla oblongata, and the pons segment. The fourth ventricle has a thick anterior wall, or floor; its posterior wall, or roof, is formed by the cerebellum and two thin membranes—one rostral and one caudal to the cerebellum. Those two membranes are (1) the *rostral*, or *superior*, *velum* and (2) the *caudal*, or *inferior*, *velum*, respectively (Fig. 1-6).

In the midbrain, the cavity is again reduced to a canal about 2 mm in diameter, called the *cerebral aqueduct*. In the diencephalon, the cavity enlarges to form the *third ventricle*. This is a median cleft-like space, with a membranous superior wall, or roof, a thin rostral wall, called the *lamina terminalis* (this is the midline part of the telencephalon) (Fig. 1-2), and a thin floor, or inferior wall. In the lateral wall of the third ventricle, within the angle formed by the roof and the lamina terminalis, we find the opening of a short canal, the *interventricular foramen*. That foramen is a large opening initially, but it is only 3 to 4 mm in diameter in the mature brain. It drains the lateral ventricle, which is the cavity of the cerebral hemisphere. The *lateral ventricle* is a **C**-shaped tubular space. Its outline is illustrated in Figure 1-6 as it would appear projected onto the medial surface of the hemisphere. In a cross section of the cerebral hemisphere, it would be cut twice, as illustrated in Figure 1-7. The lateral wall of the ventricle is thick; the medial wall is thin; and part of it is membranous and contains a tuft of vessels called a *choroid plexus*. The choroid plexus secretes cerebrospinal fluid into the ventricle and is described in the section entitled Definitions is this chapter. The right and left lateral ventricles are numerically the first and second in the series of four ventricles of the brain, but they are not identified by number.

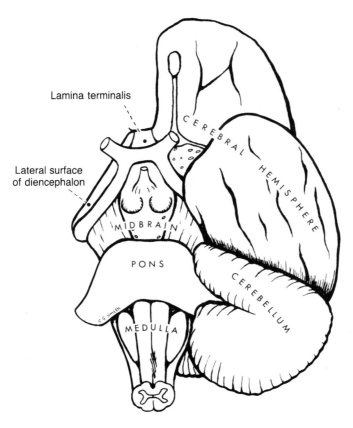

Lamina terminalis

Lateral surface
of diencephalon

Figure 1-5. Ventral aspect of the fully developed brain with the right hemisphere and the right half of the cerebellum removed.

Microscopic Structure and Organization of Nervous Tissue

The nervous system is made up of nerve cells, called *neurons,* and supporting tissue cells, called *neuroglial cells.*

A neuron has a cell body that is specialized to detect minimal changes in its environment. To increase its receptive surface, it has a variable number of short branching processes, called *dendrites* (Fig. 1-8) (*dendron,* "a tree"). A change in the environment, if great enough, will result in excitation. *Excitation* is defined as an altered state of the cell surface that is propagated through the cell and along an insulated process of the cell called its *axon,* or *nerve fiber.* That propagated excitation is called a *nerve impulse.* The insulation of the axon ends before its termination to permit naked contact with another nerve cell. In this way, excitation may be conveyed from one neuron to another.

A chain of neurons is called a *neural pathway,* and the contact of a nerve fiber terminal with a second cell body, or its dendrite, is called a *synapse* (Fig. 1-8). The synapse is the main neural computer mechanism as a result of two features. First, conduction of excitation is permitted to pass through the synapse only in one direction, that is, from the terminal end of the nerve fiber of one cell to the body, or dendrite, of the next cell.

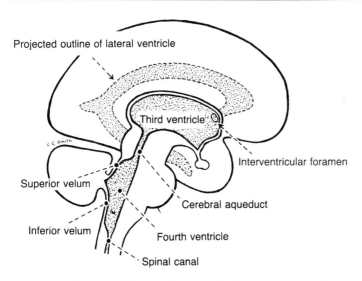

Figure 1-6. *The parts of the central cavity of the brain and spinal cord as seen in a midsagittal section.*

That process ensures that a pathway can conduct impulses in only one direction. Second, and more significant, the synapse has the capacity to function as a variable resistance. When nerve impulses arrive at the end of a nerve fiber, they release a chemical substance, for example, acetylcholine, which excites the next nerve cell. A certain amount of acetylcholine is required to attain the excitation threshold which, in turn, depends on the number of nerve impulses arriving per second, since the excitation dissipates quickly.

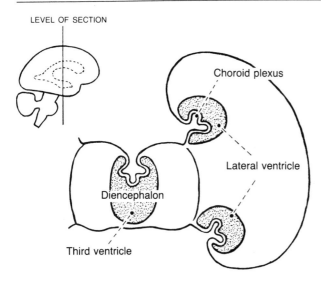

Figure 1-7. *Cross section of the embryonic forebrain, showing the thin medial wall of the lateral ventricle invaginated to form a choroid plexus.*

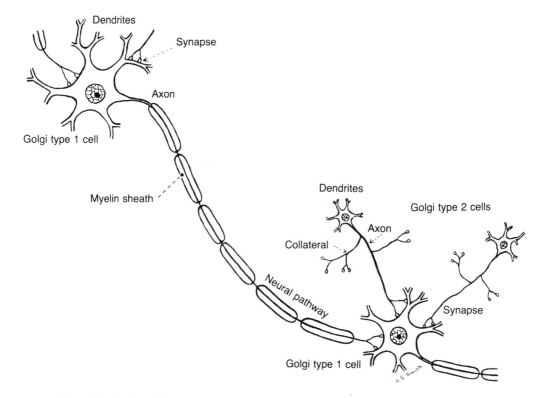

Figure 1-8. A chain of two Golgi type 1 cells (long axons) linked together by a synapse to form a neural pathway. Golgi type 2 cells (short axons) are shown synapsing with the second cell of the pathway. Axons of both types of cells may or may not be myelinated.

Acetylcholine is an example of an excitor substance, but other nerve fibers release a chemical that can counteract the action of acetylcholine. Those fibers are inhibitors, and since each cell body, including its dendrites, receives terminals from both excitor and inhibitor fibers, it follows that the activation of a cell body at a synapse depends on the summatiom of the two influences (positive and negative) at its surface.

Nerve cells are classified according to the length of their axons. Golgi type 1 cells (Fig. 1-8) have long axons. They extend long distances within the central nervous system to connect segments of the spinal cord with each other and with the brain. Golgi type 1 cells also give rise to the motor nerve fibers that leave the central nervous system to supply muscles. Golgi type 2 cells have short axons that branch freely to establish connections with nearby cells. They form a major part of the integrating (computer) mechanism of the nervous system.

Neuroglial cells (Fig. 1-9) are the supporting tissue cells of the nervous system. They are derived from neural ectoderm, which is the same source as for nerve cells. They vary in form and function, but the chief supporting cell is the *astrocyte*. Astrocytes are much smaller than nerve cells and have many processes that link up with capillaries, other astrocytes, and ependymal cells (see the following discussion) to form a mesh within

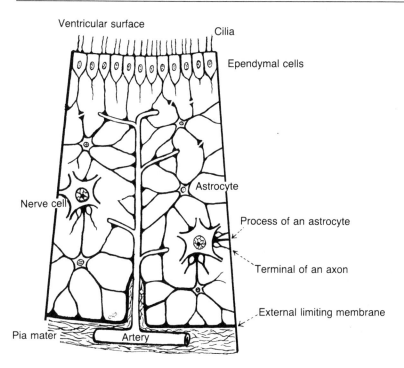

Ventricular surface

Cilia

Ependymal cells

Astrocyte

Nerve cell

Process of an astrocyte

Terminal of an axon

External limiting membrane

Pia mater   Artery

Figure 1-9. Section of the central nervous system, extending from the ventricular surface to the pia-covered external surface to illustrate its cellular structure.

which the nerve cells and their processes are lodged. Processes of astroctyes extend to the external surface of the brain and spinal cord, where they interweave to form an *external limiting membrane*. In a formalin-hardened brain, that membrane can be removed by dissection, where necessary, to demonstrate underlying fiber bundles.

In addition to their role as supporting cells, astrocytes probably have a nutrient function. Processes of astrocytes contact nerve cells and may convey materials from the capillaries.

Ependymal cells are modified neuroglial cells that form an epithelial-like lining for the spinal canal and cavities of the brain (Fig. 1-9). Ependymal cells have a columnar or cuboidal form, with a ventricular border that may be ciliated. In embryos, the deep end tapers and is prolonged as a process that extends into the substance of the brain and spinal cord to add itself to the neuroglial framework. Later in development, this basal process may be retracted. Some ependymal cells are specialized to form the gland-like cells of the choroid plexuses that secrete cerebrospinal fluid (Fig. 1-7). A choroid plexus has two components. One component is a thinned-out part of the wall of a ventricle that is reduced in thickness to a layer of ependymal cells overlaid by a few astrocytes. The other component is a plexus of capillaries applied to the outer surface of the membranous wall, causing it to bulge into the ventricle (Fig. 1-12). The specialized ependymal cells extract the constituents of cerebrospinal fluid from the capillaries and secrete them into the ventricle.

Modified neuroglial cells also form sheath-like coverings for axons. Within the central

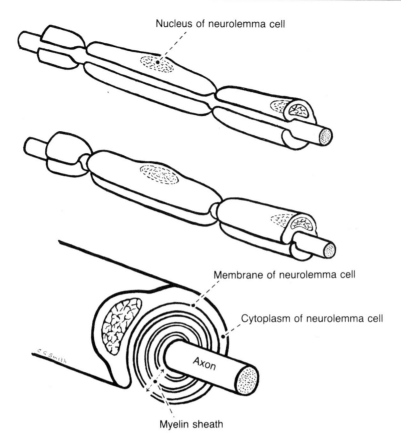

Nucleus of neurolemma cell

Membrane of neurolemma cell

Cytoplasm of neurolemma cell

Axon

Myelin sheath

Figure 1-10. Stages in the development of a myelin sheath.

nervous system, those cells are known as *oligodendroglia:* in the peripheral nervous system, they are known as *neurolemma* or *Schwann cells.* The neurolemma cells are illustrated in Fig 1-10. They are elongated cells that extend, end to end, along the length of the nerve fiber, partially enclosing it within a deep groove. When the lips of the groove come together, the fiber is completely enclosed. In this way the axon is insulated to the extent that other fibers cannot synapse with it. Such a fiber, ensheathed in neurolemma cells, is an example of an unmyelinated fiber, but it is also an example of a transient stage in the development of a myelin sheath. Fibers that are destined to remain unmyelinated usually course in small groups, with each fiber embedded in a separate deep groove within one chain of neurolemma cells.

A myelinated fiber is one that has acquired a sheath of white lipoid material, called *myelin.* The sheath is formed by a lipoid-rich, jelly-roll-like wrapping of cell membrane contributed by the neurolemma cell. Reference to the diagrams in Figure 1-10 will explain how the nucleus and cytoplasm of a neurolemma cell migrate around the axon, contributing a double layer of cell membrane with each encirclement. The thickness of the sheath depends on the number of encircling layers.

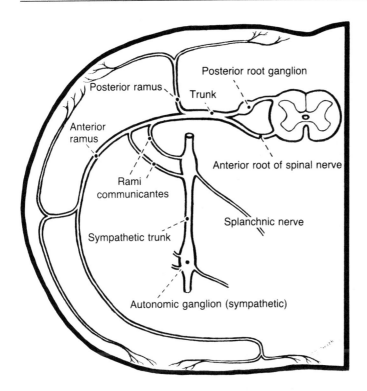

Figure 1-11. Parts of a typical spinal nerve (sixth thoracic) and its connections with the sympathetic trunk.

Parts of the Peripheral Nervous System

The peripheral nervous system is comprised of nerves and ganglia. Nerves are bundles of nerve fibers; ganglia are clusters of nerve cells located within the nerves.

Nerves may contain sensory fibers, motor fibers, or both sensory and motor fibers. Sensory fibers convey impulses from sense organs to the central nervous system; motor fibers convey impulses from cells in the central nervous system to striated muscles or via relay stations in the peripheral nervous system to smooth muscles and glands. There are 12 pairs of nerves attached to the brain (cranial nerves) and 31 or 32 pairs of spinal nerves.

All spinal nerves have a similar attachment to the spinal cord and a similar branching pattern (Fig. 1-11). The parts of a nerve are likened to the parts of a tree. Each one has roots, a trunk, and two primary rami (branches) which, in turn, branch repeatedly and are distributed to the skin and muscles. The fibers, sensory and motor, of the posterior part of the body, when traced from the skin and muscles toward the spinal cord, come together to form the *posterior ramus*. Similarly, the fibers from the anterior part come together to form the *anterior ramus*. The union of those two rami forms the short trunk of the spinal nerve. The trunk is attached to the spinal cord by two roots—a posterior root (dorsal) made up of sensory fibers and an anterior (ventral) root made up of motor fibers.

The cranial nerves, unlike the spinal nerves, are very irregular. They vary in the way they are attached to the brain and in their content of sensory and motor fibers. Some, such as the nerves that excite the muscles of the tongue and the orbit, have no sensory component; others, such as the nerves from sense organs of the nose, eye, and ear, contain no motor fibers.

The ganglia of the peripheral nervous system (Fig. 1-11) are comparable to the cell clusters within the central nervous system, where they are called *nuclei*. There are two kinds of ganglia: sensory and autonomic (motor). A sensory ganglion is present in every spinal and cranial nerve that contains sensory fibers, except the first and second cranial nerves. It is located near the nerve's attachment to the central nervous system. The sensory ganglion of a spinal nerve is a swelling on its posterior root. The cell bodies of a sensory ganglion have only one process, which divides to send one branch distally to a sense organ and another into the central nervous system. There is no synapse in a posterior root ganglion.

The autonomic ganglia are motor ganglia. They contain cells that relay impulses from fibers of cells in the central nervous system to smooth muscle, heart muscle, and glands. Developmentally each spinal nerve has an autonomic ganglion associated with it. It is located just anterior to its anterior ramus and lateral to the vertebral column. Those ganglia are connected to form a longitudinal nerve trunk, called the *sympathetic trunk*. Each of the 12 thoracic nerves and upper two lumbar nerves is connected to its associated ganglion by two nerves, a white (myelinated) ramus communicans and a gray (unmyelinated) ramus communicans (see Chapter 17). The white ramus fibers convey impulses to the ganglion; the gray ramus fibers convey impulses back to the nerve to reach the blood vessels and glands of the body wall. Some fibers of the white rami ascend in the sympathetic trunk; others descend to synapse with cells of ganglia above the first thoracic and below the second lumbar nerve, respectively. The axons of cells in each of these upper and lower ganglia form a gray ramus communicans that extends to its associated spinal nerve, where its fibers are distributed with its branches. Other branches of the sympathetic ganglia, the *splanchnic nerves,* extend medially to supply the viscera of the thorax and abdomen.

The Meninges and Circulation of the Cerebrospinal Fluid

The brain and spinal cord have a gelatinous consistency similar to that of the liver and are therefore particularly susceptible to trauma. They are, however, supported and protected by three membranous coverings (pia mater, arachnoid membrane, and dura mater), collectively known as the *meninges*. Additional protection is provided by (1) a cushion of fluid, the cerebrospinal fluid, located between the pia mater and the arachnoid membrane and (2) the rigid-walled outermost covering provided by the skull and the vertebral column.

The pia mater ("tender mother," or "protector") (Figs. 1-12 and 1-13) is the immediate covering of the brain and spinal cord. It is a very thin layer, within which blood vessels branch and anastomose freely before giving off the very fine thread-like nutrient branches that penetrate the brain and spinal cord at right angles. The pia mater, being a nutrient layer, is in contact with every part of the surface of the brain and spinal cord. At the caudal end of the spinal cord, it is prolonged on the filum terminale, a thread-like strand of neuroglia that anchors the spinal cord to the coccyx (Fig. 1-13).

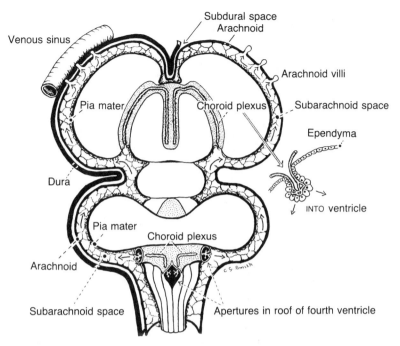

Figure 1-12. Dorsal aspect of the embryonic brain showing general relationships of its meninges and the circulation of the cerebrospinal fluid.

The arachnoid membrane (Fig. 1-11) is a thin, translucent, almost avascular membrane that may be likened to a plastic bag that is pulled tightly over the brain but forms a roomy tubular sac for the spinal cord. The sac extends to the second sacral vertebra, well below the spinal cord, which only extends to the second lumbar vertebra (Fig. 1-13). The subarachnoid space, between the the arachnoid membrane and pia mater, is filled with a watery cerebrospinal fluid. Over the elevated portions of the brain, the arachnoid membrane is adherent to the pia mater but, elsewhere, particularly at the base of the brain (anterior inferior aspect), the subarachnoid space may be very large. The enlarged portions are called *cisterns*.

The arachnoid membrane (*arachne*, "a spider") gets its name because of the cobweb-like strands that connect its deep surface to the pia mater. It does not have those attachments to the dura mater, so it has a smooth external surface.

The dura mater (Fig. 1-12) is a tough fibrous tissue membrane. Its inner surface is smooth and is separated from the arachnoid membrane by a moistened potential subdural space similar to the potential space between the chest wall and the lungs. The outer surface of the dura mater adheres to the periosteum on the inner aspect of the skull, except where large venous channels, the dural sinuses, intervene. At the foramen magnum, the dura mater separates from the periosteum of the skull and extends into the vertebral canal; it remains closely applied to the arachnoid membrane but separated from the bony wall of the vertebral canal by fatty tissue that contains a plexus of veins. At the level

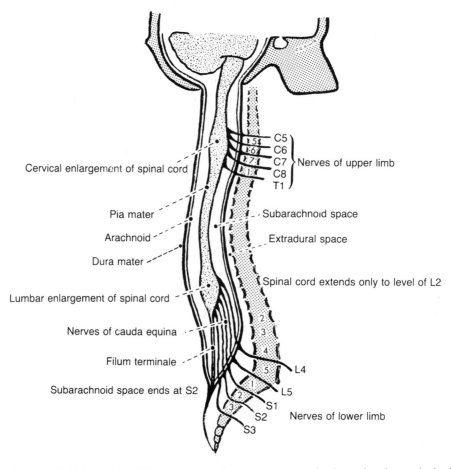

Cervical enlargement of spinal cord

C5
C6
C7 Nerves of upper limb
C8
T1

Pia mater

Arachnoid

Dura mater

Subarachnoid space

Extradural space

Spinal cord extends only to level of L2

Lumbar enlargement of spinal cord

Nerves of cauda equina

Filum terminale

Subarachnoid space ends at S2

L4

L5

S1
S2   Nerves of lower limb
S3

Figure 1-13. Relationships of the spinal cord and the meninges to each other and to the vertebral column.

of the second sacral vertebra, the arachnoid and dural sacs end and provide coverings for the filum terminale (Fig. 1-13).

Within the skull, the dura mater has folds that partially divide the cranial cavity into compartments for the cerebral hemispheres and the cerebellum. A horizontal, but tent-like, fold, the tentorium cerebelli, extends into the cleft between the cerebral hemispheres and the cerebellum to provide support for the hemispheres. Similarly, a sickle-shaped fold, the falx cerebri, extends into the fissure between the two hemispheres. Its narrower anterior end is attached to the floor of the cranial cavity, and its posterior end is attached to the tentorium cerebelli, thus anchoring the falx and providing the medial wall of a compartment for each hemisphere.

As the dura peels away from the periosteum of the skull to form the falx cerebri and the tentorium cerebelli, it leaves a space between the dura mater and the periosteum that is lined by endothelium and serves as a rigid-walled venous channel, a dural sinus. The tributaries of the dural sinuses are veins of the brain. The sinuses, in turn, are drained by the internal jugular veins.

The cerebrospinal fluid that fills the subarachnoid space is secreted into the ventricles by the choroid plexuses, one of which is present in each ventricle (Figs. 1-7 and 1-12). It escapes from the fourth ventricle into the subarachnoid space by way of three apertures, one at each angle of the triangular inferior velum (Fig. 1-12). The right and left apertures are known as the *foramina of Luschka;* the median aperture is called the *foramen of Magendie.* The fluid is removed from the subarachnoid space by arachnoid villi. Those villi return the fluid to the blood through evaginations of the arachnoid membrane (Fig. 1-12) that extend into the venous blood of the dural sinuses. Collections of villi form macroscopic moss-like masses, called *arachnoid granulations.*

Definitions

A Neural Pathway. A neural pathway is a chain of nerve cells linked together, end to end, to convey excitation from one part of the nervous system to another or from a sense organ to muscles by way of the central nervous system.

A Ganglion, a Nucleus. A ganglion is a collection of nerve cell bodies located in the peripheral nervous system. A sensory ganglion contains the cell bodies of sensory nerve fibers and has no synapses. An autonomic, or motor, ganglion contains the cell bodies of fibers that supply smooth muscle, heart muscle, and glands. The cells of an autonomic ganglion are activated by axons of cells located in the central nervous system and therefore have synapses. A nucleus is a collection of nerve cell bodies located in the central nervous system.

A Nerve, a Fasciculus, a Fiber Tract. A nerve is a cable-like bundle of fibers in the peripheral nervous system. A fasciculus and a fiber tract are bundles of fibers within the central nervous system. The term *fiber tract* is usually, but not always, reserved for a fiber bundle that contains fibers that have the same origin, function, and termination.

A Synapse, a Relay Station. A synapse is the specialized region of contact between two nerve cells, where excitation of one can be relayed to the other. Synapses are present in all nuclei and autonomic ganglia. Hence those cell masses are sometimes described as relay stations.

Gray Matter and White Matter. The central nervous system, when cut across, is seen to consist of two substances: one gray, the other white. The gray matter contains the bodies of nerve cells; the white matter is made up of nerve fibers. The myelin sheaths give the fiber masses their whiteness. When hardened by fixation in formaldehyde, gray matter is friable, whereas white matter has a rubbery consistency and can be split like wood in the direction of its fibers.

Cortex—Cerebral and Cerebellar. Cortex is a thin layer of gray matter on the surface of the cerebral hemisphere and the cerebellum. It has a limited thickness, never greater than 2 mm on the cerebellum or 4 mm on the cerebral hemisphere, and its cells are arranged in layers.

A Commissure (a Joining Together). A commissure is a band of gray or white matter that connects a portion of the brain or spinal cord on one side of the midline with its fellow of the opposite side.

A Decussation (an Intersection). The crossing of the midline by an ascending or descending fiber bundle is called a *decussation.* Since corresponding bundles of the right and left sides of the central nervous system cross at the same level, they characteristically crisscross through each other to form an X.

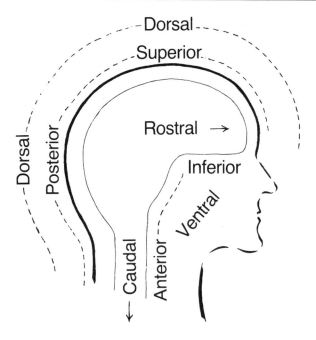

Figure 1-14. Relationships between the terminology of comparative neuroanatomy and that of human anatomy.

Descriptive Terms. The terms *dorsal, ventral, rostral,* and *caudal* are useful in describing relationships of some parts of the human central nervous system. Figure 1-14 shows how they may apply. Thus in describing the relationships of parts of the human forebrain, dorsal may be substituted for superior and ventral for inferior. Similarly, in describing the spinal cord, medulla, pons, and midbrain, dorsal and ventral may be used instead of posterior and anterior.

To locate structures relative to their position along the long axis of the central nervous system, two additional terms, rostral and caudal, may be used: rostral if nearer the nose and caudal if nearer the coccyx.

Functional Organization of the Central Nervous System

Each segment of the spinal cord and brain stem contains its own integrating mechanism, or computer. It processes the limited environmental data available to it from its own right and left sensory nerves and is capable of exciting an appropriate local segmental response. The diencephalon and midbrain segments of the brain stem are exceptions to this general statement, as will be explained later. The cerebral hemisphere also possesses an integrative mechanism, known as the *cerebral cortex*. It is a suprasegmental computer and, as such, it receives data concerning the environment from all the segments. Thus the cerebral cortex is equipped to initiate responses appropriate to the total environment—

so-called willed responses—as compared with the segmental, predictable responses that are referred to as reflex responses.

In addition to the suprasegmental computer in the cerebral hemisphere, a second suprasegmental computer exists in the cerebellum—the cerebellar cortex. It also receives data concerning the environment from all the segments of the spinal cord and brain stem, but, unlike the cerebral cortex, it does not initiate responses. Its role is to regulate the flow of impulses to the muscles during voluntary movements to ensure that they are well coordinated and to shorten and lengthen muscles without a tremor.

The computers (cell masses) of the spinal cord are centrally located in each segment. Sensory nerve fibers convey coded messages, that is, nerve impulses, into its posterior portion. Those data are processed there for local responses but are also conveyed along pathways that ascend to the suprasegmental computers located in the cortex of the cerebral hemisphere and the cortex of the cerebellum. The fibers of those pathways emerge from the gray matter of each segment to ascend and form part of the outer layer of white matter of the spinal cord and the brain stem.

To initiate voluntary movements, the cerebral cortex has descending fibers that permit it to activate the required motor nuclei of the segments of the brain stem and spinal cord. Collectively, those fibers make up the pyramidal tract. In addition to the fibers of the pyramidal tract that excite motor nuclei, the cerebral cortex has descending fibers that trigger the cerebellum into acting as a coordinator of muscles. Fibers of the descending pathways from both the cerebral and the cerebellar cortex form part of the white matter of the spinal cord.

In the chapters that follow, the guiding technique used to describe the structure of the spinal cord and the successive levels of the brain stem is the tracing of pathways. Ascending pathways are traced to their termination in the cerebral hemisphere and the cerebellum and descending pathways are located at each level and thus are traced retrogradely to their origins.

In the process of tracing the pathways, relationships of clinical importance are pointed out. Diagrams illustrating the whole length of each sensory and motor pathway are located in Chapter 15.

The nuclei of the cranial nerves and their connections are described collectively in Chapter 8.

Review Questions (Answers Available on the Pages Cited)

1. How does the function of the central nervous system differ from that of the peripheral nervous system (p. 1)?
2. Name the structures that form the posterior wall of the fourth ventricle (p. 5).
3. What are the first and second ventricles of the brain named (p. 5)?
4. Give one reason why a nerve cell may have more than one dendrite (p. 6).
5. What is a neural pathway (p. 6)?
6. What are the two basic functions of a synapse (p. 6)?
7. Name the two components of a choroid plexus (p. 9).
8. How does a myelin sheath increase in thickness (p. 10)?
9. State two ways in which cranial nerves differ from spinal nerves (p. 12).
10. Locate the sensory ganglia of spinal nerves and the motor ganglia of the sympathetic trunk (p. 12).
11. Why do all parts of the external surface of the central nervous system have a covering of pia mater (p. 12)?

12. How does the subdural space differ from the subarachnoid space (p. 13)?
13. What is a subdural venous sinus (p. 13)?
14. What is the function of the choroid plexus and the arachnoid villi (p. 15)?
15. How does the input of a spinal cord segment differ from that of the cerebral cortex (p. 16)?
16. How would responses be altered by an injury of (1) the cerebral cortex (p. 16) and (2) the cerebellar cortex (p. 17)?

2

Neuroanatomical Investigative Procedures

The study of nerve cells and their connections to form neural pathways has evolved in stages, each one dependent on the use of a new technique.

Golgi Technique

Late in the nineteenth century, Golgi, in Italy, and Cajal, in Spain, developed methods of impregnating nerve cells and their processes with gold or silver to make (Fig. 2-1) them either opaque (Golgi) or partially opaque (Cajal). That technique made it possible for investigators to follow axons for relatively long distances, particularly in fetal brains, where large portions could be included in a section prepared for microscopic study. The techniques were particularly useful because they selectively stained only a very small fraction of the cells in a given region, leaving them clearly outlined in an unstained background. Cajal, in particular, used this technique to trace many pathways and arrive at a basic understanding of the organization of the brain and spinal cord. In 1906, Golgi and Cajal received the Nobel Prize for their work.

Degeneration Studies

Although the Golgi technique enabled investigators to trace single nerve fibers, it was often difficult to follow those fibers over long distances through many tissue sections. In addition, the Golgi technique was capricious, staining different neurons and different numbers of neurons on different occasions. Those limitations led to the development of

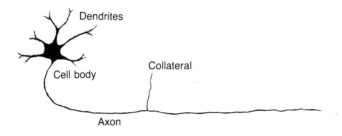

Figure 2-1. Diagram of a cell stained using the Golgi technique.

selective degeneration stains. In particular, Nauta and his colleagues, in the 1950s, produced silver stains that specifically marked degenerating neurons. Thus lesions could be made in specific brain nuclei of experimental animals, and the long axonal projections of those degenerating neurons could be traced to their terminations. For over 20 years, degeneration studies were the primary vehicle for revealing the organization of brain pathways. The major limitation of those studies was that the experimental lesions destroyed not only neuronal cell bodies at the lesion site but, also, fibers of passage that originated in various other brain nuclei.

Axonal Transport

The modern age of experimental neuroanatomy began in the early 1970s with the realization that normal axonal transport systems of neurons could be employed to trace the projections of neurons. It is known that neurons transport various proteins and structural elements of the cell anterogradely (forward) from the cell body, down the axon, to the axon terminal and that neurons also have a retrograde (backward) intraaxonal transport system that serves to transport intracellular elements from the axon terminal back to the cell body. Researchers have learned that certain substances (e.g., radioactively labeled amino acids) are primarily taken up by cell bodies and transported anterogradely down axons to terminal processes (Fig. 2-2A), and that other substances (e.g., horseradish peroxidase and fluorescent dyes) are primarily taken up by axon terminals and transported retrogradely in axons back to neuronal cell bodies (Fig. 2-2B). The anterograde and retrograde axonal tracers are transported from one part of the brain of a living experimental animal to another, using the natural intraaxonal communication systems of the neurons. These tracers have revolutionized the study of brain pathways. Besides bringing an extraordinary sensitivity to the tracing of neuronal projections, they have also enabled investigators to achieve considerable specificity. For example, the anterogradely transported, radioactively labeled amino acids are only taken up, synthesized into proteins, and transported from cell bodies (where protein synthesis takes place) and not by neuronal fibers that pass through the injection site. Thus the major fiber-of-passage problem that made degeneration studies difficult to interpret can be avoided. The radioactive label is attached to the amino acids so that the transported amino acids can be

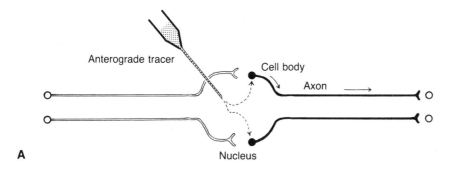

A

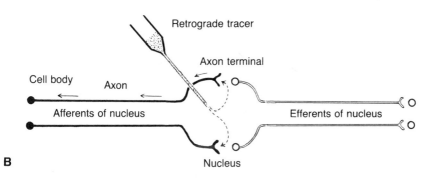

B

Figure 2-2. *Axonal transport techniques.*

readily visualized. Other transported tracers in the brain can be visualized by their fluorescence.

Axonal tracers also have been used along with other techniques to reveal additional aspects of brain organization. First, although axonal tracers are used primarily at light-microscopic levels to show projection pathways, many of the tracers also can be used at electron-microscopic levels to demonstrate that the labeled terminal projections actually form synapses with the neurons within the brain nuclei where they end. Second, labeled antibodies that combine with specific neurotransmitters (the chemical communicators between neurons) have been employed to locate the neurons containing each transmitter. These immunocytochemical procedures can be carried out in the same brain in which axonal tracing techniques are used, so that both the description of a neuronal pathway and the biochemical characterization of its neurotransmitter can be described concurrently. Third, anterograde and retrograde tracers can be injected together to study the frequent reciprocity of connections between two brain nuclei. Finally, intracellular injection of axonal tracers may be made through electrodes while recording the physiologic activity of a single neuron. Thus the shape and axonal projections of a single physiologically identified neuronal cell body can be traced. The modern axonal transport tracing techniques have already revealed (and continue to reveal) new connections in the brain and provide better and more detailed descriptions of previously known pathways.

Review Questions (Answers Available on the Pages Cited)

1. How does the Golgi technique reveal the processes of a nerve cell (p. 19)? What is its chief limitation (p. 19)?
2. Why would you be in doubt about the origin of degenerating fibers emanating from a cell cluster that has been destroyed (p. 19)?
3. Why does a cell's ability to synthesize protein make it possible to trace its axon (p. 20)?
4. What technique is available to identify the location of neurons containing a certain neurotransmitter (p. 21)?

3

The Spinal Cord

Form and External Features

The spinal cord is a cylindrical structure, flattened somewhat dorsoventrally, so its cross section has an oval outline. Its maximum diameter does not exceed that of the little finger. It is connected to the medulla oblongata at the foramen magnum and tapers to a point at the upper border of the second lumbar vertebra (Fig. 3-1). The caudal end of the spinal cord is connected to the back of the lowest coccygeal vertebra by the filum terminale, a thread-like strand of neuroglia overlaid by pia mater and also, below S2, by extensions of the arachnoid membrane and dura mater. Surrounding the filum terminale, within the subarachnoid space, are the roots of the spinal nerves that leave the vertebral column below the second lumbar vertebra. Those long roots form a leash of nerves known as the *cauda equina* ("tail of horse") (see Fig.1-13). A needle can be inserted into the subarachnoid space that contains those nerve roots to remove cerebrospinal fluid without endangering the spinal cord.

The spinal cord is segmented (one segment for each of its 31 pairs of spinal nerves), but there is nothing in its structure, externally or internally, to betray this fact. The lack of a segmental enlargement at the points at which spinal nerves attach is explained by the manner in which nerves are joined (Fig. 3-2). Instead of entering or leaving the spinal cord in one bundle, the fibers of the nerve are first segregated into a sensory posterior root and a motor anterior root, and then the fibers of each of those roots are evenly distributed in a series of filaments along the segment's length. Since the filaments' attachments form an unbroken series, it is not possible to identify the limits of the individual segments after the roots are cut and the continuity with the trunk of the nerve has been lost.

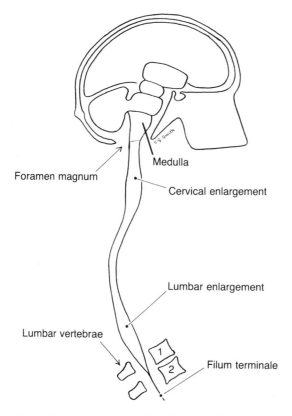

Figure 3-1. Form of the spinal cord and its relationships to the vertebral column.

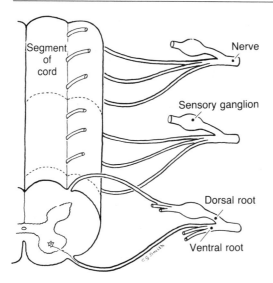

Figure 3-2. Attachment of a spinal nerve to its segment of the spinal cord.

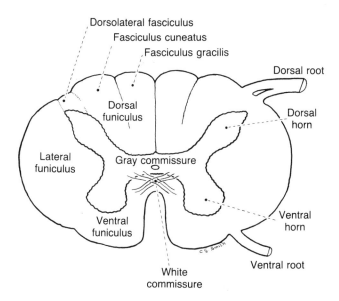

Figure 3-3. Cross section of a cervical segment of the spinal cord, showing the subdivisions of gray and white matter.

The lines of attachment of the posterior and anterior rootlets are marked by shallow longitudinal grooves. A similar groove is present in the midline posteriorly. Anteriorly, a deep median fissure extends the length of the spinal cord and serves to identify its anterior surface.

The spinal cord has two fusiform enlargements: a cervical enlargement that involves segments C5 to T1 and a lumbar enlargement that involves segments L4 to S3. Those segments are enlarged because of an increase in the amount of gray matter. The increase in cellular content is required to serve the increased sensory input from the limbs and to provide an increased number of anterior horn cells, whose axons supply the large number of limb muscles.

Internal Structure

All the segments of the spinal cord basically have the same structure. Each one has a central canal, a layer of gray matter around it, and an outer covering of white matter (see Fig. 3-3).

Gray Matter

Subdivisions
In a cross section, the gray matter of the spinal cord has the form of the letter H (Fig. 3-3). The crossbar is the gray commissure. It contains the central canal, which is about 1 mm in diameter, and it may be obliterated in later life.

The posterior limb of the H-shaped gray matter (*posterior horn*) extends toward the entering fibers of the sensory posterior root. It receives the terminals of the sensory fibers. The anterior limb (*anterior horn*) contains the cell bodies of the motor fibers of the anterior root, and it extends toward the exit of those fibers. The gray matter between the posterior and anterior horns is the intermediate gray matter. Its cells convey impulses from the cells of the posterior horn to the anterior horn (for segmental reflexes), to higher and lower levels of the spinal cord (for intersegmental reflexes), and to the brain (for sensation). Some cells of the intermediate gray matter receive input from the brain and serve as relay stations for the motor pathways, for example, the pathway for voluntary movement.

Cells of the Gray Matter

The cells of the gray matter are arranged in layers that are more or less parallel to the posterior surface of the spinal cord. That basic stratification is evident when thick sections are examined. In some cases, the nuclei of the spinal cord involve an entire layer; in others, they are secondary groups of cells within a layer (Fig. 3-4A and B).

Lamina I, also known as the posterior marginal nucleus, is a thin layer at the apex of the posterior horn. It contains cells of varying size but, significantly, some large cells that have axons that ascend to the brain. Lamina I forms a thin covering for the thick, well-defined lamina II, called the *substantia gelatinosa*. Lamina II is a jelly-like layer (in a fresh section) that is composed of closely packed, very small cells with short unmyelinated axons. Therefore, it is clearly defined as an unstained area in sections stained for myelin, for example, using the Weigert technique.

Laminae III and IV together comprise the nucleus proprius, or proper sensory nucleus. The two layers are penetrated by many myelinated fibers of the dorsal nerve root. Many end there, but some reach other laminae. The cells are loosely disposed and have a wide range of form and size. The large cells of lamina IV give rise to axons that ascend to the brain.

Lamina V forms the constricted part of the posterior horn that is described as its neck. A feature of that layer is its lateral part, known as its *reticular process*, which is invaded by crisscrossing myelinated fibers.

Lamina VI forms the basal part of the posterior horn. It is absent in most thoracic segments.

Lamina VII is an intermediate zone between posterior and anterior horns. It includes three named cell clusters. (1) The intermediolateral nucleus is present only in the thoracic and first two lumbar segments. It forms an extension of gray matter into the lateral funiculus, called the *lateral horn*. That nucleus contains the small cell bodies of visceral motor (preganglionic) fibers of the sympathetic part of the autonomic nervous system. (2) The nucleus dorsalis (Clarke's column) is coextensive segmentally with the intermediolateral nucleus. It bulges into the dorsal funiculus and contains large cells with axons that extend to the cerebellum. (3) The intermediomedial nucleus is present in all segments in the medial part of lamina VII. It contains small cells that receive terminals of sensory nerve fibers and may relay impulses to the preganglionic cells of the lateral horn. The intervening portions of lamina VII contain medium-sized cells that relay impulses (1) to the motor nuclei of the anterior horn (lamina IX), (2) to the other segments of the spinal cord, and (3) to the brain.

Lamina VIII stretches across the base of the ventral horn in the thoracic segments, but, in the limb segments, the cells are crowded into the medial portion of the anterior

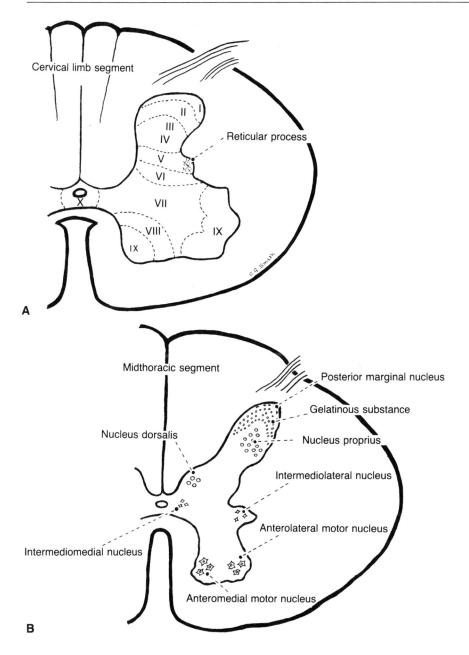

Figure 3-4. (A) Section of the cervical enlargement of the spinal cord, showing the stratification of the cells of the gray matter. (B) A section of a midthoracic segment, showing the nuclei of the gray matter.

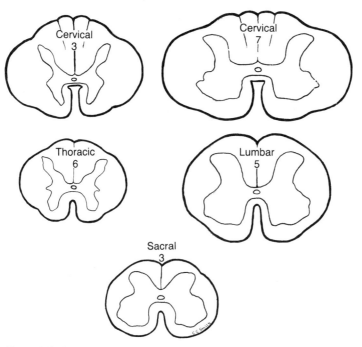

Figure 3-5. Cross sections of the spinal cord at representative levels showing identifiable features.

horn by the large laterally located motor nuclei of lamina IX. The axons of lamina VIII cells extend to other segments on the same side (fasciculi proprii) and on the opposite side (commissural fibers).

Lamina IX is a discontinuous layer. Its large and medium-sized cells aggregate in clusters separated by the cells of layers VII and VIII. Those clusters are composed of the nuclei of motor nerves that supply skeletal muscles. A medial group of nuclei have axons that supply the muscles of the back by way of the posterior rami of spinal nerves. The lateral group of motor nuclei have axons that supply the muscles of limbs and the lateral and anterior parts of the body by way of the anterior rami. The increase in size of the lateral nuclei in the limb segments accounts for the large size of the anterior horn, which is a feature of those segments (Fig. 3-5). Lamina X is a layer that surrounds the central canal. It is made up chiefly of neuroglia cells, but it also contains the terminals of some nerve fibers.

Functional Organization of the Gray Matter
In general, the posterior horn laminae I, II, III, and IV receive terminals from cutaneous sensory fibers; laminae V, VI, and VII receive terminals of fibers from the sense organs in muscles, tendons, and joints; and lamina IX contains the cell bodies of motor nerve fibers.

Lamina VIII and most of the other laminae contain cells that relay impulses to anterior horn cells (IX) of the same segment and other segments of the spinal cord on both the right and left sides. Some of the cells in laminae I, IV, and V relay impulses along sensory pathways to the brain; other cells located in laminae V, VI, and VII relay impulses to the cerebellum.

The cells of lamina II have a special role. They modulate, that is, inhibit or facilitate, the flow of impulses along the sensory pathways for pain.

White Matter of the Spinal Cord

Major Subdivisions: Funiculi

The white matter of the spinal cord is composed of fibers that course longitudinally. Those are fibers grouped into three large bundles, called *funiculi* (Fig. 3-3). The posterior funiculus is located between the posterior median neuroglial septum and the posterior horn. The anterior funiculus is located between the anterior median fissure and the anterior horn; and the lateral funiculus is located lateral to the gray matter of the spinal cord and between the entering and departing fibers of the nerve roots.

Composition of the Posterior Funiculus

As the fibers of a posterior root enter the spinal cord, the myelinated fibers separate from the unmyelinated fibers and form a bundle that courses medially between the tip of the posterior horn and the posterior funiculus. Fibers of that bundle enter the posterior horn after contributing a short descending and a long ascending branch to the posterior funiculus. The unmyelinated fibers of the posterior root form a lateral bundle that enters the apex of the posterior horn. Before doing so, however, each of its fibers gives off branches that ascend and descend one or two segments at the tip of the posterior horn to form a bundle of unmyelinated fibers, called the *dorsolateral fasciculus*, or *tract of Lissauer.* Its fibers convey impulses from pain and temperature sense organs to adjacent segments.

Most of the fibers that ascend in the posterior funiculus extend to the brain. As they course upward, they are crowded medially by fibers entering at higher levels. In the upper thoracic and cervical region of the spinal cord, a neuroglial septum intervenes between the fibers that entered the funiculus below the sixth thoracic segment and those that entered above that level. The slender medial bundle is the fasciculus gracilis (*gracilis*, "slender"); the lateral bundle, wedge-shaped in cross section, is the fasciculus cuneatus (*cuneus*, "wedge).

Fibers of the posterior funiculus that do not reach the brain end in the gray matter of the spinal cord. Some form the fasciculus proprius of the posterior funiculus, a thin layer applied to the posterior horn that provides intersegmental connections.

Composition of the Lateral and Anterior Funiculi

The fiber content of the lateral and anterior funiculi is basically different from that of the posterior funiculus. The fibers that ascend to the brain have cell bodies in the gray matter of the spinal cord, not in the posterior root ganglia. Those fibers are grouped into bundles according to function, but they are not isolated by neuroglial septa and cannot be identified in a cross section of normal spinal cord. Also, unlike the posterior funiculus, the lateral and anterior funiculi contain pathways that descend from the brain. Some excite voluntary movements and others excite reflex movements in response to special sense stimuli (e.g., visual and auditory).

All three funiculi contain a fasciculus proprius that is composed of intersegmental fibers. Fibers that connect the right and left halves of the spinal cord form the *white commissure*—a bundle of fibers that crosses the midline anterior to the gray commissure.

Distinguishing Features of Cross Sections of Spinal Cord at Different Levels

The thoracic segments of the spinal cord contain a minimal amount of gray matter; the intermediate gray matter contains two readily identified nuclei, the nucleus dorsalis and the intermediolateral nucleus, which project into the posterior and lateral funiculi, respectively (Fig. 3-5).

Segments of both the cervical and lumbar enlargements have massive anterior horns, but the size of the funiculi is much greater in the segments of the cervical enlargement. In addition, the posterior funiculus at cervical levels has a neuroglial septum that separates the fasciculus gracilis from the fasciculus cuneatus.

Sections of upper cervical segments have a small amount of gray matter, similar to the thoracic segments, but they lack the nucleus dorsalis and the intermediolateral nucleus.

The sacral segments are readily identified by small funiculi, which are reduced to a thin covering for the gray matter.

Pathways of the Spinal Cord

The primary pathway of the spinal cord is a reflex pathway that connects the sense organ of a spinal nerve with a muscle.

Secondary pathways convey impulses to and from the brain. Pathways to the cerebral hemisphere are sensory pathways. When a sensory pathway is cut, sensation is lost. Pathways to the cerebellum provide information necessary to coordinate muscles for a given response. Pathways descending from the cerebral hemisphere excite voluntary movements, while other descending pathways from the brain stem effect reflex responses to special sense stimuli, such as auditory or visual stimuli or those from the special position sense organs of the internal ear.

Proprioceptive Pathways: Pathways Excited by Position Sense Organs

The position sense provides a person with an awareness of how the parts of his or her body are positioned without visual clues. Sense organs are located deep in the skin, muscles, tendons, and joint capsules. They excite (1) posture-regulating reflexes, (2) pathways to the cerebellum, and (3) sensory pathways to the cerebral cortex.

Reflex Pathways. The *stretch reflex pathway* (Fig. 3-6) excites contraction of a muscle in response to its being stretched (elongated) and thus prevents any change in muscle length from occurring. The sense organ is a muscle spindle, and the reflex arc is composed of a *chain of two neurons.* The sensory nerve fiber extends all the way from the sense organ to the anterior horn cells of the motor fibers that supply the muscle.

The muscle spindle is a bundle of modified muscle fibers (intrafusal) enclosed in a spindle-shaped connective tissue capsule. The fibers are attached to the capsule at each end and, through it, to the supporting tissue and, indirectly, to the tendon of the muscle. The muscle fibers of the spindle are arranged parallel to the working muscle fibers and therefore increase in length when the muscle is stretched. That action excites the naked terminal of a thick myelinated fiber that is wound around the noncontractile middle portion of the intrafusal fibers. When the muscle contracts, the spindle is permitted to shorten, and its sensory ending is no longer stimulated.

The *lengthening,* or *clasp-knife, reflex* (Fig. 3-6) is a protective reflex that acts to reduce tension in the tendon of an overactive muscle. It is a *chain of three or more neurons.* The sense organ is in the tendon (the tendon sense organ of Golgi). The cell body of the

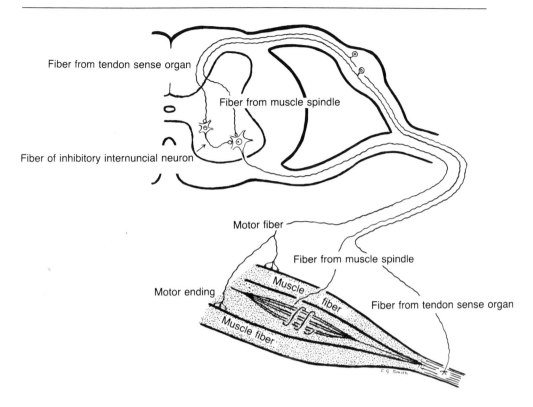

Figure 3-6. Two reflex pathways: the stretch reflex and the clasp-knife reflex (lengthening reaction).

sensory fiber is located in the posterior root ganglion and extends to synapse with an internuncial cell in lamina VII. That cell relays inhibitory impulses to the anterior horn cells in lamina IX, which are exciting excessive contraction of the muscle. The inhibition permits the muscle to relax. The reflex gets its name, clasp-knife reflex, because the sudden loss of resistance that is encountered clinically when a contracted muscle is force-fully stretched resembles that experienced in closing a spring-loaded folding knife.

Pathways to the Cerebellum. Impulses that reach the cerebellum from proprioceptive sense organs, and also some from cutaneous sense organs, enable it to regulate the flow of impulses to muscles to ensure a smoothly executed, precise movement. When those pathways are cut sensation is not lost, but voluntary movements are awkward and tremu-lous.

There are four direct pathways to the cerebellum. Two of them (one for the lower half of the body, the *posterior spinocerebellar tract,* and one for the upper half, the *cu-neocerebellar tract*) convey data from sensory fibers with small receptive fields. The afferent fibers are chiefly from muscles and tendons. The other two (one for the lower part of the body, the *anterior spinocerebellar tract,* and one for the upper part of the body, the *rostral spinocerebellar tract*) convey data from sensory fibers with large receptive fields. Impulses conveyed by the latter two tracts are chiefly from cutaneous and tendon sense organs.

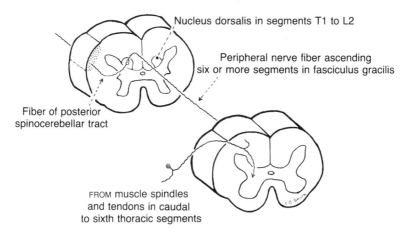

Figure 3-7. The posterior spinocerebellar tract.

The *posterior spinocerebellar tract* (Fig. 3-7) is composed of axons of cells in the nucleus dorsalis. Those cells receive terminals of ascending branches of myelinated proprioceptive fibers that enter the spinal cord caudal to the sixth thoracic segment. Impulses conveyed by those sensory fibers are relayed by cells of the nucleus dorsalis along axons that ascend on the surface of the posterior half of the lateral funiculus, located on the same side. The posterior spinocerebellar tract enters the cerebellum as part of the inferior cerebellar peduncle.

The *cuneocerebellar tract* (Fig. 3-8) supplements the posterior spinocerebellar tract in

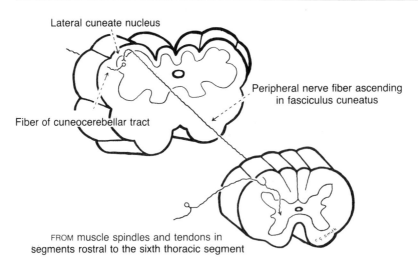

Figure 3-8. The cuneocerebellar tract.

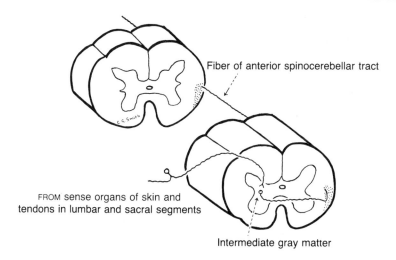

Fiber of anterior spinocerebellar tract

FROM sense organs of skin and
tendons in lumbar and sacral segments

Intermediate gray matter

Figure 3-9. The anterior spinocerebellar tract.

that it conveys impulses from comparable sense organs, located in the segments above the sixth thoracic segment.

The nucleus that corresponds to the nucleus dorsalis is the lateral cuneate nucleus, a short column of cells that is found in the caudal part of the medulla oblongata. To reach that nucleus, the sensory fibers enter the spinal cord above the midthoracic level and ascend in the posterior funiculus. Axons of the lateral cuneate nucleus join the posterior spinocerebellar tract, on the same side, to enter the cerebellum.

The *anterior spinocerebellar tract* (Fig. 3-9) conveys impulses from cutaneous sense organs and the Golgi tendon organ. The cells originate in the intermediate gray matter (laminae V, VI, and VII) of the sacral and lumbar segments of the spinal cord. Axons of those cells cross the midline in the anterior white commissure and ascend on the surface of the anterior half of the lateral funiculus.

The anterior spinocerebellar tract relays impulses of sensory fibers that have a larger receptive field than those sensory fibers from the same portion of the body that end in the nucleus dorsalis. A single fiber may have a receptive field that includes synergistic muscles of each joint in the lower limbs.

The *rostral spinocerebellar tract* (Fig. 3-10) is the upper limb equivalent of the anterior spinocerebellar tract. Sensory nerve fibers of cutaneous and tendon sense organs enter the spinal cord in the nerves of the upper portion of the body and synapse with cells of the intermediate gray matter. Axons of those cells, unlike the fibers of the anterior spinocerebellar tract, ascend without crossing. They join the fibers of the anterior spinocerebellar tract on the surface of the anterior half of the lateral funiculus.

The rostral spinocerebellar tract, like the anterior spinocerebellar tract, is activated by sensory fibers with a large receptive field. As fibers of that tract, which serves the upper limb, enter the cerebellum, they branch to reach both right and left sides. In addition, their distribution within the cerebellum overlaps the area where fibers from the lower limb terminate. This distribution within the cerebellum suggests that the rostral

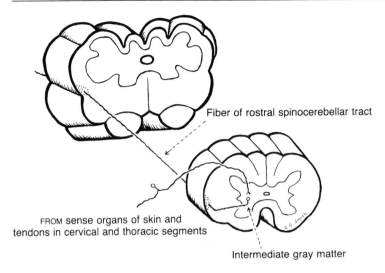

Fiber of rostral spinocerebellar tract

FROM sense organs of skin and tendons in cervical and thoracic segments

Intermediate gray matter

Figure 3-10. The rostral spinocerebellar tract.

spinocerebellar tract conveys information that is utilized in coordinating movements that involve the upper and lower limbs.

Pathways to the Cerebral Hemisphere: Position Sense (Fig. 3-11). The sense of position, that is, the awareness of the degree of angulation at a given joint, is obtained from data provided by sense organs in joints and muscles but also, in part, from sense organs in the skin near joints. *Changes* in position are recorded by rapidly adapting sense organs, but awareness of *position at rest* is the function of slowly adapting sense organs. The chief slowly adapting sense organs are the muscle spindles and the tendon sense organ of Golgi.

Impulses from the lower and upper limbs follow different routes to the brain. Sensory nerve fibers that enter the spinal cord below the sixth thoracic segment ascend in the posterior funiculus to end in the nucleus dorsalis. That part of the sensory pathway is the same as the posterior spinocerebellar pathway to the cerebellum. Collateral branches of individual fibers of the posterior spinocerebellar tract peel off as they enter the medulla oblongata to synapse with cells of a rostral subdivision of the nucleus gracilis.

The position sense fibers of the nerves of the upper half of the body extend all the way to the brain in the fasciculus cuneatus to synapse with cells in the nucleus cuneatus. The cells of that nucleus and those of the rostral part of the nucleus gracilis relay impulses along fibers that cross the midline to ascend in a bundle, called the *medial lemniscus.*

Sensory Pathways for Pain and Temperature: The Lateral Spinothalamic Tract
The pathways for pain and temperature have the same course, share the same relay stations (nuclei), and have the same termination in the brain. The sensory nerve fibers are composed of unmyelinated and thinly myelinated fibers of small cells in the dorsal root ganglia. The central processes of those cells enter the apex of the dorsal horn, but before doing so, they give off branches that ascend and descend to end in the posterior horn of adjacent segments. Those ascending and descending fibers are joined by un-myelinated axons of cells in the dorsal horn to form the dorsolateral fasciculus (Lissauer's

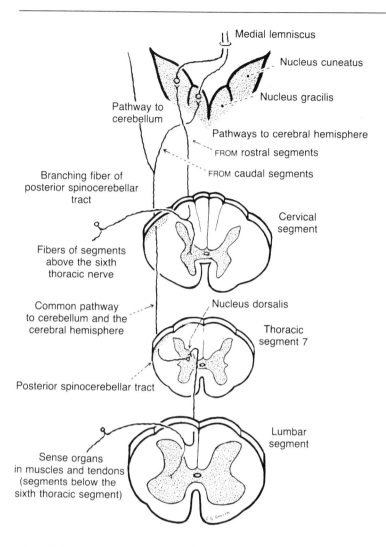

Medial lemniscus

Nucleus cuneatus

Nucleus gracilis

Pathway to cerebellum

Pathways to cerebral hemisphere

FROM rostral segments

FROM caudal segments

Branching fiber of posterior spinocerebellar tract

Cervical segment

Fibers of segments above the sixth thoracic nerve

Common pathway to cerebellum and the cerebral hemisphere

Nucleus dorsalis

Thoracic segment 7

Posterior spinocerebellar tract

Lumbar segment

Sense organs in muscles and tendons (segments below the sixth thoracic segment)

Figure 3-11. Position sense pathways from lower and upper limbs.

tract). The terminals of the sensory fibers, including those of the dorsolateral fasciculus, synapse with cells located primarily in the most superficial laminae of the dorsal horn.

The lateral spinothalamic tract (Fig. 3-12) originates from cells in lamina I (cells that receive direct input from dorsal root fibers) as well as from several deeper laminae, especially laminae IV to VII, which are activated indirectly by means of internuncial cells. Fibers of that tract cross the midline in the anterior commissure and ascend in the anterior half of the lateral funiculus. Some of the fibers that ascend along the spinothalamic tract, the spinoreticular fibers, end in the core of the brain stem; others, the spinotectal fibers, end in the roof (tectum) of the midbrain. As the fibers of the lateral spinothalamic tract ascend, they are crowded laterally by fibers crossing at higher levels. Hence in the cervical

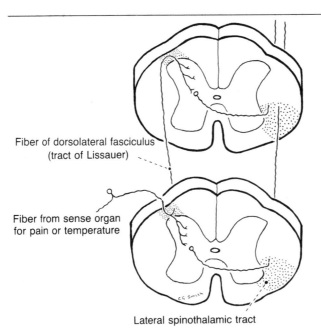

Fiber of dorsolateral fasciculus
(tract of Lissauer)

Fiber from sense organ
for pain or temperature

Lateral spinothalamic tract

Figure 3-12. Sensory pathways for pain and temperature. A short uncrossed pathway that is one or two segments long and the long crossed pathway. Note that the crossing fibers reach the opposite side in the segment above their origin (not shown here to simplify the diagram).

region, the fibers of the sacral, lumbar, thoracic, and cervical segments form successively deeper layers. Surgical sectioning of the lateral spinothalamic tract (anterolateral tractotomy) is required in some cases to relieve intractable pain. To obtain analgesia on one side of the body up to the level required, the depth of the cut must be considered. However, in many cases, pain relief is only temporary, indicating that there are other pathways along which pain impulses reach the brain.

The function of the small cells of lamina II is not understood. The evidence available indicates that they control access of impulses to the sensory pathways and thus have a role in pain appreciation.

Sensory Pathways for Touch
An adequate sense of touch includes the ability to recognize (1) two stimuli that are closely related spatially as being discrete (two-point discrimination) and (2) closely related successive stimuli as being discontinuous (usually tested with a vibrating tuning fork).

Spatial discrimination depends, in part, on the size of the area that receives the terminals of a sensory fiber; the smaller the area supplied, the more precise the localization. Temporal discrimination depends on the rate at which the sense organs for touch adapt, that is, cease to respond to a contact that is maintained.

Most of the pathways from rapidly adapting sense organs and from small receptive fields ascend to the brain without crossing the median plane in the spinal cord. But some, along with pathways from slowly adapting sense organs and from larger receptive fields, ascend to the brain after crossing the median plane. Thus cutting one of the

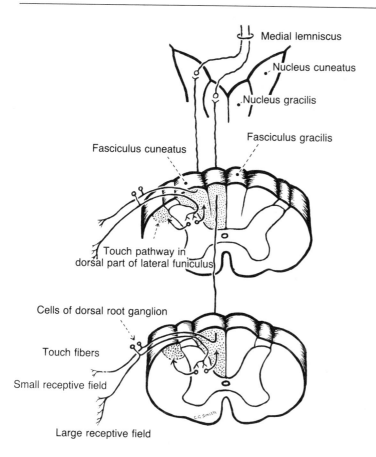

Figure 3-13. *The uncrossed touch pathways. The pathways that have a relay station in the spinal cord (lamina IV) ascend to the nuclei gracilis and cuneatus in the lateral and dorsal funiculi as indicated.*

ascending tracts will not seriously impair the sense of touch. However, *if the uncrossed pathway is cut*, careful testing will reveal reduced two-point discrimination and a loss of the sense of vibration. The sense organ for the "vibratory" sense is the pacinian corpuscle, a rapidly adapting encapsulated nerve ending.

The Uncrossed Touch Pathway of the Spinal Cord. The sensory nerve fibers are the myelinated processes of large cells in the posterior root ganglion. Those fibers ascend in the posterior funiculus. Some continue all the way to the brain to end in the nucleus gracilis or cuneatus. Others ascend only a short distance and then enter the posterior horn to synapse with a cell in lamina IV. The cells relay impulses to the appropriate nucleus gracilis or cuneatus by way of fibers that ascend either in the posterior funiculus or in the posterior part of the lateral funiculus (Fig. 3-13).

The Crossed Touch Pathway of the Spinal Cord: The Anterior Spinothalamic Tract. Myelinated fibers of large cells in the posterior root ganglion enter the posterior horn and synapse with cells in laminae III and IV. Impulses conveyed to some of those posterior horn cells play a part, through interneurons, in regulating conduction in the pain path-

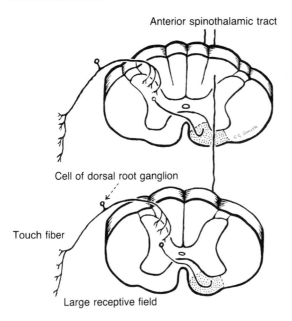

Anterior spinothalamic tract

Cell of dorsal root ganglion

Touch fiber

Large receptive field

Figure 3-14. The crossed pathway for touch, the anterior spinothalamic tract.

ways. Other cells in laminae III and IV relay impulses by means of internuncials to cells of deeper layers V, VI, and VII, which give rise to fibers of the anterior spinothalamic tract (Fig. 3-14). Fibers of that tract cross the midline in the anterior commissure and ascend in the anterior funiculus. As the fibers ascend, they are crowded anteriorly and laterally by fibers crossing at higher levels, as previously described, for the fibers of the lateral spinothalamic tract.

Descending Tracts of the Spinal Cord
Tracts that descend from the brain contribute fibers to the gray matter of each segment of the spinal cord. Most of those fibers excite motor responses, but some tracts contain fibers that end in the posterior horn to influence conduction in ascending pathways, for example, the pain pathways.

Motor responses may be excited voluntarily by pathways from the cerebral cortex, or reflexly, by pathways from (1) the midbrain (auditory and visual reflexes) and (2) the hindbrain (equilibrium reflexes). In addition to the pathways that form moderately compact bundles, tracts of loosely disposed fibers with a variety of functions descend from the reticular formation of the brain stem. The fibers of the reticulospinal tracts mingle with the fibers of the lateral and anterior funiculi. At this time, only the direct pathways from the cerebral cortex are described. The other descending pathways are described and traced from origin to termination after the study of the brain stem is completed.

The Corticospinal Tracts. The fibers of the corticospinal tracts (Fig. 3-15) are the axons of cells that are located in the cerebral cortex. Those fibers descend to the junction of the brain stem and the spinal cord, where about four-fifths of the fibers cross the midline to form the lateral corticospinal tract of the spinal cord. The crossing fibers are capable

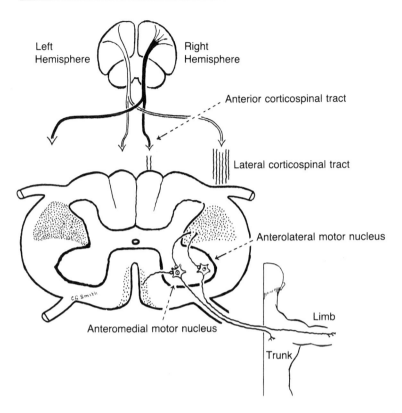

Figure 3-15. The corticospinal tracts. Anterior horn cells may be activated directly or by way of internuncial cells. Note that the anteromedial nuclei can be activated by both hemispheres.

of exciting all the motor nuclei of one side of the spinal cord. They descend in the posterior half of the lateral funiculus between the posterior horn and the posterior spinocerebellar tract.

Some fibers that do not cross form the *anterior corticospinal tract.* That tract descends in the anterior funiculus in the wall of the anterior median fissure. Other uncrossed fibers descend in the lateral funiculus, where they mingle with the fibers of the lateral corticospinal tract that have entered the lateral funiculus from the opposite hemisphere. Occasionally, all the fibers that descend without crossing follow this course; in that case, the anterior corticospinal tract is missing.

Fibers of the lateral corticospinal tract from the opposite hemisphere drop out in each segment to activate *all* the motor cells of lamina IX in the anterior horn. They may do so directly or by way of internuncial cells in lamina VII. Direct connections of corticospinal fibers with anterior horn motor cells have only evolved in primates to mediate, in particular, delicate independent movements of the fingers and thumb. Some fibers that descend into the spinal cord from the hemisphere on the same side also drop out in each segment to provide extra input to the anteromedial nuclei—that is, the motor nuclei of the muscles of the trunk and the proximal portions of the limbs (Fig. 3-15).

The muscles in the medial portions of the body can be controlled by both hemispheres.

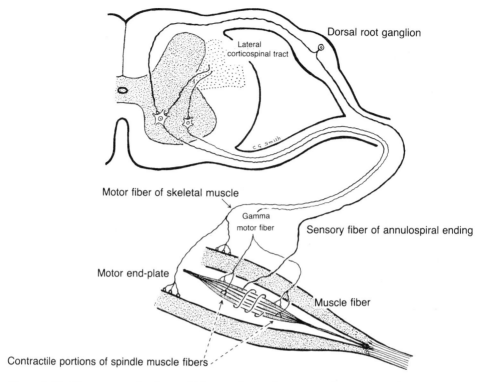

Lateral corticospinal tract

Dorsal root ganglion

Motor fiber of skeletal muscle

Gamma motor fiber

Sensory fiber of annulospiral ending

Motor end-plate

Muscle fiber

Contractile portions of spindle muscle fibers

C.G. Smith

Figure 3-16. The gamma reflex loop, which strengthens voluntary muscle contraction by increasing the sensitivity of the muscle spindle.

Therefore, the muscles of the trunk and limb girdles will not be paralyzed when a lesion in one hemisphere interrupts all its corticospinal fibers.

The corticospinal fibers, already described, can excite voluntary movements by activating anterior horn cells directly or indirectly by way of internuncial cells of the intermediate gray matter. They can, however, also facilitate, if not actually excite, motor responses by increasing the sensitivity of the muscle spindles. To do that, some corticospinal fibers activate small so-called gamma motor neurons, included in lamina IX (Fig. 3-16), which have axons that supply the contractile portions of the spindle muscle fibers. By causing those intrafusal fibers to contract, the noncontractile middle portions are stretched and the annulospiral sensory ending is stimulated (Fig. 3-16). That action reflexly activates the anterior horn cells and thus reinforces the activation by means of the more direct corticospinal pathways.

Review Questions (Answers Available on the Pages Cited)

1. At what vertebral level is the fifth sacral segment of the spinal cord located (see Fig. 1-13)?
2. If the dorsal aspect of the spinal cord is exposed, how could you locate the upper and lower limits of the seventh cervical segment (p. 23)?
3. Account for the cervical and lumbar enlargements of the spinal cord (p. 25).

4. What is the function of the cells in lamina II of the posterior horn of the spinal cord (p. 29)?
5. Where are the cell bodies of the fibers that make up the posterior funiculus at the level of the first sacral segment of the spinal cord (p. 29)?
6. What are the identifying features of a section of the cervical enlargement of the spinal cord (p. 30)?
7. Where are the cell bodies of the two neurons of the stretch reflex arc (p. 30)?
8. Explain the retention of position sense in the lower limbs when a lesion involves the posterior funiculi in the cervical part of the spinal cord (p. 34).
9. What parts of the body would lose pain sensation following a midline section of the anterior commissure of the sixth thoracic segment (p. 35; see also p. 193)?
10. If the fibers of the posterior funiculus are cut, what loss of touch sensation may be expected (p. 37)?
11. Explain the retention of voluntary control of the trunk muscles when the corticospinal fibers leaving one cerebral hemisphere are interrupted (p. 39).
12. How could strong stimulation of gamma motor neurons excite contraction of a muscle (p. 40)?

4

The Medulla Oblongata

The medulla oblongata, the caudal segment of the brain stem (Fig. 4-1), is imperceptibly continuous with the spinal cord. It extends up to the border of the strap-like band of fibers that crosses the surface of the pons segment. Its precise junction with the spinal cord is at the level where the highest rootlets of the first cervical nerve attach. The medulla oblongata increases in all diameters toward its upper end and, for descriptive purposes, may be considered to be shaped like the basal segment of a four-sided pyramid. It has an anterior, right, left, and posterior surface.

External Features

Anterior Surface

The anterior surface of the medulla oblongata has only one feature, the pyramid (Fig. 4-1), which is a band of fibers that enters the medulla oblongata from the pons and descends adjacent to the midline; it becomes continuous with the anterior funiculus of the spinal cord. The pyramid contains corticospinal fibers—a pathway for impulses that excite voluntary movements (Fig. 4-2A). As those fibers enter the spinal cord, most of them cross to form the lateral corticospinal tract of the lateral funiculus. The crossing fibers can be seen by opening the anterior median fissure. The fibers that do not cross descend in the anterior funiculus or in the posterior part of the lateral funiculus, where they mingle with the fibers of the lateral corticospinal tract.

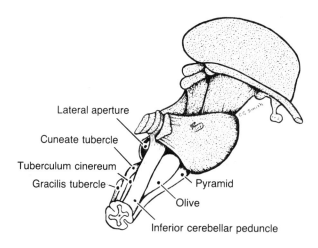

Lateral aperture

Cuneate tubercle

Tuberculum cinereum

Gracilis tubercle

Pyramid

Olive

Inferior cerebellar peduncle

Figure 4-1. Features of the lateral and anterior surfaces of the medulla.

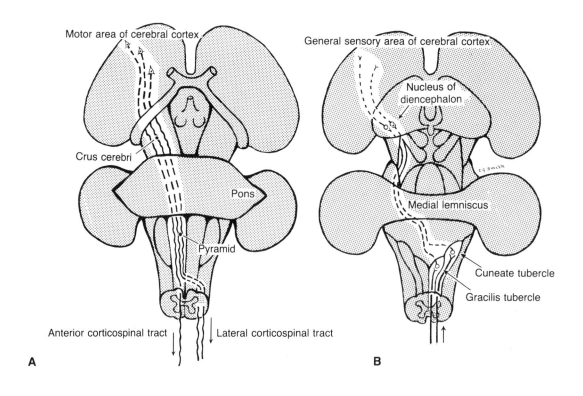

Motor area of cerebral cortex

Crus cerebri

Pons

Pyramid

Anterior corticospinal tract | ↓ Lateral corticospinal tract

A

General sensory area of cerebral cortex

Nucleus of diencephalon

Medial lemniscus

Cuneate tubercle

Gracilis tubercle

B

Figure 4-2.(A) Course of the corticospinal tracts on the ventral surface of the brain. (B) Course of the sensory pathways of the fasciculi gracilis and cuneatus on the dorsal aspect of the brain.

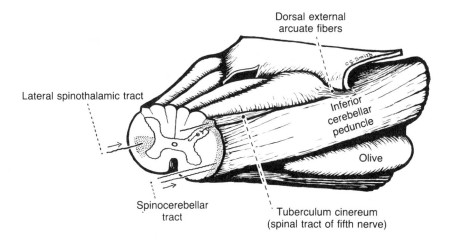

Dorsal external
arcuate fibers

Inferior
cerebellar
peduncle

Olive

Lateral spinothalamic tract

Spinocerebellar
tract

Tuberculum cinereum
(spinal tract of fifth nerve)

Figure 4-3. Posterolateral aspect of the medulla.

The Lateral Surface

The lateral surface of the medulla oblongata has three features: the inferior cerebellar peduncle, the tuberculum cinereum, and an ovoid elevation, the *olive*, which contains a large nucleus (Fig. 4-1).

The inferior cerebellar peduncle is a composite bundle composed of spinocerebellar fibers and other fibers that it acquires as it ascends through the medulla. As the anterior and posterior spinocerebellar tracts enter the medulla, they cover almost the entire lateral surface. As they ascend, mingling with fibers of the spinothalamic tracts, and are joined by medullary fibers, the enlarging bundle shifts dorsally and is separated from the pyramid by the olive. The olive contains the inferior olivary nucleus. It is covered externally by a thin layer of afferent fibers that descends from the midbrain. The cells of the nucleus relay impulses along fibers that cross the midline to become a major part of the inferior cerebellar peduncle (see Fig. 4-10). Just before the peduncle reaches the attachment of the cerebellum, it receives the dorsal external arcuate fibers from the cuneate tubercle (Fig. 4-3). Those fibers relay impulses from position sense organs in the upper part of the body, including the upper limbs.

The tuberculum cinereum (*cinereus*, "ashy") is an ashen gray external feature that is formed by a bundle of unmyelinated fibers that descend from the pons. That fiber bundle, the *spinal tract of the fifth nerve*, comes to the surface in the caudal part of the medulla, where it forms a narrow gray band between the posterior spinocerebellar tract and the fasciculus cuneatus, both of which are composed of myelinated fibers. The spinal tract of the fifth nerve is made up of the pain and temperature fibers of the fifth, seventh, ninth, and tenth nerves, but the fifth nerve contributes most of the fibers (Fig. 4-4). The tuberculum cinereum, it must be emphasized, is only the exposed part of that bundle. Most of it, including its thick underlying column of nerve cells, is covered by a thin layer of spinocerebellar fibers and accounts for the bulging lateral surface of the caudal half of the medulla.

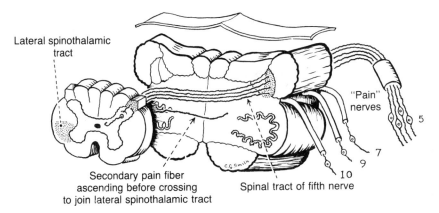

Lateral spinothalamic tract

"Pain" nerves

5

7

9

10

Secondary pain fiber
ascending before crossing
to join lateral spinothalamic tract

Spinal tract of fifth nerve

Figure 4-4. Posterolateral aspect of the upper portion of the medulla and the first cervical segment, showing the composition and termination of fibers of the spinal tract of the fifth nerve.

Posterior Surface

The posterior surface of the medulla oblongata has three features: the inferior velum, cuneate tubercle, and gracilis tubercle (Fig. 4-5).

As the fasciculi gracilis and cuneatus ascend into the medulla, they diverge from the midline to form the borders of the triangular inferior velum. They terminate in nuclei that form the club-shaped gracilis and cuneate tubercles. Those nuclei are relay stations of the discriminatory pathways for touch and position that ascend in the dorsal funiculus

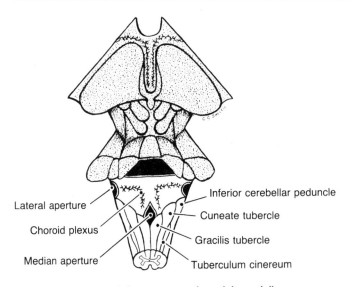

Lateral aperture

Choroid plexus

Median aperture

Inferior cerebellar peduncle

Cuneate tubercle

Gracilis tubercle

Tuberculum cinereum

Figure 4-5. Features of the posterior surface of the medulla.

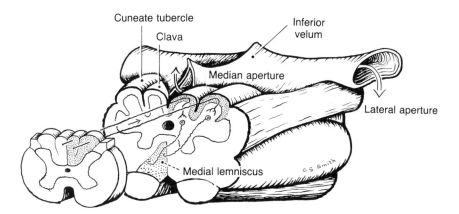

Figure 4-6. *Posterolateral aspect of the medulla, with a segment removed to show the decussation of the sensory pathways that ascend in the posterior funiculus.*

of the spinal cord. Axons of those relay stations course ventrally within the medulla and cross the midline to ascend, as illustrated in Figures 4-2B and 4-6. It is the progressive departure of those pathways (from a posterior to an anterior location within the medulla) that reduces the thick posterior wall of the central canal to the thinness of a membrane, allowing the central canal to enlarge and form the fourth ventricle.

The inferior velum contains the choroid plexus of the fourth ventricle. It is a T-shaped structure. The stem of the T is in the midline and has right and left portions; the cross piece extends the full width of the rostral part of the medulla. Each angle of the inferior velum is perforated to allow cerebrospinal fluid to escape into the subarachnoid space. The lateral apertures are known as the *foramina of Luschka;* the median aperture is the *foramen of Magendie.*

Nerve Attachments of the Medulla

Four of the twelve cranial nerves are attached to the medulla: the hypoglossal nerve (12), the accessory nerve (11), the vagus nerve (10), and the glossopharyngeal nerve (9) (Fig. 4-7).

The hypoglossal nerve is the motor nerve of the tongue. It emerges as a series of rootlets along the lateral border of the pyramid, in line with the motor rootlets of the first spinal nerve.

The accessory nerve is also a motor nerve. It arises as a longitudinal series of rootlets from the lateral surface of the rostral five segments of the spinal cord and the caudal part of the medulla. The fibers of the emerging rootlets of the spinal segments ascend within the subarachnoid space and unite to form a nerve that enters the skull through the foramen magnum, where it is joined by rootlets from the medulla. The spinal part supplies the sternomastoid and trapezius muscles; the cranial part contributes fibers to the vagus nerve to supply the muscles of the larynx and pharynx.

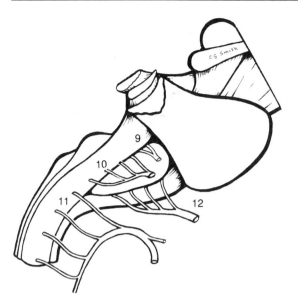

Figure 4-7. Attachment of the nerves of the medulla.

The vagus nerve is a mixed nerve. Its sensory and preganglionic fibers have a wide distribution, including the heart and most of the alimentary tract and its derivatives. It also contains the motor fibers to the larynx and pharynx that are contributed by the accessory nerve. Its rootlets emerge from the middle portion of the medulla along the dorsal border of the olive, in line with those of the accessory and glossopharyngeal nerves.

The glossopharyngeal nerve contains visceral sensory fibers (taste), preganglionic fibers (salivary glands), and some general sensory and motor fibers to the pharynx. Its two or three rootlets emerge in line with the vagal rootlets at the posterior border of the olive, adjacent to the pons.

Internal Structure

The change that occurs in the internal structure of the medulla between its lower and upper ends is gradual. Nevertheless, the medulla can be divided into three portions, each with a characteristic feature. A caudal portion contains the crossing fibers of the corticospinal tracts and is known as the *region of motor decussation*. A middle portion, the *region of sensory decussation*, contains the crossing fibers of the nuclei gracilis and cuneatus, a continuation of the sensory pathways that ascend in the posterior funiculi. An upper portion contains the decussation of olivocerebellar fibers, but it is known as the *region of the open medulla*. At that level, the entire posterior surface is formed by a delicate inferior velum.

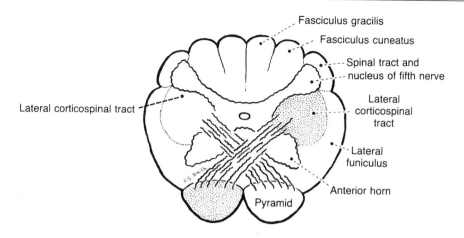

Figure 4-8. *Cross section of the medulla at the level of decussation of the corticospinal tracts.*

Region of Motor Decussation

The region of motor decussation (Fig. 4-8) is about 9 mm long, and most of the descending fibers of the pyramid cross its midline to form the lateral corticospinal tract. The fibers of the pyramid that do not cross form the anterior corticospinal tract of the anterior funiculus (Fig. 4-2A).

Region of Sensory Decussation

Above the level of motor decussation, the **H**-shaped form of the gray matter that is characteristic of the spinal cord is altered. The gray matter that contains sensory nuclei and corresponds to the posterior horn rotates, using the central canal as an axis, until it points laterally. In doing so, it fills the space that is taken up more caudally by the lateral corticospinal tract. The anterior horn also shifts, but posteriorly and medially, to lie next to the midline, anterior to the central canal. That gray matter contains motor nuclei (as in the spinal cord), but as it migrates, some cells are left behind to form a longitudinal series of motor nuclei for cranial nerves 10, 9, 7 and 5. The gray matter corresponding to the intermediate gray matter of the spinal cord extends into the medulla to form a core of loosely dispersed cells in a network of fibers called the *reticular formation* (Fig. 4-9). That network is described in Chapter 9.

As the sensory gray matter assumes its new position, clusters of its cells bulge posteriorly to form the nuclei of fasciculi gracilis and cuneatus. Those fasciculi contain sensory fibers of the spinal nerves that ascend to end at this level. Axons of the nuclei gracilis and cuneatus course anteriorly, through the reticular formation as internal arcuate fibers, to cross the midline and ascend. They form a sagittally oriented ribbon-like bundle, the medial lemniscus, which is located adjacent to the median plane and posterior to the pyramid.

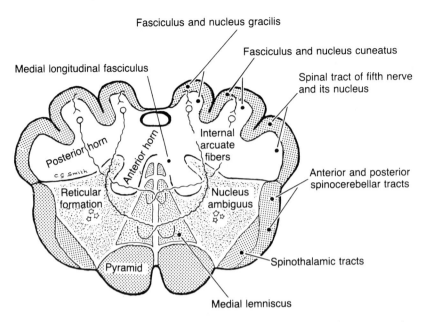

Fasciculus and nucleus gracilis

Fasciculus and nucleus cuneatus

Medial longitudinal fasciculus

Spinal tract of fifth nerve and its nucleus

Posterior horn

Anterior horn

Internal arcuate fibers

c.g smith

Anterior and posterior spinocerebellar tracts

Reticular formation

Nucleus ambiguus

Pyramid

Spinothalamic tracts

Medial lemniscus

Figure 4-9. Cross section of the medulla at the level of decussation of the sensory pathways that ascend in the fasciculus gracilis and fasciculus cuneatus.

The apical portion of the posterior horn of the spinal cord, that is, the gelatinous substance, retains its characteristic structure in the medulla. It serves as the nucleus of the spinal tract of the fifth nerve, which descends lateral to it and forms the external feature, called the *tuberculum cinereum.*

The spinocerebellar and spinothalamic fibers ascend on the lateral surface of the medulla. At that level, the fibers of the lateral and anterior spinothalamic tracts mingle and form a single bundle, known as the *spinal lemniscus.*

Level of the Open Medulla

At the level of the open medulla (Fig. 4-10), the pathways of the posterior funiculi have all decussated and the change in structure, from spinal cord to brain stem, is completed. The gray matter containing motor and sensory nuclei that corresponds to the gray matter of the anterior and posterior horns now extends mediolaterally and forms the floor of the fourth ventricle. A parasagittal groove, the *sulcus limitans,* intervenes between the motor nuclei medially and the sensory nuclei laterally. The extension of the intermediate gray matter of the spinal cord to the medullary level forms the reticular formation of the core of the medulla.

The ribbon-like medial lemniscus is applied to the median plane. Its posterior border is separated from the motor nucleus of the hypoglossal nerve by a fiber bundle, the medial longitudinal fasciculus, which is a vestibular reflex pathway.

Anteriorly, the medial lemniscus contacts the pyramid. Laterally, fibers of the hypoglossal nerve course anteriorly to emerge at the lateral border of the pyramid. Those

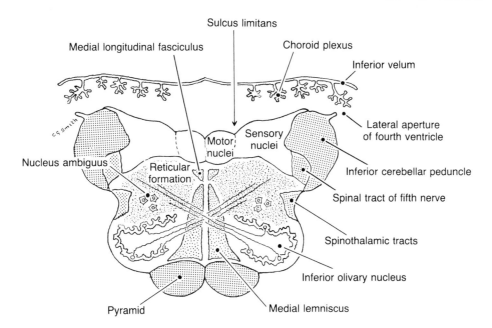

Figure 4-10. Cross section of the open medulla. The decussation of the olivocerebellar fibers is a feature of this level.

fibers pass between the medial lemniscus and the nuclei of the inferior olivary complex. The large principal nucleus is a wrinkled layer of gray matter that is folded to form a sac, with its opening directed medially and its lateral portion bulging onto the lateral surface to form the olive. Its external surface is covered by a thin layer of afferent fibers that descend from the midbrain. Its efferent olivocerebellar fibers leave the inner aspect of the sac-like nucleus and cross the midline to ascend into the cerebellum in the inferior cerebellar peduncle. The crossing fibers are joined dorsally and medially by fibers of two small accessory olivary nuclei.

The inferior cerebellar peduncle is located lateral to the spinal tract of the fifth nerve and forms the floor of the lateral recess of the fourth ventricle. Anterior to it, in the groove between the inferior cerebellar peduncle and the olive, the fibers of the spinothalamic tracts are crowded into a compact bundle. The rootlets of nerves 9, 10, and 11 emerge through that bundle. The motor fibers of those nerves originate in the nucleus ambiguus, a long column of cells that extends the length of the medulla, posterior to the inferior olivary nucleus.

Review Questions (Answers Available on the Pages Cited)

1. What is the function of the fibers of the pyramid (p. 43)?
2. Name the three sources of nerve fibers that make up the inferior cerebellar peduncle (p. 45).
3. Where are the cell bodies of the fibers of the tuberculum cinereum (p. 45 and Fig. 4-6)?

4. What are the features of the inferior velum that have a role in the production and circulation of cerebrospinal fluid (p. 47)?
5. Locate a lesion that causes paralysis of the right arm and leg and the left half of the tongue (p. 47).
6. Where are the cell bodies of the bundles of fibers that cross the midline in the caudal, middle, and rostral portions of the medulla (p. 48)?
7. In what way are the nuclei gracilis and cuneatus comparable to nuclei of the posterior horn of the spinal cord (p. 49)?
8. Name the nucleus of the medulla that is an upward extension of the gelatinous substance (p. 50).
9. What portion of the gray matter of the spinal cord corresponds to the reticular formation of the brain stem (p. 50)?

5

The Pons Segment

The pons segment is the rostral half of the embryonic hindbrain. The cerebellum is attached to its posterior surface, and a transverse band of fibers (the *pons*, "a bridge") stretches across its anterior and lateral surfaces, uniting the right and left halves of the cerebellum. That bridge-like band, the basilar part of the pons segment, is phylogenetically a recently acquired structure and gives the segment its name. The portion of the pons segment that is crossed by the pons is the tegmental part.

External Features

Anterior Surface

The anterior surface of the pons segment (Fig. 5-1) has just one feature, the pons. It covers the entire surface.

Lateral Surface

As the fibers of the pons course around the side of the pons segment, they join to form the compact middle cerebellar peduncle and leave the rostral portion of the tegmental part exposed (Fig. 5-1). In that exposed area, a wide ribbon-like band of fibers ascends onto the lateral surface of the midbrain. The posterior fibers of the band arch toward the back of the midbrain. Those fibers are the lateral lemniscus, a part of the auditory pathway, which is described in conjunction with the internal structure of the pons segment. The anterior portion of that composite ribbon of fibers is the medial lemniscus.

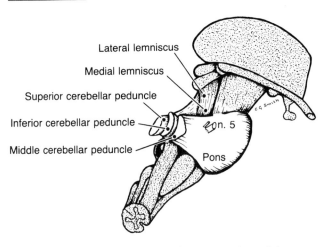

Lateral lemniscus
Medial lemniscus
Superior cerebellar peduncle
Inferior cerebellar peduncle
Middle cerebellar peduncle
n. 5
Pons

Figure 5-1. Features of the lateral and anterior surfaces of the pons segment.

It spirals onto the lateral surface as it ascends through the pons segment to lie alongside the spinal lemniscus, which is formed by the spinothalamic tracts (lateral and anterior). The lemnisci partly cover the superior cerebellar peduncle, an efferent fiber bundle of the cerebellum.

Posterior Surface

The attachment of the cerebellum extends across the back of the caudal part of the pons segment (Fig. 5-2). In the lateral part of the attachment, on each side, are three fiber bundles: the inferior, middle, and superior peduncles. Those peduncles convey data to and from the cerebellum and are named according to their relationship within the brain stem. The lateral bundle is called the *middle peduncle,* which conveys impulses from the cerebral hemisphere by way of the basilar part of the pons. Immediately medial to the middle peduncle is the *inferior peduncle,* which ascends from the medulla oblongata to reach the cerebellum; it conveys data from the sense organs. The most medial of the three bundles is the *superior cerebellar peduncle,* which ascends into the midbrain. As the right and left superior peduncles course along the lateral border of the superior velum, they gradually encroach on it until they almost meet at the midline. Thus the superior velum, like the inferior velum, is triangular. Those two delicate membranes, plus a small intervening portion of the cerebellum, form the roof of the fourth ventricle.

Nerve Attachments of the Pons Segment

Four of the eight nerves of the hindbrain are attached to the pons segment (Fig. 5-3).

The fifth nerve, the trigeminal, resembles a spinal nerve in that it has sensory and motor roots. The sensory fibers convey impulses from sense organs for touch, position, pain, and temperature, which are located in the head region. Its motor fibers supply the

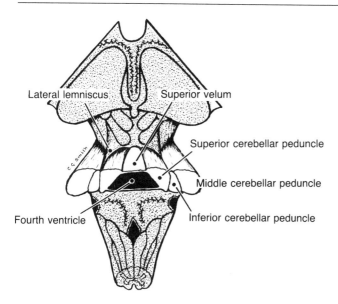

Figure 5-2. Features of the posterior surface of the pons segment.

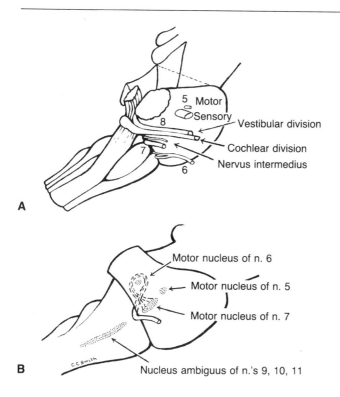

Figure 5-3. (A) The nerve attachments of the pons segment. (B) The motor nuclei of nerves 5, 6, 7, 9, 10, and 11 and the fibers of nerve 7 projected onto the lateral surface of the hindbrain.

muscles for mastication and some smaller muscles.. The large sensory root and the much smaller motor root penetrate the middle of the lateral surface of the pons together.

The sixth nerve is the abducens nerve. It is the motor nerve of the abductor muscle of the eye (hence its name). It emerges at the caudal border of the pons lateral to the pyramid.

The seventh nerve is the facial nerve. That nerve supplies the muscles for facial expression. It emerges at the caudal border of the pons in line with the rootlets of the glossopharyngeal nerve. The nervus intermedius, attached posterior to the facial nerve, is considered to be its sensory root. It contains fibers that convey impulses from taste buds on the anterior part of the tongue.

The eighth nerve is the vestibulocochlear nerve, which is a composite sensory nerve. A cochlear portion conveys impulses from sense organs for hearing; a vestibular portion is a special position sense nerve that supplies sense organs to record movement and changes in position relative to the force of gravity. The two parts reach the brain together just posterior to the nervus intermedius at the anterior border of the inferior cerebellar peduncle. The vestibular division enters the pons segment ventral to the peduncle. The cochlear division ends in nuclei on its dorsolateral surface.

Internal Structure

Basilar Part

The basilar part of the pons segment is acquired after the fourth month of intrauterine life. It is composed of pathways from the cortex of the right and left cerebral hemispheres that descend superficially on the midbrain to decussate anterior to the rostral half of the hindbrain and end in the cerebellar hemisphere (Fig 5-4). Each of those pathways is a chain of two nerve cells. The cell in the cerebral cortex sends its axon to synapse with a cell located anterior to the tegmental part of the pons segment. Those latter cells form the pontine nuclei and relay impulses along axons that extend superficially across the midline to end in the cerebellar cortex. The pontocerebellar fibers form the middle cerebellar peduncle.

The cells of the pontine nucleus form in layers separated by sheets of transverse pontocerebellar fibers (Figs. 5-5 and 5-6). The fibers of the corticopontine and corticospinal tracts descend into these cell layers where the corticopontine fibers end, but the corticospinal fibers continue into the pyramid of the medulla.

The Tegmental Part of the Pons Segment

The tegmental portion of the pons segment has a structure similar to that of the medulla (Fig. 5-5A and 5-B). Its core is a part of the reticular formation. Like the medulla, the floor of the fourth ventricle in the pons segment contains motor and sensory nuclei.

The medial lemniscus enters the pons segment from the medulla medial to the reticular formation. It spirals around it as it ascends to form an outer layer of fibers, first on the anterior and then on the lateral surface of the tegmentum (see Fig. 5-8). That development brings it alongside the spinothalamic tracts. The lateral and anterior spinothalamic tracts together form a single bundle, at that level, called the *spinal lemniscus*.

The inferior cerebellar peduncle makes a sharp turn into the stalk of the cerebellum

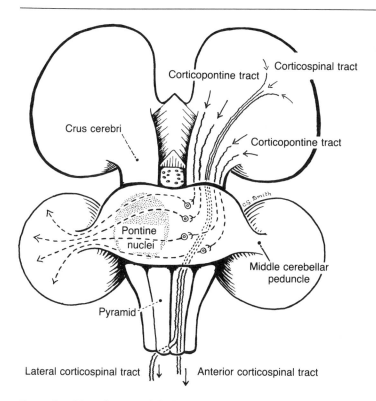

Figure 5-4. Ventral aspect of the brain, showing how the pons is formed by pathways descending from the cerebral hemisphere to the cerebellum. Only the pathways from the left hemisphere are charted.

as it enters the pons segment (see Fig. 5-1), leaving the spinal tract of the fifth nerve in contact with the middle cerebellar peduncle. Just rostral to that point, the fifth nerve penetrates the middle cerebellar peduncle and encounters its ovoid principal sensory nucleus (Fig. 5-6). There the sensory fibers of the nerve sort themselves out according to function. The thickly myelinated fibers from touch and position sense organs end in the principal sensory nucleus; the unmyelinated and thinly myelinated fibers descend to form the spinal tract. A slender bundle of myelinated fibers, the mesencephalic tract, extends up into the midbrain. That bundle is composed of afferent fibers for the stretch receptors in the muscles of mastication as well as other muscles of the head.

In the caudal part of the tegmentum's central core, the superior olivary nucleus replaces the large sac-like inferior olive of the medulla. It is a very small irregularly shaped nucleus that serves as a relay station in the auditory system. Posterior to it and within the reticular formation is the motor nucleus of the seventh nerve; rostral to it is the motor nucleus of the fifth nerve. Those two nuclei are in line with the nucleus ambiguus of the medulla. The motor nucleus of the sixth nerve is located in the floor of the fourth ventricle—at the midline—in the caudal part of the pons segment. The motor fibers of the seventh nerve loop around it, as illustrated in Figure 5-3. The nucleus of the seventh nerve is only a few millimeters from its exit from the brain stem, but its fibers course to the

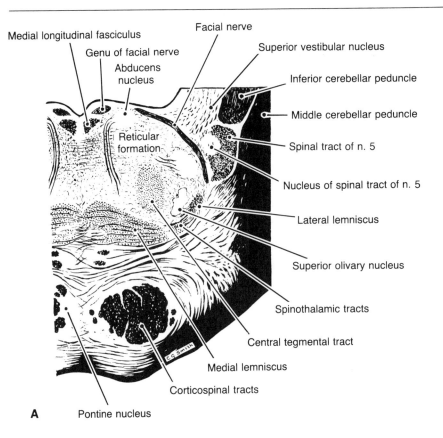

Medial longitudinal fasciculus

Genu of facial nerve

Abducens nucleus

Facial nerve

Superior vestibular nucleus

Inferior cerebellar peduncle

Middle cerebellar peduncle

Reticular formation

Spinal tract of n. 5

Nucleus of spinal tract of n. 5

Lateral lemniscus

Superior olivary nucleus

Spinothalamic tracts

Central tegmental tract

Medial lemniscus

Corticospinal tracts

A Pontine nucleus

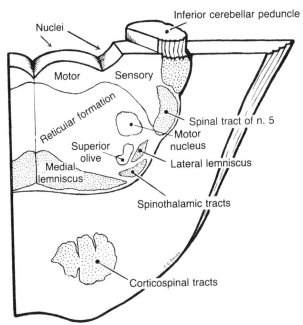

Nuclei

Inferior cerebellar peduncle

Motor   Sensory

Reticular formation

Spinal tract of n. 5

Motor nucleus

Superior olive

Medial lemniscus

Lateral lemniscus

Spinothalamic tracts

Corticospinal tracts

B

Figure 5-5.(A) Diagram of a myelin-stained cross section of the pons segment at the level of the nucleus of the sixth nerve. (B) The same section, showing its major features.

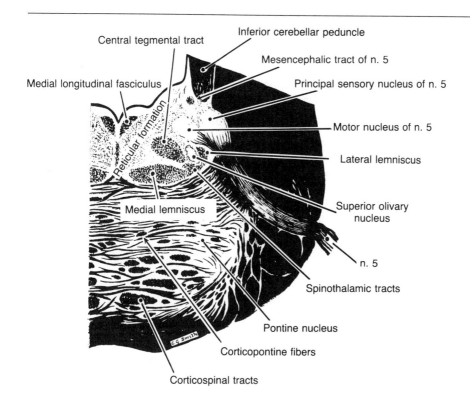

Figure 5-6. Diagram of a myelin-stained cross section of the pons segment at the level of the principal sensory nucleus of nerve 5.

caudal border of the sixth-nerve nucleus. At that point, the seventh-nerve fibers ascend medial to the sixth-nerve nucleus and then turn back between the nucleus and the floor of the ventricle to emerge at the caudal border of the pons.

The central tegmental tract is made up of fibers that descend from the red nucleus to the inferior olive and contain some ascending reticulothalamic fibers. It is located in the lateral part of the reticular formation, and it is a moderately compact bundle.

The sensory nuclei of the cochlear and vestibular divisions of the eighth nerve, along with their connections, are described under separate headings.

Cochlear Nuclei and Auditory Pathways
The cells of the sense organ for hearing are located in the walls of a fluid-filled tube, called the *cochlear duct*. The duct is a part of the membranous labyrinth of the inner ear (Fig. 5-7). It coils to form a spiral with two and a half turns, and sensory cells extend along its length. The cells in the basal turn respond to high frequencies; those in the apical turn, to low frequencies. The bipolar ganglion cells also extend along the length of the cochlear duct. Each one sends a short process to contact one or more sensory cells and a long process to the brain. The latter form the cochlear division of the vestibulocochlear nerve.

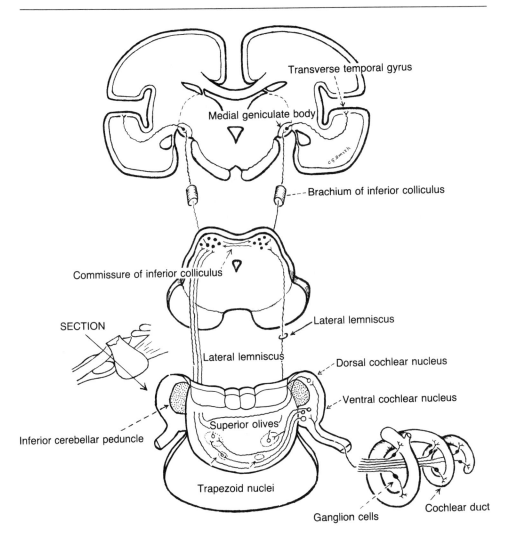

Transverse temporal gyrus

Medial geniculate body

Brachium of inferior colliculus

Commissure of inferior colliculus

SECTION

Lateral lemniscus

Lateral lemniscus

Dorsal cochlear nucleus

Ventral cochlear nucleus

Inferior cerebellar peduncle

Superior olives

Trapezoid nuclei

Ganglion cells

Cochlear duct

Figure 5-7. Auditory pathways to the cerebral cortex.

Fibers of the cochlear nerve terminate in two cell masses, the dorsal and ventral cochlear nuclei, located on the dorsal and lateral surfaces of the inferior cerebellar peduncle. The dorsal nucleus forms an eminence, the acoustic tubercle, on the floor of the lateral recess of the fourth ventricle (Fig. 5-8). When the nerve fibers reach the brain stem, they bifurcate, sending a branch to both the dorsal and the ventral nucleus. Each nucleus has its own pathway to the cerebral hemisphere of the opposite side, but the ventral nucleus also has an ascending pathway to the cerebral hemisphere on its own side. Fibers of cells in the dorsal nucleus pass posterior to the inferior cerebellar peduncle to cross the midline just anterior to the gray matter in the floor of the fourth ventricle. After crossing, they form part of a ribbon-like band, the lateral lemniscus, that ascends along the spiraling lateral border of the medial lemniscus.

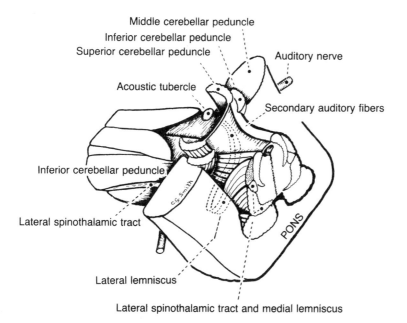

Middle cerebellar peduncle
Inferior cerebellar peduncle
Superior cerebellar peduncle
Auditory nerve
Acoustic tubercle
Secondary auditory fibers
Inferior cerebellar peduncle
Lateral spinothalamic tract
PONS
Lateral lemniscus
Lateral spinothalamic tract and medial lemniscus

Figure 5-8. Dorsolateral aspect of the hindbrain. The bundles in the stalk of the cerebellum have been isolated, and the course of the crossing auditory fibers, to form the lateral lemniscus on the right side, is indicated.

The ventral cochlear nucleus is larger than the dorsal one. Its fibers pass medially, deep to the inferior cerebellar peduncle and anterior to the superior olivary nucleus. When they encounter the medial lemniscus on the anterior surface of the tegmentum (see Fig. 5-5), some penetrate it and others pass anterior to it and cross the midline to continue anterior to the superior olivary nucleus. The crossing fibers form a strap-like band, called the *trapezoid body*. Lateral to the superior olive, the fibers ascend to join the fibers that crossed in the dorsal part of the tegmentum to form the lateral lemniscus. A few fibers of the trapezoid body, after crossing, end in trapezoid nuclei, located anterior to the superior olive. Cells of those nuclei relay impulses to the superior olive, which, in turn, relays them along fibers that join the lateral lemniscus.

As previously indicated, impulses relayed by the ventral cochlear nuclei can reach both hemispheres. The homolateral pathway is provided by fibers that synapse with cells of the superior olivary nucleus of the same side. Some cells of that nucleus relay impulses along fibers that ascend without crossing in the lateral lemniscus. Since impulses from the cochlea of one ear ascend in both the right and left lateral lemniscus, a lesion of that bundle does not result in significant loss of hearing.

The superior olivary nucleus has additional important functions. It serves as a relay station on reflex pathways and it is the origin of fibers that extend, by means of the eighth nerve, to terminate in the sensory cells of the cochlear duct. Impulses conveyed by those efferent fibers can selectively modulate the sensitivity of the sensory cells.

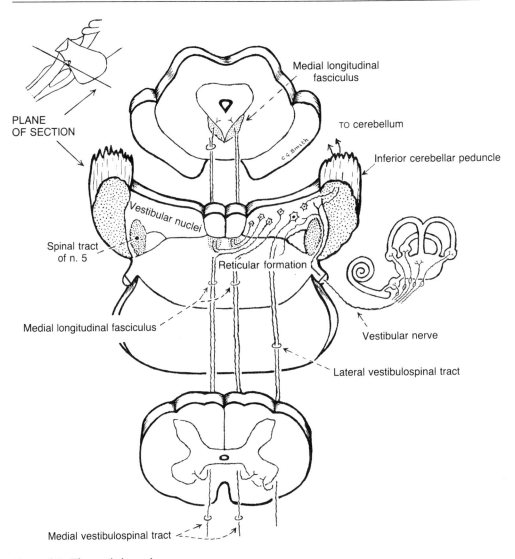

Figure 5-9. The vestibular pathways.

Vestibular Pathways

The Vestibular Nerve and Its Sensory Nuclei. The vestibular nerve carries the sensory stimuli of the position sense organs in the ampullae of the semicircular canals and (2) in the maculae of the utricle and saccule of the inner ear (Fig. 5-9). The sensory cells of the semicircular canals are stimulated by angular movements of the head; those of the utricle and saccule respond to changes in gravitational forces.

The sensory ganglion of the vestibular nerve, like that of the the cochlear nerve, is close to the sense organ. The long, centrally directed processes of its bipolar cells form a compact bundle that is enclosed in a common connective-tissue sheath with the cochlear nerve. The two nerves separate when they reach the brain (Fig. 5-3). The vestibular nerve fibers course deep to the inferior cerebellar peduncle to reach the vestibular nuclei, which are located in the lateral part of the floor of the fourth ventricle. There are four of those nuclei: superior, inferior, medial, and lateral. Some fibers continue into the cerebellum through the inferior cerebellar peduncle; a few end in the reticular formation.

The Efferent Fibers of the Vestibular Nuclei. The major efferent fibers of the vestibular nuclei mediate reflex responses. Sensory pathways to the cerebral cortex have been demonstrated physiologically by recording electrical activity, but they have not been traced. The reflex responses are adjustments of the eyes and all parts of the body to angular movements of the head and changes in position relative to the force of gravity. Those postural adjustments always involve both sides of the body, so most of the pathways are paired.

The reflex pathways can be divided into two groups: ascending and descending. The ascending pathways extend to the motor nuclei that control movements of the eyes. The descending pathways extend to motor nuclei that excite the muscles used in maintaining equilibrium. The ascending pathways originate in the rostral part of the vestibular nuclei. Crossed and uncrossed fibers form compact bundles that ascend on each side of the midline, anterior to the motor nuclei of eye muscles, in the pons and midbrain. Those fiber bundles are the medial longitudinal fasciculi. Similarly, crossed and uncrossed fibers descend from cells in the caudal parts of the medial and the inferior nuclei, and those fibers form caudal extensions of the medial longitudinal fasciculi. They extend into the anterior funiculi of the spinal cord where they are known as the *medial vestibulospinal tracts*. Those tracts convey impulses to the anterior horn cells.

In addition to the paired, crossed and uncrossed medial vestibulospinal tracts, there is an unpaired, uncrossed, lateral vestibulospinal tract. It arises from the lateral vestibular nucleus and descends as a bundle of loosely disposed fibers in the reticular formation of the medulla, and it continues into the lateral part of the anterior funiculus. Its fibers activate anterior horn cells that supply extensor muscles. Cutting that tract relieves the extensor rigidity that follows transection of the upper brain stem in experimental animals.

The vestibular nerve, like the cochlear nerve, contains some efferent fibers. Those fibers have cell bodies in the reticular formation and extend to the special position sense organs of the vestibular nerve. They modulate the excitability of the vestibular sensory cells.

Review Questions (Answers Available on the Pages Cited)

1. What are the two external features that identify the pons segment (p. 53)?
2. Justify the names, superior and inferior cerebellar peduncles, for the two medial bundles in the stalk of the cerebellum (p. 54).
3. Name and locate the nerve attachments of the pons segment (a) that contain no sensory fibers and (b) that contain no motor fibers (p. 56).
4. What are the pathways that (a) decussate in the basilar part of the pons segment (b) pass through the basilar part without a synapse (p. 57)?
5. Locate the lesion that can result in a homolateral paralysis of the muscles of expression and the abductor of the eye (p. 57).
6. Describe the homolateral pathway for hearing (p. 61).
7. What is the function of the reflex pathways (a) that ascend (b) that descend from the vestibular nuclei (p. 63)?

6

The Midbrain

The midbrain is the cube-shaped segment of the brain stem that is located between the pons segment of the hindbrain and the diencephalon. It may be identified by the four mound-like elevations, known as the *corpora quadrigemina,* that form its posterior surface.

Functionally, the midbrain plays a major role in motor activity. It contains the nuclei that reflexly control movements of the head and eyes, and it also contains nuclei that have a role in voluntary movements. One of them, the red nucleus, is the origin of the rubrospinal tract, which conveys impulses from the cerebellum and from the cerebral cortex to the spinal cord. Another, the substantia nigra, is part of a feedback pathway that relays impulses to the origin of the corticospinal tract. Lesions of those nuclei result, respectively, in intention tremor and rigidity associated with a tremor present at rest.

External Features

All the external features of the midbrain are illustrated in Figure 6-1. Each one is part of a sensory or motor pathway, and they are described in order in the following sections, starting with the medial lemniscus on the lateral surface, which is progressively overlapped by features posterior and anterior to it as it is followed from the pons to the diencephalon.

Medial Lemniscus

The fibers of the medial lemniscus are axons of cells of the nuclei gracilis and cuneatus. They convey impulses from sense organs for touch and position. The ribbon-like medial lemniscus, after a spiral course within the pons segment, reaches its lateral surface and

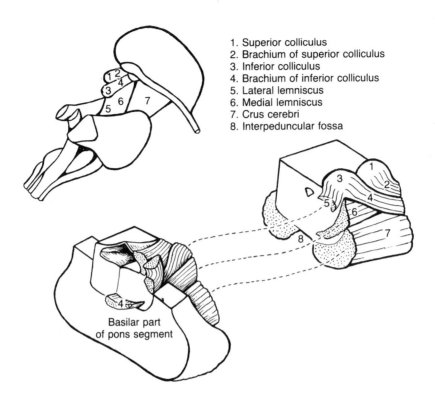

1. Superior colliculus
2. Brachium of superior colliculus
3. Inferior colliculus
4. Brachium of inferior colliculus
5. Lateral lemniscus
6. Medial lemniscus
7. Crus cerebri
8. Interpeduncular fossa

Basilar part
of pons segment

Figure 6-1. External features of the midbrain.

retains that position in the midbrain. As it approaches the diencephalon, it is overlapped progressively by the brachium of the inferior colliculus and the crus cerebri.

Crus Cerebri (Basis Pedunculi) and Interpeduncular Fossa

The crus cerebri is a rope-like bundle that includes fibers of the corticopontine tract, the corticobulbar tract, and the corticospinal tract. It descends on the anterior surface of the midbrain, separated from its fellow of the opposite side by a deep, wide fossa, the interpeduncular fossa. The right and left crura converge as they descend from the diencephalon, narrowing the interpeduncular fossa and leaving increasingly more of the medial lemniscus uncovered. Between the two crura, the anterior surface of the midbrain is penetrated by many fine vessels. That area is called the *posterior perforated area*, because there is a similar area on the anterior part of the inferior surface of the cerebral hemisphere. Occlusion or rupture of those vessels is one cause of stroke, resulting (as will be explained later) in ipsilateral paralysis of the muscles supplied by the third nerve, and in contralateral ataxia (incoordination) due to involvement of the red nucleus. This loss of function is known as the *syndrome of Benedikt*.

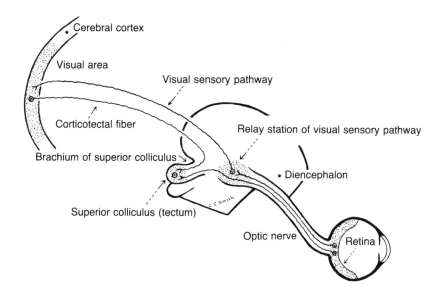

Figure 6-2. *The optic pathway, showing the direct and indirect pathways from the retina to the superior colliculus.*

Lateral Lemniscus, Inferior Colliculus, and Brachium of the Inferior Colliculus (Parts of the Auditory Pathway)

The lateral lemniscus, which is located along the posterior border of the medial lemniscus, makes a sharp turn posteriorly as it enters the midbrain to end in a relay station, called the *nucleus of the inferior colliculus*. That cell mass bulges onto the posterior surface to form a large round eminence, called the *inferior colliculus*, ("little hill"). The inferior colliculus, with its fellow of the opposite side, covers the caudal half of the posterior surface of the midbrain. Most of the neurons of that relay station are part of the auditory pathway to the cerebral hemisphere. Their fibers form a compact bundle, the brachium ("arm") of the inferior colliculus, that extends upward on the lateral surface. The bundle ascends superficial to the medial lemniscus and continues to shift anteriorly until it contacts the posterior border of the crus cerebri at the upper end of the midbrain.

Superior Colliculus and Its Brachium (Parts of the Reflex Pathway for Eye Movements)

The superior colliculus is a dome-like eminence of gray matter that, with its fellow of the opposite side, forms the upper, or rostral, half of the posterior surface of the midbrain. It receives impulses from the retina directly by way of a small number of optic nerve fibers and indirectly by way of a large bundle of fibers that relays impulses from the area of the cerebral cortex, in which the visual pathway ends.

All those afferent fibers form the fiber bundle that is called the *brachium of the superior colliculus* (Fig. 6-2). It reaches the lateral surface of the midbrain from the diencephalon at the posterior border of the brachium of the inferior colliculus and courses parallel to it to enter the superior colliculus. Its fibers spread out and end in a superficial layer of cells to provide a point-to-point projection of the retina.

In humans, the function of the superior colliculus is to control movements of the head and eyes. Injury of the superior colliculus impairs a person's ability to keep the eyes fixed on a moving object, but it does not cause blindness.

Nerve Attachments of the Midbrain

Two nerves, the third and the fourth, are attached to the midbrain. Both are motor nerves. The third, the oculomotor nerve, emerges at the medial border of the crus cerebri at the level of the superior colliculus. It contains motor fibers that supply four of the muscles attached to the eyeball and one muscle of the upper eyelid. The nerve also contains the parasympathetic preganglionic fibers that convey impulses by means of the ciliary ganglion to the smooth muscles that control pupil size and tension on the lens for near and far vision. The fourth, the trochlear nerve, emerges from the back of the midbrain at the midline, just caudal to the inferior colliculus. It is a thread-like nerve that supplies the superior oblique muscle of the eye.

Internal Structure

The internal structure of the midbrain can be studied in cross sections. Comparing a section of the midbrain with a section of the pons, we find that the membranous roof of the fourth ventricle is replaced by the nervous tissue of the superior and inferior colliculi—the *tectum of the midbrain*. Anteriorly, the basilar part of the pons segment is replaced in cross section by the crus cerebri and a layer of pigmented cells deep to it, called the *substantia nigra*. The portion of the midbrain between the substantia nigra and the tectum is called the *tegmentum*. It contains an extension of the reticular formation of the pons and a number of nuclei and fiber bundles.

Cerebral Aqueduct (Cavity of the Midbrain)

The cavity of the midbrain is reduced to a canal, called the *cerebral aqueduct* (Fig. 6-3). It is located in the median plane close to the posterior surface. The name is fitting because it serves as a drainage channel for the watery cerebrospinal fluid produced in the third and lateral ventricles of the forebrain. It is only 2 mm or less in diameter and may be blocked by inflammatory debris or by the pressure of a tumor. In that case, fluid accumulates in the ventricles of the forebrain, a condition known as *hydrocephalus*. If that occurs in a child, the head can and will enlarge; in an adult, the head cannot enlarge because the bones of the skull are synostosed. As a result, there is an enlargement of the ventricles at the expense of nervous tissue, leading to mental deterioration.

Central (Periaqueductal) Gray Matter

The central gray matter is the thick layer that surrounds the aqueduct (Fig. 6-4). Its anterior part contains cranial nerve nuclei. The *nucleus of the fourth nerve* (motor) is

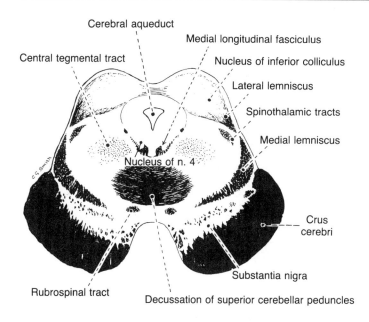

Cerebral aqueduct
Medial longitudinal fasciculus
Central tegmental tract
Nucleus of inferior colliculus
Lateral lemniscus
Spinothalamic tracts
Medial lemniscus
Nucleus of n. 4
Crus cerebri
Substantia nigra
Rubrospinal tract
Decussation of superior cerebellar peduncles

Figure 6-3. Cross section of the midbrain at the level of the inferior colliculus.

adjacent to the median plane at the level of the inferior colliculus; the *nucleus of the third nerve* (motor) is in line with it at the level of the superior colliculus. A mesencephalic portion of the *sensory nucleus of the fifth nerve* is a slender column of cells that is prolonged rostrally into the midbrain, lateral to both motor nuclei. The cells in the posterior portion of the central gray matter are not grouped into well-defined nuclei. Some relay impulses from pain sense organs to the limbic portion of the forebrain, which is associated with emotional responses and feeling. The afferent fibers ascend within the spinothalamic tracts. Other cells of the central gray matter give rise to descending fibers that are part of a pathway (to the spinal cord) that regulates nerve conduction from sense organs for pain.

Nucleus of the Inferior Colliculus

The nucleus of the inferior colliculus (Fig. 6-3) is located posterior to the central gray matter in the caudal half of the midbrain. It is an ovoid mass that is encapsulated by the fibers of the lateral lemniscus, which end in it. Its neurons serve as relay stations on diverging auditory pathways. Most of its efferent fibers form the brachium of the inferior colliculus, which is the continuation of the auditory pathway to the forebrain. It is the sensory pathway for hearing. Other fibers extend across the midline to form the *commissure of the inferior colliculus,* thus ensuring that each colliculus receives impulses from both ears. Cutting one brachium does not cause appreciable deafness in either ear. Reflex responses to auditory stimuli are excited by means of fibers that pass into the deeper layers of the superior colliculus, which has efferent pathways to muscles (see the following discussion).

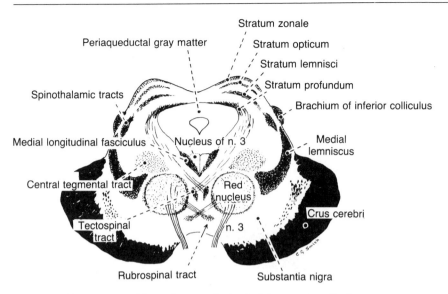

Figure 6-4. Cross section of the midbrain at the level of the superior colliculus.

Gray Matter of the Superior Colliculus

The superior colliculus is a laminated structure that consists of alternate layers of white and gray matter (Fig. 6-4). From the surface inward, those layers are (1) a thin layer of optic nerve fibers, the stratum zonale; (2) an outer gray layer; (3) a fiber layer, the stratum opticum, containing afferent fibers from the cerebral hemisphere; (4) a middle gray layer; (5) a fiber layer, stratum lemnisci, containing spinotectal fibers that ascend with the fibers of the spinothalamic tracts (also known as the spinal lemniscus); (6) a deep gray layer; and (7) a deep fiber layer, the stratum profundum, composed of efferent fibers.

The efferent fibers of the stratum profundum course anteriorly, lateral to the central gray matter, to cross the midline in the *posterior tegmental decussation,* and descend close to the midline to end in the motor nuclei of the brain and spinal cord. They are known as fibers of the *tectobulbar tract (bulb,* "the hindbrain") and the *tectospinal tracts.* Impulses conveyed by those tracts excite movements of the eyes and head in response to visual and auditory stimuli.

Red Nucleus

The red nucleus (Fig. 6-4) is a conspicuous feature of the central part of the tegmentum of the midbrain. It is an ovoid mass of cells, circular in cross section, that extends from the middle of the midbrain into the caudal part of the diencephalon. It gets its name from its pink color in a freshly cut, unfixed brain. It is pink because it contains more capillaries than the adjacent nervous tissue. The red nucleus is an integrating nucleus that is interpolated at the convergence of two major pathways. One of those pathways, the corticorubral, originates in the area of cerebral cortex that gives rise to the corti- cobulbar and corticospinal tracts, which excite voluntary movements. Fibers of the *cor-*

ticorubral tract enter the midbrain in the crus cerebri and pass posteriorly to end in the red nucleus on the same side. The other pathway to the red nucleus originates in the cerebellum of the opposite side. Fibers of that pathway leave the cerebellum to emerge as the *superior cerebellar peduncle* (brachium conjunctivum). That large fiber bundle ascends with an anterior inclination to enter the midbrain medial to the lateral lemniscus and anterior to the inferior colliculus. Anterior to the periaqueductal gray matter, the fibers of the right and left peduncles cross the midline in the caudal half of the tegmentum to form the decussation of the superior cerebellar peduncles (Fig. 6-3). Having crossed, the fibers turn rostrally to enter the red nucleus, where some end and synapse with the cells that also receive the terminals of the corticorubral fibers; the rest continue on to end in the diencephalon.

The cells of the red nucleus give rise to two efferent tracts: a *rubrospinal tract* and a *rubroolivary tract*. The fibers of the rubrospinal tract cross the midline in the anterior tegmental decussation and descend in the core of the brain stem to reach the middle of the lateral funiculus of the spinal cord, where they mingle with the fibers of the lateral corticospinal and the lateral spinothalamic tracts.

The fibers of the rubroolivary tract descend without crossing the midline as part of a *centrally located tegmental tract* to end in the inferior olivary nucleus. That tract is a feedback pathway that utilizes the inferior olive as a relay station to convey impulses back to the cerebellum, the origin of the cerebellar pathway to the red nucleus.

It is of interest that the corticorubrospinal pathway has the same site of origin and the same site of termination as the corticospinal pathway, which conveys impulses to excite voluntary movements. Unlike the corticospinal pathway, however, the impulses conveyed by the corticorubral fibers come under the modulating influence of the cerebellum in the midbrain.

Substantia Nigra

The substantia nigra is a thick layer of cells that intervenes between the crus cerebri and the tegmentum of the midbrain (Figs. 6-3 and 6-4). It extends the length of the midbrain in line with the laminated gray matter of the pontine nuclei and extends a short distance into the diencephalon, where it abuts against the subthalamic nucleus. Its cells are remarkable for the black pigment (melanin) they contain. Hence the nucleus is identifiable as a black band in an unstained section.

The substantia nigra has two parts: a posterior layer of closely crowded cells, the *pars compacta,* and an anterior layer, the *pars reticulata,* which is composed of more loosely disposed cells that partly invade the crus cerebri. The function of the substantia nigra is to control the flow of impulses into motor pathways. The chief pathway controls voluntary movements and originates in the cerebral cortex. When the substantia nigra is destroyed by disease, as in paralysis agitans, there is no paralysis of voluntary movement, but a disabling rigidity occurs because of maintained contraction of flexors and extensors. This problem is usually associated with a rhythmic tremor while the person is at rest. The pathways involved are described after the study of the cerebral hemisphere.

Spinothalamic Tracts

The fibers of the lateral and anterior spinothalamic tracts continue into the midbrain in one bundle, called the *spinal lemniscus.* That bundle reaches the midbrain just deep to the dorsal border of the medial lemniscus and then ascends deep to the brachium of the inferior colliculus. The neurosurgeon utilizes this relationship to locate the pain pathway in the midbrain. By cutting across the brachium deep enough to include the spinal lemniscus, it is possible to relieve pain on the entire opposite side of the body. Cutting the brachium of the inferior colliculus does not significantly impair hearing, because auditory pathways in the brachium of the opposite side convey impulses from both ears.

As the so-called spinothalamic tracts ascend through the brain stem, there is a progressive decrease in fiber content. That decrease occurs because they also contain fibers that end in the reticular formation (*spinoreticular fibers*) and in other parts of the brain stem such as the tectum (*spinotectal fibers*) and the central gray matter.

Medial Longitudinal Fasciculus

The medial longitudinal fasciculus is a well-defined bundle that extends from the hindbrain to the diencephalon, anterior to the central gray matter. Most of its fibers are axons of cells in the vestibular nuclei. They synapse with cells of the fourth and third motor nuclei to complete reflex pathways that excite eye turning in response to head movements.

Review Questions (Answers Available on the Pages Cited)

1. What are the external features that identify the midbrain (p. 65)?
2. Name the external features of the midbrain that are parts of the auditory pathway (p. 67).
3. Locate the lesion that could result in homolateral paralysis of eye muscles and paralysis of the muscles of the limbs on the opposite side (p. 68).
4. Why is the cerebral aqueduct well named (p. 68)?
5. What is the function of each of the groups of efferent fibers of the inferior colliculus (p. 69)?
6. Name four sources of afferent fibers to the superior colliculus (pp. 69 and 70).
7. Name two major afferent pathways of the red nucleus (pp. 70 and 71).
8. How does the substantia nigra influence voluntary movement (p. 71)?
9. Why does the spinal lemniscus (spinothalamic tracts) get smaller as it ascends through the brain stem (p. 72)?

7

The Diencephalon

The diencephalon is the rostral portion of the brain stem. The cerebral hemispheres are attached to its lateral surfaces. It is wedge-shaped (Fig. 7-1), and the edge of the wedge is its vertical anterior border. Its triangular superior and inferior surfaces meet posteriorly to form a smoothly rounded base. The base is notched in the midline by a posterior extension of a median gutter on the superior surface. The midbrain is attached to the middle of the inferior surface.

Subdivisions of the Diencephalon

The subdivisions of the diencephalon (Fig. 7-2) are groups of association nuclei. They integrate data from all the sense organs of the body as well as from the cerebellum and the cerebral hemisphere. Many of those subdivisions have two-way connections with a portion of the cerebral cortex to form corticothalamic association units.

Two subdivisions, the *subthalamus* and the *hypothalamus,* form the inferior part of the diencephalon. The subthalamus is located directly above the tegmentum of the midbrain. The hypothalamus is anterior and partly lateral to the subthalamus; it forms the inferior surface of the diencephalon anterior to the midbrain attachment. The subthalamus has a role in the motor function of skeletal muscles; the hypothalamus controls vital visceral functions.

The *thalamus* is located above the two inferior divisions, separated from them by a plane that arches from the aqueduct of the midbrain to the middle of the anterior border of the diencephalon. It contains the principal association nuclei of the diencephalon and forms its superior surface, lateral to the epithalamus. The *epithalamus* is a slender

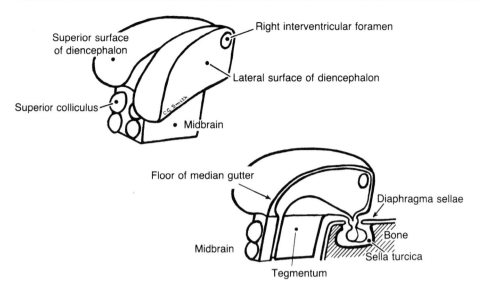

Figure 7-1. Form and relationships of the diencephalon.

cell column, called the *habenular trigone,* located along the border of the roof of the third ventricle; it receives olfactory and visceral impulses.

The *metathalamus* contains two nuclei: the lateral and medial geniculate bodies. Those nuclei are located under the portion of the thalamus that projects back above the colliculi. They receive impulses by way of the visual and auditory pathways, respectively.

External Features

Superior Surface

The membranous roof of the third ventricle forms the floor of the median gutter (Fig. 7-3). Anteriorly, it is continuous with the roof of the interventricular foramen, which extends from the anterior tubercle of the thalamus to the fornix. The fornix is a bundle of fibers that conveys impulses from the hippocampal portion of the cerebral cortex to the hypothalamus. Between the right and left fornices, the anterior border of the dien-cephalon contains commissural fibers of the attenuated recurring anterior portion of the corpus callosum. The corpus callosum connects the cortex of the right and left cerebral hemispheres.

The posterior part of the roof of the ventricle is outlined by the habenular trigone laterally and by the habenular commissure posteriorly. The habenular trigone is a slender ridge that tapers from a width of 2 mm posteriorly to end short of the interventricular foramen. Posterior to the habenular trigone, the transition zone between the diencephalon and the tectum of the midbrain is called the *pretectal area.* It contains relay nuclei of the light reflex pathway. The pupillary constrictor muscles of both eyes are activated by that pathway when a pencil of light enters one eye. Lateral to the pretectal area, the thalamus

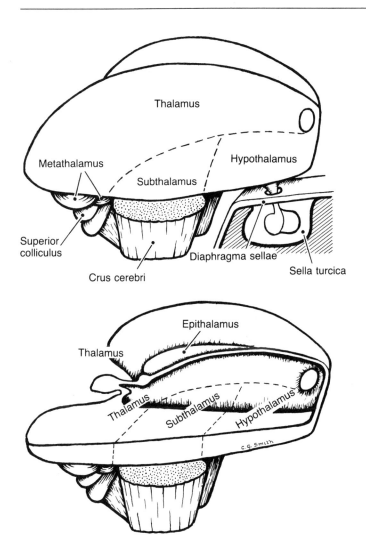

Figure 7-2. The diencephalon, showing its subdivisions.

extends posteriorly, above the superior colliculus, to form a cushion-like mass known as the *pulvinar*. The pineal gland is attached to the habenular commissure in the midline.

Inferior Surface

The midbrain attachment takes up the middle and largest part of the inferior surface (Fig. 7-4). In front of that attachment is the free triangular ventral surface of the hypothalamus. The apex of the surface is formed by the lamina terminalis, which is the anterior wall of the third ventricle. Just behind that wall, the right and left optic nerves are attached. About half the fibers of each nerve cross the midline to a form a transverse

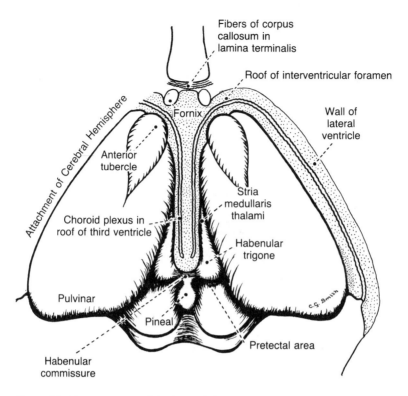

Figure 7-3. *Superior aspect of the diencephalon.*

bar, called the *optic chiasma.* Those crossing fibers join the fibers of the opposite nerve that do not cross and form the optic tract. The optic tract courses back along the lateral border of the diencephalon, hugging the lateral side of the crus cerebri. The optic tract fibers end in the lateral geniculate body, located dorsolateral to the crus cerebri on the inferior aspect of the pulvinar. That cell station has a lateral portion that forms a poorly defined swelling and a medial portion that is located in the floor of a groove, known as the *hilum of the lateral geniculate body.*

The medial geniculate body is a well-defined swelling, located dorsal to the crus, at the end of the brachium of the inferior colliculus. It may be mistaken for the poorly defined lateral geniculate body, because the medial fibers of the optic tract appear to end in it.

On the ventral surface of the hypothalamus, immediately in front of the midbrain, are two spherical masses: the right and left mammillary bodies. Those masses are nuclei of the hypothalamus. Between the mammillary bodies and the optic chiasma, the floor of the third ventricle is drawn down into a funnel-like projection, called the *infundibulum.* The stem of the funnel has a terminal enlargement, called the *infundibular process* (Fig. 7-4). Surrounding the base of the stem is an elevation, called the *median eminence.* That eminence, the infundibular stem, and the process are all parts of the posterior part of the hypophysis, that is, the posterior lobe of the pituitary gland. Lateral to the median

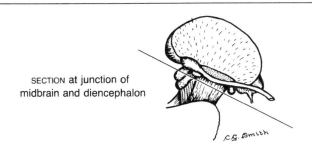

SECTION at junction of
midbrain and diencephalon

C.G. Smith

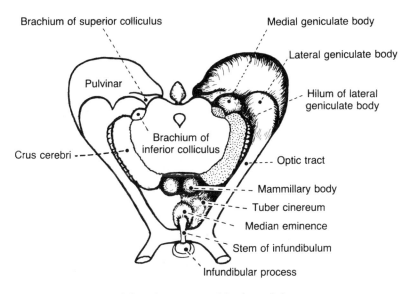

Brachium of superior colliculus

Medial geniculate body

Lateral geniculate body

Pulvinar

Hilum of lateral
geniculate body

Brachium of
inferior colliculus

Crus cerebri

Optic tract

Mammillary body

Tuber cinereum

Median eminence

Stem of infundibulum

Infundibular process

Figure 7-4. Features of the inferior aspect of the diencephalon.

eminence, the nuclei of the hypothalamus form the irregularly nodular area that is known as the *tuber cinereum.*

Lateral Surface

The lateral surface of the diencephalon serves as an area of attachment for the cerebral hemisphere (Fig. 7-5). Through that surface pass almost all the fibers that connect the brain stem and the cerebral hemisphere. They are called *projection fibers;* their cell bodies may be in the hemisphere and convey impulses to the brain stem, or they may be in the brain stem and convey impulses to the hemisphere. Immediately lateral to the diencephalon those fibers are crowded into a fan-shaped layer, called the *internal capsule,* by a large lens-shaped cell mass, the lentiform nucleus (Fig. 7-6). The internal capsule has the following parts: a posterior limb between the lentiform nucleus and the diencephalon, an anterior limb composed of fibers that course medial to the anterior part of the lentiform nucleus, and a sublenticular limb, located inferior to the posterior part of the lentiform nucleus. The knee-like bend between the anterior and posterior limbs is called the *genu.*

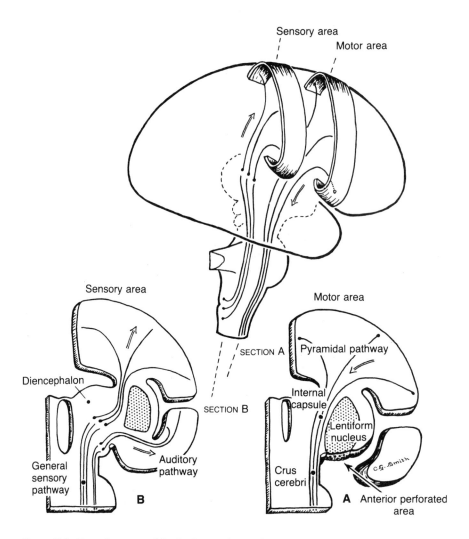

Figure 7-5. Frontal sections of the forebrain, showing how the fibers that connect the cerebral hemisphere and diencephalon are crowded together to form the internal (medial) part of the capsule of the lentiform nucleus.

The contributions of the diencephalic fibers and the fibers that form the crus cerebri are illustrated in Figure 7-7.

Figure 7-7A is a diagram of the lateral aspect of the diencephalon, with its subdivisions outlined. In Figure 7-7B, the two-way connections of the diencephalon with the cerebral cortex have been added. Those connections radiate so that anterior, middle, and posterior portions of the diencephalon are connected with corresponding portions of the cerebral cortex. In Figure 7-7C, the fibers of the corticospinal, corticobulbar, and corticopontine

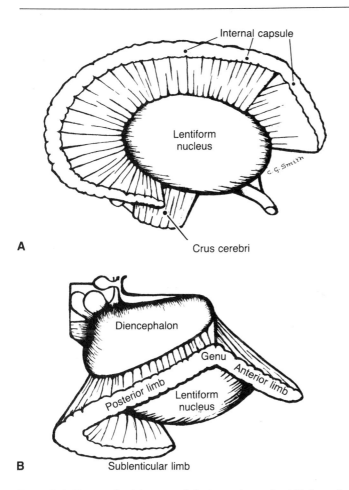

Internal capsule

Lentiform
nucleus

C.G.Smith

A

Crus cerebri

Diencephalon

Genu

Anterior limb

Posterior limb

Lentiform
nucleus

B

Sublenticular limb

Figure 7-6. Form and subdivisions of the internal capsule. (A) Lateral aspect of the lentiform nucleus and the emerging fibers of the internal capsule. (B) Superior aspect of the right half of the diencephalon and the internal capsule.

tracts have been added. Most of those tracts descend in the posterior limb and pass lateral to the subthalamus to converge and form the crus cerebri. The lateral aspect of the hypothalamus is left uncovered and in direct contact with the lentiform nucleus, which is lateral to the area outlined by the broken line shown in Figure 7-7C.

The portion of the lentiform nucleus lateral to the hypothalamus is a subdivision called the *innominate substance*. It has olfactory and hypothalamic connections and extends to form a small part of the inferior surface of the hemisphere, called the anterior perforated area (Fig. 7-5). The remainder of the lentiform nucleus is divided into a medial and a lateral part. The lateral part is the putamen; it receives most of the afferent fibers of the lentiform nucleus (Fig. 7-8). The medial part is the globus pallidus, which looks paler than the putamen because of its content of myelinated fibers. The cell bodies of many of the efferent fibers of the lentiform nucleus are located in the globus pallidus.

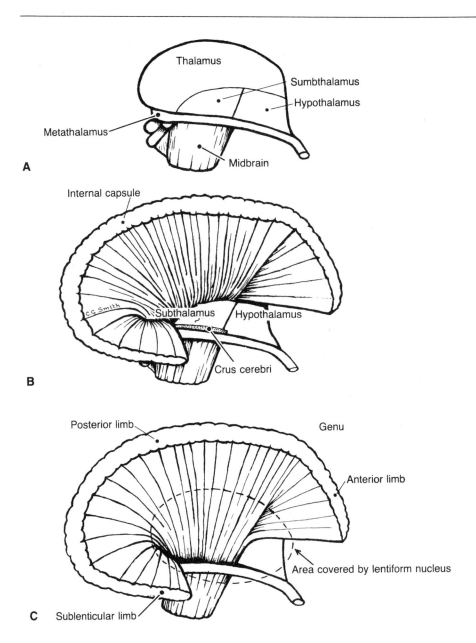

A

B

C

Figure 7-7. Structure of the internal capsule. (A) Lateral aspect of the diencephalon and midbrain. (B) Fibers that connect the thalamus and metathalamus with the cerebral cortex. (C) Addition of the fibers that descend in the crus cerebri.

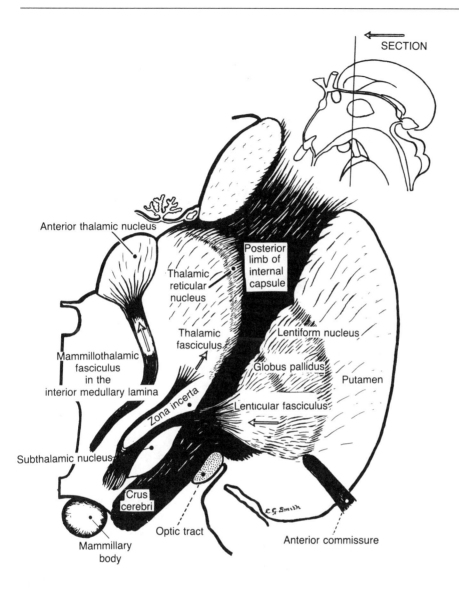

SECTION

Anterior thalamic nucleus

Thalamic reticular nucleus

Posterior limb of internal capsule

Thalamic fasciculus

Lentiform nucleus

Mammillothalamic fasciculus in the interior medullary lamina

Globus pallidus

Putamen

Zona incerta

Lenticular fasciculus

Subthalamic nucleus

C. G. Smith

Crus cerebri

Optic tract

Anterior commissure

Mammillary body

Figure 7-8. Frontal section of the right half of the diencephalon, internal capsule, and lentiform nucleus in the plane shown in the upper diagram.

Midsagittal Section of the Diencephalon: The Third Ventricle

The right and left portions of the diencephalon are almost completely separated from each other by the cleft-like third ventricle. That cavity has lateral walls, a roof, a floor, and an anterior wall. No posterior wall exists because the roof and floor approach each other to form the dorsal and ventral walls of the aqueduct (Fig. 7-9).

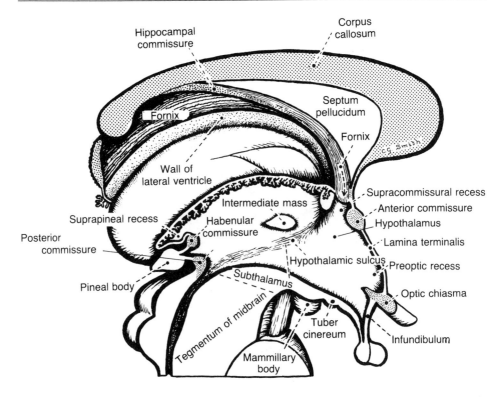

Figure 7-9. Midsagittal section of the midbrain, diencephalon, and the commissural band connecting the cerebral hemispheres to show the form and relationships of the third ventricle.

Floor of the Third Ventricle

The posterior half of the floor of the third ventricle is formed by the subthalamus, which, in a sense, is an upward extension of the tegmentum of the midbrain. As the rostral (anterior) portions of the right and left halves of the subthalamus shift laterally, away from the midline, the third ventricle expands ventrally between them. Anterior to the subthalamus, the thin floor of the ventricle is formed by nuclei of the hypothalamus that bulge inferiorly on each side of the midline to form the mammillary bodies. In front of those nuclei, the floor is pulled down to form a funnel-shaped evagination, called the *infundibulum* ("funnel"). It is a part of the neural lobe of the hypophysis, and it contains no nerve cell bodies, only axons and blood vessels. Anterior to the infundibulum, the floor of the ventricle is pulled upward and backward by the optic chiasma and its right and left connections with the optic tracts. The midsagittal section of the optic chiasma is shaped and hangs like a pear; its long axis is vertical, with a slight inclination forward and downward. This is an anatomical fact to be remembered, because the crossing fibers at its lower edge come from the inferior nasal quadrants of the retina. They would be the first ones to be interrupted, therefore, by a tumor expanding upward from the sella turcica.

Anterior Wall of the Third Ventricle

The anterior wall of the third ventricle is formed by the lamina terminalis, which is the rostral border of the embryonic neural tube. It is a thin membrane that stretches from the lower part of the front of the chiasma to the anterior commissure. The pocket-like space between the chiasma and the lamina terminalis is called the *preoptic recess*. The anterior commissure is a bundle of fibers, about 2 mm in diameter, which connects the parts of the right and left cerebral hemispheres that lie deep to the temporal bones. It arches medially from the temporal lobe to reach the lamina terminalis and then uses it as a bridge to cross the midline. It is interesting that, in humans, the larger part of the anterior commissure is a new structure that connects the parts of the brain that are associated with memory. In lower animals, its fibers connect the olfactory bulbs, which are the recipients of the olfactory nerves, and related portions of the cortex.

Above the anterior commissure, there is a small supracommissural recess; above that, at the junction of the anterior wall and the roof of the third ventricle, the wall is formed by the fibers of the thin edge of the corpus callosum. Immediately behind the corpus callosum, the fornices of the right and left hemispheres are pressed against each other to form a small part of the wall. The corpus callosum consists of commissural fibers that connect the two cerebral hemispheres. The fornix is a bundle of fibers that courses from the posterior part of the hemisphere to enter the anterior end of the diencephalon on its way to the mammillary body.

Roof of the Third Ventricle

The larger part of the roof of the third ventricle is membranous. It is a paper-thin membrane that is formed by the ependymal epithelium of the wall of the third ventricle, a supporting layer of neuroglia, and a covering of pia mater. It extends from the fornix, in front, to the habenular commissure. It is attached on each side to the medial margin of the habenular trigone, and in front of that structure, it is directly continuous with the roof of the interventricular foramen. The roof of the interventricular foramen, in turn, is continuous with the membranous part of the medial wall of the lateral ventricle. The roof of the third ventricle is not stretched taut between its lateral attachments. It is ballooned dorsally to fill partially the deep median gutter on the dorsal surface of the diencephalon. That dorsal expansion of the third ventricle projects back over the pineal gland to form the suprapineal recess, recognizable in radiologic examination of the air-filled ventricle. In spite of its dorsal evagination, the whole length of the ventricle's roof has a linear choroid plexus on either side of the middle. Anteriorly, each plexus is prolonged laterally into the roof of the interventricular foramen to become continuous with the choroid plexus in the wall of the lateral ventricle.

The posterior, smaller part of the roof of the third ventricle is formed by the walls of the pineal gland's hollow stalk and the posterior commissure. The posterior commissure is located at the entrance to the cerebral aqueduct. The pointed extension of the third ventricle, contained in the stalk of the pineal gland, is called the *pineal recess*. The posterior commissure contains the crossing fibers of the light reflex pathway. Both pupils contract when a pencil of light strikes the temporal half of the retina of one eye. The habenular commissure usually has wart-like masses on its ventricular surface. Those masses are never found on the posterior commissure. They are usually calcified and thus show up on radiologic examinations. Their significance is not known.

Lateral Wall of the Third Ventricle

The right and left walls of the third ventricle may be 1 to 10 mm apart. Each wall has three features: the interventricular foramen, the hypothalamic sulcus, and the intermediate mass, which connects the right and left thalami.

Interventricular Foramen

The interventricular foramen is a short canal that is 3 to 5 mm in diameter. Its medial end is located in the angle between the roof and the anterior wall of the third ventricle. The fornix forms its anterior and inferior borders; the anterior tubercle of the thalamus forms its posterior border. Its roof is membranous, and the choroid plexus it contains almost fills the opening.

The Hypothalamic Sulcus. The hypothalamic sulcus is a poorly defined groove that extends from the floor of the interventricular foramen to the aqueduct. It divides the lateral wall of the ventricle into dorsal and ventral halves. The dorsal part is the thalamus proper. The ventral part consists of (1) the hypothalamus anteriorly and (2) the subthalamus posteriorly. A line parallel to the lamina terminalis and passing through the posterior border of the mammillary body corresponds roughly to the junctions of the two ventral portions of the diencephalon.

The Intermediate Mass. The intermediate mass is an adhesion between the right and left walls of the third ventricle. It unites the right and left thalami proper and is located just above the hypothalamic sulcus, anterior to its midpoint. It may be thread-like, or it may have a diameter equal to the ventricular surface of the thalamus proper, that is, a diameter of about 15 mm. The intermediate mass apparently has no functional significance. It is present in only about two-thirds of brains examined at autopsy.

Nuclei and Fiber Connections of Each of the Subdivisions of the Diencephalon

Subthalamus

The subthalamus serves as a reception hall for the diencephalon. Fiber tracts that convey impulses from the brain stem and the lentiform nucleus pass through it to reach the thalamus and the hypothalamus.

Form and Relationships

The subthalamus is, in part, an extension of the tegmentum of the midbrain (Fig. 7-9). It rises to the level of the hypothalamic sulcus and extends forward in the wall of the third ventricle as far as a line parallel to the lamina terminalis and just caudal to the mammillary body. Laterally, the subthalamus is applied to the posterior limb of the internal capsule (Fig. 7-10) and reaches as far forward as its anterior border. The plane that separates the subthalamus from the hypothalamus anterior to it is poorly defined.

Nuclei and Fiber Tracts of the Subthalamus

The upper end of the ovoid red nucleus and the upper border of the plate-like substantia nigra project into the caudal part of the subthalamus from the midbrain (Fig. 7-10). The upper border of the substantia nigra is partly overlapped by the subthalamic nucleus, which is the major nucleus of that subdivision. It is a flattened, biconvex mass of unpigmented cells that is applied to the posterior limb of the internal capsule.

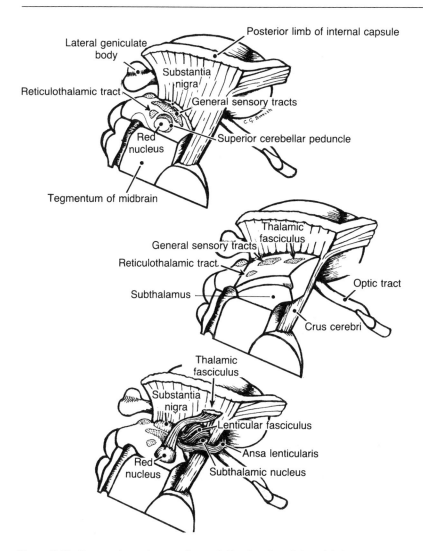

Figure 7-10. Form, relationships, nuclei, and fiber bundles of the subthalamus.

The subthalamic nucleus receives impulses from the lentiform nucleus by way of two fiber bundles: the lenticular fasciculus and the ansa lenticularis. The fibers of the lenticular fasciculus penetrate the posterior limb of the internal capsule and sweep over its medial surface. The fibers of the ansa lenticularis detour around the anterior border of the posterior limb. Most of the efferent fibers of the subthalamic nucleus serve as a feedback pathway to the lentiform nucleus. They form part of the ansa and fasciculus lenticularis. Collaterals of the efferent fibers of the subthalamus extend to the substantia nigra.

A large number of the fibers that enter the subthalamus from the lentiform nucleus bypass the subthalamic nucleus and are joined by fibers of the superior cerebellar peduncle at the rostral pole of the red nucleus. There they form a densely woven mass known as the *field H of Forel* before continuing as the thalamic fasciculus to enter the thalamus. Their termination is described with the nuclei of the thalamus.

As the thalamic fasciculus ascends, it is separated from the fiber capsule of the sub-thalamic nucleus by a lamina of gray matter, known as the *zona incerta* (Fig. 7-8). Its diffuse cell groups are continuous laterally with the thalamic reticular nucleus, which is a thin layer of cells within an external medullary lamina, lateral to the thalamic nuclei. The function of those cell layers is not known.

The posterior part of the subthalamus receives two afferent pathways of the thalamus: (1) the general sensory pathway that includes the medial lemniscus, the spinothalamic tract, and the trigeminothalamic fibers that accompany the medial lemniscus, and (2) the reticulothalamic tract. Some fibers of the reticulothalamic tract reach the hypo-thalamus.

Hypothalamus

Function of the Hypothalamus
The function of the hypothalamus is to maintain the internal environment of the body within limits that are compatible with life and to integrate emotional responses. Its output is chiefly to visceral effectors that are controlled by the autonomic nervous system. These are activated by neural pathways or hormones ("chemical messengers") that reach the effectors through the bloodstream.

The hypothalamus monitors the changes in the body's environment (1) by using data provided by neural pathways from the sense organs and (2) by means of its nerve cells that are sensitive to physical and chemical changes in the blood.

Form and Relationships
The hypothalamus is wedge-shaped (Fig. 7-11). Its anterior vertical border, the lamina terminalis, is the thin edge of the wedge. The *inferior surface* of the hypothalamus (Figs. 7-4 and 7-9) is triangular and free. The apical limit of that surface is the lamina terminalis, and behind it, from front to back, we find the optic chiasma, the tuber cinereum (with the stalk of the hypophysis attached to it), and the mammillary bodies. Those structures form the floor of the third ventricle, which connects the right and left halves of the hypothalamus. The lateral border of the inferior surface is the optic tract. The *medial surface of each half of the hypothalamus* forms that part of the wall of the third ventricle that lies ventral to the hypothalamic sulcus and in front of a vertical line behind the mammillary body. The *lateral surface* extends from the lamina terminalis to the anterior border of the posterior limb of the internal capsule; it is directly continuous with the gray matter of the anterior inferior portion of the lentiform nucleus. Through that surface, the hypothalamus receives many fibers from the cerebral hemisphere. The *superior surface* is triangular. Its apical part is crossed by the anterior commissure that connects the right and left hemispheres. Behind the commissure, the fornix enters the superior surface of the hypothalamus, and immediately behind it again is the floor of the interventricular foramen. The rest of the superior surface of the hypothalamus carries the anterior portion of the thalamus.

Nuclei of the Hypothalamus
The hypothalamus is divided into regions, and those regions, in turn, are divided into smaller portions, called *nuclei*, or areas, depending on whether the cells are in clusters

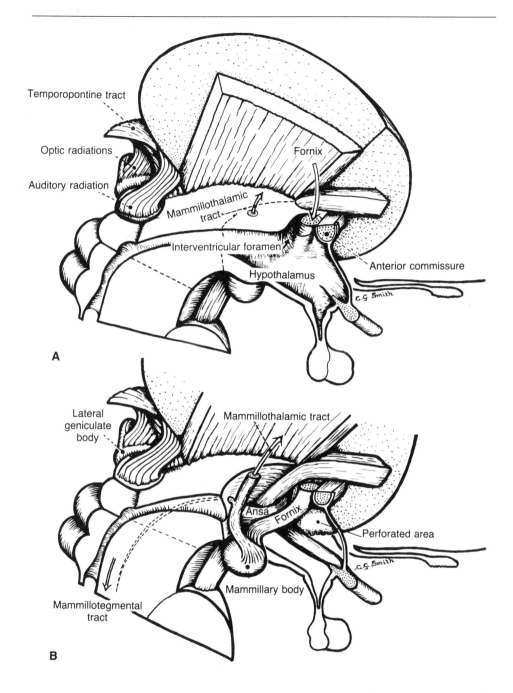

Temporopontine tract

Optic radiations

Auditory radiation

Fornix

Mammillothalamic tract

Interventricular foramen

Hypothalamus

Anterior commissure

c.g. Smith

A

Lateral geniculate body

Mammillothalamic tract

Ansa

Fornix

Perforated area

c.g. Smith

Mammillary body

Mammillotegmental tract

B

Figure 7-11. Form, relationships, and dissectable fiber bundles of the hypothalamus.

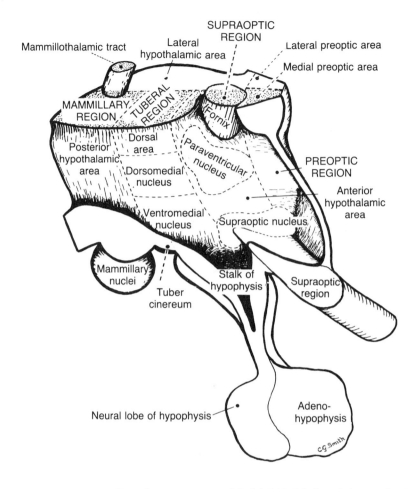

Figure 7-12. *Ventricular and superior aspects of the left half of the hypothalamus, showing its subdivisions and nuclei.*

or dispersed (Fig. 7-12). The hypothalamus has a lateral portion that contains the longitudinal fibers of the medial forebrain bundle, which are afferent and efferent fibers of the hypothalamus. The parasagittal plane between the medial and lateral portions contains the terminal part of the fornix, an afferent bundle from the cerebral hemisphere, and the mammillothalamic tract, an efferent bundle to the anterior nucleus of the thalamus. The medial portion is divided into four regions from front to back. Each portion is given the name of the external feature at its ventral border. (1) The *supraoptic region* lies above the optic chiasma and at the beginning of the optic tract. (2) The *preoptic region* is a small part that is located in front of that region. (3) The *tuberal region* is located above the tuber cinereum and the stalk of the hypophysis. (4) The *mammillary region* is above the mammillary body.

The named parts of the supraoptic region include (1) a supraoptic nucleus, which is

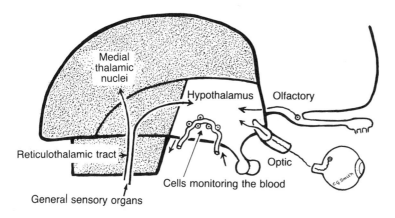

Figure 7-13. *Input of the hypothalamus by means of pathways from sense organs and by means of cells that monitor the blood.*

applied to the medial side of the lower end of the optic tract, (2) a paraventricular nucleus, which is applied to the medial side of the fornix, and (3) a mass of scattered cells that constitutes the anterior hypothalamic area.

The tuberal region also has three parts: ventral, dorsal, and intermediate. The ventral and intermediate portions are the ventromedial and dorsomedial nuclei of the hypothalamus. The scattered cells in the dorsal part make up the dorsal area.

The mammillary region has a ventral and a dorsal portion. The ventral part contains the mammillary nuclei. The cells of the dorsal part make up the posterior hypothalamic area.

The lateral part of the hypothalamus has a small anterior and a large posterior portion. The anterior small portion is the lateral preoptic region. The posterior portion is the lateral hypothalamic area. The entire lateral division of the hypothalamus serves, in part, as an input and output region for the hypothalamus. Impulses it receives by means of ascending reticulothalamic fibers and descending pathways of the medial forebrain bundle are relayed to the medial region for processing. It also contains some relatively large cells, whose axons serve as one of the efferent pathways of the hypothalamus.

Input Pathways of the Hypothalamus

Hypothalamic Cells that Monitor Physical and Chemical Changes in the Blood. Certain cells of the hypothalamus are selectively sensitive to particular changes in the blood (Fig. 7-13). The following examples are cited. Cells of the supraoptic and paraventricular nuclei are sensitive to changes in osmotic pressure and release an antidiuretic hormone as required. Cells of the preoptic and anterior hypothalamic area are selectively sensitive to temperature changes and activate vasomotor neural pathways and responses that involve skeletal muscles, such as those that cause shivering or changes in respiratory movements. Glucose receptor cells are present in the ventromedial nucleus. They may activate feeding responses. Pressure-sensitive neurons that are stimulated reflexly by a rise in blood pressure are found in the posterior hypothalamus.

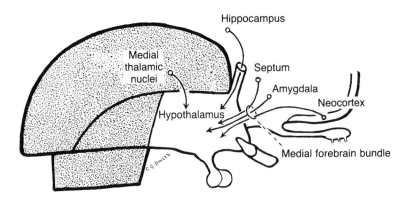

Figure 7-14. *Input of the hypothalamus from the thalamus and the cerebral hemisphere.*

Neural Afferent Pathways. Impulses from the sense organ for smell reach the anterior part of the hypothalamus by means of the medial forebrain bundle (Fig. 7-13). Those fibers have cell bodies either in a nucleus within the olfactory tract or in cell stations of indirect olfactory pathways, located in the amygdala or septal region of the cerebral hemisphere.

Impulses from the retina are conveyed by optic nerve fibers that enter the hypothalamus at the level of the optic chiasma. Such fibers provide the stimuli that, in lower animals, cause changes in skin color to match the environment. The sense organs associated with the remaining cranial and spinal nerves convey impulses to the hypothalamus by means of fibers that ascend with the reticulothalamic tract. That tract provides fibers to the hypothalamus as it passes through the subthalamus on its way to the thalamus. In addition, some fibers extend directly to the hypothalamus from taste and other visceral sensory nuclei of the hindbrain.

The pathways that reach the hypothalamus from the cerebral hemisphere and from the association nuclei of the thalamus excite emotional responses (Fig. 7-14). They are part of the limbic system of pathways, which includes structures in the cerebral hemisphere and upper brain stem that are concerned with visceral processes, and especially with those associated with changes in mood.

Fibers from a portion of the cerebral cortex, called the *hippocampus* (three-layered cortex), form the fornix. That bundle follows an arched course (*fornix,* "an arch") and enters the hypothalamus just anterior to the interventricular foramen (Fig. 7-11). It ends chiefly in the mammillary body.

Fibers from the neocortex (six layers) enter the anterior inferior portion of the hypothalamus as part of the medial forebrain bundle, along with fibers from two other noncortical cell masses in the hemisphere, namely the *amygdala* and the *septum.* Some fibers from the amygdala take an indirect route and enter the hypothalamus lateral to the fornix. That bundle is known as the *stria terminalis.* Those cerebral structures and their connections are described with the cerebral hemisphere.

Fibers from the medial thalamus reach the hypothalamus in a thin periventricular layer and also as part of a large bundle, called the *inferior thalamic peduncle.* Those fibers reach

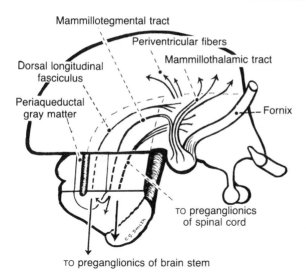

Figure 7-15. Efferent pathways of the hypothalamus.

the lateral preoptic and hypothalamic regions. The main bundle of the inferior thalamic peduncle continues into the hemisphere.

Efferent Pathways of the Hypothalamus

The hypothalamus can excite effector fibers by means of neural pathways, by conducting nerve impulses, and by elaborating hormones that are released into the bloodstream.

Efferent Neural Pathways

Pathways to Preganglionic Nuclei. Some pathways to preganglionic nuclei (Fig. 7-15) travel by means of direct fibers that descend from the hypothalamus, uncrossed, in the lateral part of the reticular formation of the brain stem and in the lateral funiculus. Lesions of those fibers that occur above the first thoracic segment interrupt the pupil dilator pathway. A small pupil, drooping eyelid, and hot dry skin of the head and neck are features of such a lesion. The condition is known as *Horner's syndrome.*

Other pathways to preganglionic nuclei of the brain stem make up part of the dorsal (not medial) longitudinal fasciculus fibers. They leave the medial part of the hypothalamus and course along the wall of the third ventricle; then they descend in the floor of the aqueduct and the fourth ventricle. They end in the preganglionic nuclei of cranial nerves 3, 7, 9, and 10.

Pathways to the Thalamus. Pathways to the thalamus by means of periventricular fibers extend into the wall of the third ventricle to the medial nuclei of the thalamus (Fig. 7-15). From there, impulses may be relayed to the cerebral cortex.

Pathways to the thalamus also exist via the mammillothalamic tract—a large compact fiber bundle—that arches from the mammillary body upward and forward to end in the

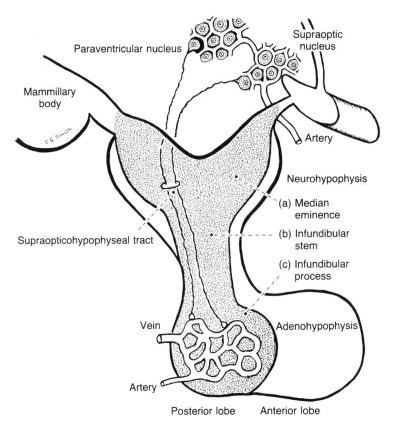

Figure 7-16. *Supraopticohypophyseal tract of the hypothalamus.*

anterior nucleus of the thalamus. That bundle lies in the same parasagittal plane as the fornix, between the medial and lateral portions of the hypothalamus.

Pathways to the Tegmental Nuclei of the Midbrain. The tract of pathways to the tegmental nuclei of the midbrain (Fig. 7-15) leaves the mammillothalamic fiber bundle and curves caudally to end in the dorsal and ventral tegmental nuclei of the caudal part of the midbrain. Those nuclei are located in the central gray matter and just ventral to the medial longitudinal fasciculus, respectively. They have feedback connections with the mammillary body and the septal region of the cerebral hemisphere.

Efferent Pathways that Discharge Hormones

Pathways for Hormones from the Supraoptic and Paraventricular Nuclei. Two nuclei—the supraoptic and paraventricular—comprise the pathways for hormones. They contain large, densely packed cells that stain deeply and contain neurosecretory granules (Fig. 7-16). Both contain cells that manufacture vasopressin, an antidiuretic hormone, and cells that elaborate oxytocin, a hormone that acts on the smooth muscle of the uterus and on

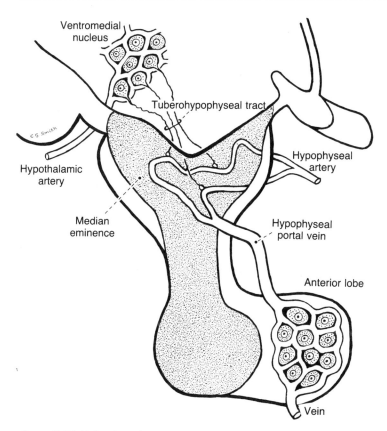

Figure 7-17. Tuberohypophyseal tract of the hypothalamus and the hypophyseal portal vein.

myoepithelial cells of the mammary gland. The hormones are conveyed along axons that form the supraopticohypophyseal tract. The fibers end on the perivascular membrane of capillaries in the distal portion, that is, the infundibular process, of the posterior lobe of the hypophysis, or pituitary gland.

Pathways for Hormones from Ventromedial and Other Medial Nuclei. Small cells of the medial hypothalamus elaborate hormone-like substances, called *hormone-releasing factors*, which are conveyed along axons that form the tuberohypophyseal tract to a capillary plexus. That plexus is located in the median eminence, a proximal part of the neural hypophysis. The hormone-releasing factors enter the blood at that point and are carried by the hypophyseal portal vein, which breaks up into a second set of capillaries in the anterior lobe of the hypophysis. A specific hormone-releasing factor exists for each of the several hormone-producing cells of the anterior lobe. When the appropriate cell is activated, it discharges its hormone into the bloodstream of the capillary plexus. The plexus is drained by a vein that empties into the cavernous sinus, and the hormones are carried to their target organ (Fig. 7-17). Some of the hormones of the anterior lobe are the thyrotropic, adrenocorticotropic, and gonadotropic hormones.

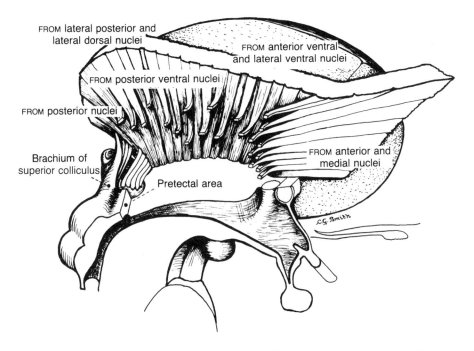

FROM lateral posterior and
lateral dorsal nuclei

FROM anterior ventral
and lateral ventral nuclei

FROM posterior ventral nuclei

FROM posterior nuclei

Brachium of
superior colliculus

FROM anterior and
medial nuclei

Pretectal area

C.G. Smith

Figure 7-18. Medial aspect of internal capsule, showing fibers contributed by each of the thalamic nuclei.

Metathalamus

The lateral and medial geniculate bodies make up the metathalamus. Those two nuclei are located side by side on the inferior aspect of the pulvinar. They serve as relay stations along the special sensory pathways from the eye and the ear, respectively. The lateral geniculate body receives the optic tract at its anterior end; the medial geniculate body receives the brachium of the inferior colliculus, that is, the auditory pathway at its posteromedial border.

The cells of the lateral geniculate body are arranged in six layers that are parallel to the inferior surface. The optic fibers enter the clefts between the cell layers anteriorly. The efferent fibers course laterally between the cell layers to emerge from the lateral side of that nucleus and continue on into the sublenticular part of the internal capsule. That part of the optic pathway is called the *optic radiation*. The cells of the medial geniculate body form a well-circumscribed cluster. The fibers that leave the nucleus and go to the cerebral hemisphere emerge from its superior aspect and course laterally above the optic pathway to help form the sublenticular limb of the internal capsule. That bundle is called the *auditory radiation*.

The relationships of the optic radiation and the auditory radiation are shown in Figure 7-11. In Figure 7-18, the brachium of the superior colliculus is shown descending from the visual area of the cerebral hemisphere to reach the superior colliculus. Its fibers mingle with those of the optic radiation in the sublenticular part of the internal capsule;

then they course within the diencephalon to emerge from the inferior surface of the pulvinar, just medial to the medial geniculate body.

Thalamus

Form and Relationships

The thalamus is a very large subdivision—an ovoid mass—that forms the superior portion of the diencephalon and extends its full length. Inferior to it, from front to back, are, in turn, the hypothalamus, subthalamus, and metathalamus (Fig. 7-2). Medial to the thalamus are the third ventricle and the habenular trigone. Lateral to it are the genu and the posterior limb of the internal capsule (Fig. 7-6).

Nuclei of the Thalamus

There are three groups of nuclei in the thalamus (Fig. 7-19C): anterior, medial, and lateral. The anterior nuclei form a conical, or horn-shaped, mass (Fig. 7-19A) that forms the anterior tubercle of the superior surface. It extends back along the upper border of a thin partition of fibers that divides the thalamus into medial and lateral portions. That partition, called the *internal medullary lamina* (Fig. 7-8), is prolonged backward beyond the pointed posterior end of the anterior thalamic nucleus and curves toward the midline at the level of the habenular commissure. Thus the lateral portion of the thalamus expands medially, at the posterior end of the diencephalon, to form the entire pulvinar.

The Anterior Thalamic Nuclei. The hypothalamus is the principal source of afferent fibers of the anterior thalamus. They travel by way of the mammillothalamic tract (Fig. 7-15). The data provided by those fibers plus those provided by possible connections with the medial and lateral thalamic nuclei are processed and relayed by a massive projection to the anteromedial cortex of the cerebral hemisphere by way of the anterior limb of the internal capsule (Fig. 7-19). That area of the cerebral hemisphere serves as an integrator of somatic and visceral data and is an essential part of the neural mechanism of emotional feeling and response.

The Medial Thalamic Nuclei. The medial thalamus (Fig. 7-19) contains, phylogenetically, the oldest and newest nuclei of the thalamus. The older nuclei have been crowded laterally and medially by the development of a cell mass, known as the *dorsomedial nucleus*, which receives its chief input from other thalamic nuclei. It serves as the highest level of association in the diencephalon. The lateral part of that nucleus has a two-way connection through the anterior limb of the internal capsule, with a comparable, phylogenetically new portion of cerebral cortex, known as the *prefrontal area.* The medial part of that recently acquired cell mass is the origin of a bundle of fibers, known as the *inferior thalamic peduncle,* which enters the hemisphere through the superior lateral part of the hypothalamus. It ends in the orbital cortex and in two subcortical cell masses: the amygdaloid nucleus and the septal gray matter.

The older nuclei, crowded laterally by the dorsomedial nucleus, form a thin layer within the loosely woven network of fibers that forms the internal medullary lamina. They are known as *intralaminar nuclei.* Those nuclei receive terminals of the reticulo-thalamic tract, and all project to the lentiform nucleus. One of those nuclei, the centromedian nucleus, is a large ovoid mass. It is located posterior to the dorsomedial nucleus and directly above the subthalamus. It appears to have enlarged in step with the newest part of the lentiform nucleus. The centromedian nucleus receives fibers from the cortical areas that give origin to the corticospinal tracts, and it projects a large number of fibers

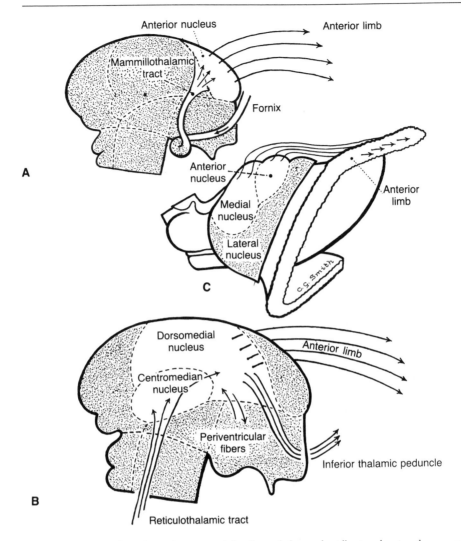

Figure 7-19.(A and B) Sagittal sections of the diencephalon and midbrain, showing the connections of the anterior and medial thalamic nuclei. (C) Superior aspect of the right half of the diencephalon, showing the contribution of fibers from the anterior and medial thalamic nuclei to the anterior limb of the internal capsule.

to the lentiform nucleus, which has a major role in motor activity. It is of interest that some cells of the intralaminar nuclei also project diffusely to the cerebral cortex. Electrical stimulation of the intralaminar nuclei is capable of exciting a change in the electroencephalogram, known as the *alerting response*. The precise pathways involved in that response have not been established.

The remaining nuclei of the medial thalamus are the midline nuclei. They form a thin layer in the wall of the third ventricle and have cortical and hypothalamic projections.

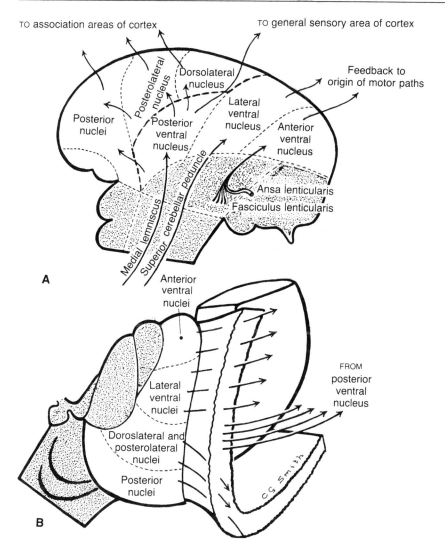

TO association areas of cortex

TO general sensory area of cortex

Dorsolateral nucleus

Posterolateral nucleus

Feedback to origin of motor paths

Lateral ventral nucleus

Posterior nuclei

Posterior ventral nucleus

Anterior ventral nucleus

Ansa lenticularis

Fasciculus lenticularis

Medial lemniscus

Superior cerebellar peduncle

A

Anterior ventral nuclei

Lateral ventral nuclei

Doroslateral and posterolateral nuclei

Posterior nuclei

FROM posterior ventral nucleus

C. G. Smith

B

Figure 7-20. (A) Sagittal section of the diencephalon and midbrain, showing the connections of the lateral nuclei of the thalamus. (B) The superior aspect of the right half of the diencephalon, showing how the posterior limb of the internal capsule is formed, in part, by fibers from each of the lateral nuclei of the thalamus.

The Lateral Nuclei of the Thalamus. The location and relationships of the nuclei of the lateral thalamus are shown diagrammatically along the lateral aspect of the diencephalon (Figs. 7-20 and 7-21). In the diagram, the border between the lateral thalamus and the inferior division of the diencephalon is shown by a line that represents the lateral projection of the hypothalamic sulcus.

Three nuclei of the lateral thalamus form a ventral group to serve as input nuclei.

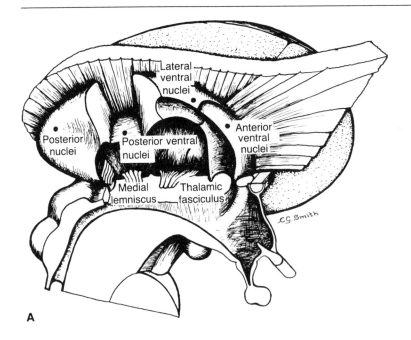

A

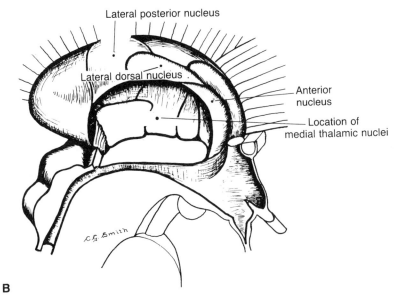

B

Figure 7-21. Form and relationships of the thalamic nuclei. (A) The three ventral and the posterior thalamic nuclei in position on the medial surface of the posterior limb of the internal capsule. Note that two of the ventral nuclei reach the superior surface of the diencephalon. (B) The lateral posterior nucleus, the lateral dorsal nucleus, and the anterior nucleus of the thalamus have been added to part A.

Their afferent fibers compose bundles that originate outside the diencephalon. The dorsal group receives input from other nuclei of the thalamus and from the metathalamus. Those nuclei are classified as *association nuclei*. The plane between the input and association nuclei is curved; it is represented by a dashed line that extends from the posterior border of the subthalamus to about the middle of the superior surface.

The afferent fiber bundles of each of the ventral nuclei of the lateral thalamus reach them by way of the subthalamus. The posterior ventral nucleus is the point at which the general sensory pathway terminates, that is, the medial lemniscus, the trigeminal thalamic fibers, and the spinothalamic tracts. It rests on the posterior portion of the subthalamus, but it does not extend to the superior surface of the diencephalon. The middle nucleus of the ventral group is called the *lateral ventral nucleus*—a term that is difficult to justify from its location. It receives fibers of the superior cerebellar peduncle by way of the thalamic fasciculus. The lateral ventral nucleus is located above the middle of the subthalamus and extends to form the middle third of the superior surface. The anterior ventral nucleus lies above the anterior part of the subthalamus, above the hypothalamus, and extends to the superior surface, lateral to the anterior thalamus. Its afferent fibers come from the lentiform nucleus. They are included in the thalamic fasciculus that enters from the subthalamus.

The three ventral input nuclei are also referred to as relay nuclei, because each of them forms part of a pathway that extends from other parts of the brain and spinal cord to the cerebral cortex. The posterior ventral nucleus is a relay station in the general sensory pathway; the lateral ventral, on the cerebellocerebral pathway; and the anterior ventral, on the lentiform-cerebral pathway.

The dorsal portion of the lateral thalamus contains three nuclei, but for practical purposes they may be treated as a unit. They integrate data received from other thalamic nuclei and from the metathalamus, and all three project to the same general area of association cortex. Lesions of those nuclei, or the cortex with which they are connected, impair comprehension. A person with this affliction loses the ability to identify objects, although no sensory loss occurs. The posterior nucleus forms the pulvinar. Anterior to it and dorsal to the posterior nucleus of the ventral group is the lateral posterior nucleus. In front of it, in turn, is the lateral dorsal nucleus, a conical cell mass that lies along the dorsal border of the internal medullary lamina. Its tapered anterior end extends as far as the posterior end of the anterior thalamic nucleus.

Epithalamus

The nuclei of the epithalamus are located in the habenular trigone. The afferent fibers of those nuclei form the slender fasciculus, called the *stria medullaris thalami*. That fasciculus begins in the region of the anterior perforated substance, where it picks up olfactory impulses from the olfactory tract. It ascends to the lateral border of the roof of the third ventricle and then follows it to reach the habenular trigone. Commissural fibers connect the right and left habenular nuclei to form the habenular commissure. The efferent fibers of the epithalamus form the slender fasciculus retroflex (see Fig. 14-2), which penetrates the medial part of the red nucleus. It ends in the interpeduncular nucleus, which is a cluster of cells that is located between the two crura in the caudal part of the midbrain. The fasciculus retroflexus also ends in nearby nuclei that are the origin of some reticulospinal fibers.

Review Questions (Answers Available on the Pages Cited)

1. Contrast the functions of the metathalamus and the hypothalamus (pp. 86 and 94).
2. Name the three parts of the floor of the third ventricle that make up the posterior lobe of the hypothalamus (p. 76).
3. Name the two commissures separated by the pineal recess of the third ventricle (p. 83).
4. Name four fiber bundles that pass through the subthalamus to enter the thalamus (pp. 85 and 86).
5. How is the hypothalamus alerted to changes in the body's environment (p. 86)?
6. Name the fiber bundle immediately lateral to (a) the paraventricular nucleus; (b) the supraoptic nucleus (p. 89).
7. Describe the pathway from the hypothalamus that excites dilation of the pupil (p. 91).
8. How does the ventromedial nucleus of the hypothalamus influence the release of hormones of the anterior lobe of the pituitary gland (p. 93)?
9. Name the nuclei of the thalamus that receive their major input (a) from the hypothalamus (p. 96); (b) from the globus pallidus (p. 99).

8

The Cranial Nerves

There are 12 pairs of cranial nerves. Each one has a number and a name. The number indicates the order of attachment to the brain; the name indicates its function or some anatomical characteristic.

Cranial nerves contain one or more functional components. Each component, except for nerves 1 and 2, has its origin or termination, as the case may be, in its own longitudinal series of nuclei within the brain stem. There are three kinds of motor fibers: (1) somatic, supplying striated muscles derived from the mesoderm of somites, (2) branchial, also supplying striated muscles but derived from the mesoderm of branchial arches, and (3) visceral motor, supplying smooth muscles, the heart, and glands. The visceral motor fibers are the preganglionic fibers of the parasympathetic nervous system.

The sensory fibers of cranial nerves are classified as *general sensory, special sensory,* and *visceral sensory.* General sensory fibers convey impulses from the widely distributed sense organs for temperature changes, pain, and touch, and from sense organs in muscles, tendons, and joints, known as *proprioceptors,* or position sense organs. Special sense fibers convey impulses from the localized special sense organs for smell, taste, vision, hearing, and equilibrium. Visceral sensory fibers record changes in the alimentary tract and other viscera in the thorax and abdomen.

Functional Components of Each Cranial Nerve

Nerve 1. The Olfactory Nerve

The olfactory nerve carries stimuli from the sense organ for smell. It has several unique features. First, its ganglion cells are located in the epithelium of the nose, not in a cluster near the brain. Second, its nerve fibers are grouped into many small bundles that enter the brain (olfactory bulb) like the bristles of a brush, and third, its sensory nucleus is in the olfactory bulb, not in the brain stem.

Nerve 2. The Optic Nerve

The optic nerve conveys impulses from the retina of the eye to the diencephalon. It is not really a nerve but, rather, a fiber tract, because, developmentally, the retina is a part of the brain. The retina has three concentric layers of cells. The outer layer contains light-sensitive cells. Impulses are relayed by means of cells of the intermediate layer to cells of the innermost layer, whose axons form the optic nerve.

Nerve 3. The Oculomotor Nerve

The oculomotor nerve gets its name because it is a motor nerve that supplies most of the muscles of the eye. It supplies striated muscles derived from somite mesoderm and also some smooth muscles—the constrictor of the pupil and the ciliary muscle.

Nerve 4. The Trochlear Nerve

The trochlear nerve is a motor nerve that supplies one striated muscle of the eye; it is derived from somite mesoderm. The tendon of that muscle plays over a pulley (trochlea).

Nerve 5. The Trigeminal Nerve

The trigeminal nerve has many of the characteristics of a spinal nerve. Its sensory fibers are from sense organs of pain, temperature, touch, and position and enter the brain in a separate root. Its motor fibers supply striated muscles and leave the brain in a bundle that corresponds to a ventral root. The motor fibers differ developmentally from those of spinal nerves, however, because they supply muscles that are derived from the mesoderm of the first branchial arch (muscles of mastication), not from the mesoderm of a somite.

The nerve gets its name (trigeminal, "three buds") because it has three large branches: one to the eye region (sensory), one to the upper jaw region (sensory), and one to the lower jaw region (sensory and motor). Its sensory ganglion is the semilunar (Gasserian) ganglion.

Nerve 6. The Abducens Nerve

Like the trochlear nerve, the abducens nerve is a motor nerve that supplies a striated muscle, which is derived from the mesoderm of a somite. It supplies the muscle that turns the eye outward (abducts it).

Nerve 7. The Facial Nerve

The facial nerve contains four kinds of fibers. (1) Motor fibers innervate striated muscles that are derived from the mesoderm of the second branchial arch. Most of those muscles are attached to the skin of the head and neck and are known as the *muscles of expression*. (2) Visceral motor (preganglionic) fibers carry impulses destined for the lacrimal, nasal, palatal, and salivary glands. (3) Sensory fibers travel from sense organs of pain and possibly temperature and touch in some areas of the skin and mucous membrane that are supplied by the trigeminal nerve. Those areas of overlapping nerve supply are on the tongue, palate, in the external auditory meatus, and on the outer aspect of the eardrum. (4) Visceral sensory fibers carry impulses from sense organs of taste on the anterior two-thirds of the tongue.

The nerve gets its name because its large motor branches fan out over the face. Its sensory ganglion is the geniculate ganglion.

Nerve 8. The Vestibulocochlear Nerve

The vestibulocochlear nerve has two kinds of sensory fibers in two bundles, known as the *cochlear* (auditory) and the *vestibular nerves*. The vestibular nerve comes from special sense organs that detect movement of the head and record its position relative to the pull of gravity. The sensory ganglia of the two nerves are within the temporal bone in the vestibule and the cochlea.

Nerve 9. The Glossopharyngeal Nerve

The glossopharyngeal nerve, like the facial nerve, contains four kinds of fibers. (1) Motor fibers excite a striated muscle of the pharynx (stylopharyngeus) that is derived from the mesoderm of the third branchial arch. (2) Visceral motor (preganglionic) fibers carry impulses destined for the parotid and also the other salivary glands. (3) Sensory fibers travel from sense organs of pain, temperature, and touch, in the wall of the pharynx, in the posterior third of the tongue, and from the middle ear. Stimulating the sensory endings in the pharynx initiates swallowing. (4) Visceral sensory fibers carry impulses from sense organs of taste in the posterior third of the tongue and from chemoreceptors and pressure receptors in the carotid sinus (for the regulation of respiration and blood pressure).

The glossopharyngeal nerve gets its name from its chief areas of distribution: the tongue and the pharynx. The ganglion cells of the sensory part of the nerve are in two clusters that are located in the portion of the nerve in the jugular foramen.

Nerve 10. The Vagus Nerve

The vagus nerve also has four kinds of fibers. (1) Motor fibers go to the striated muscles of the larynx and pharynx. They are derived from the mesoderm of the fourth and fifth branchial arches. (2) Visceral motor (preganglionic) fibers carry impulses destined for the thoracic and abdominal viscera as far as the left colic flexure. (3) Sensory fibers travel from sense organs of pain and possibly temperature and touch in the skin of the external auditory meatus. That is an area of skin also supplied by the trigeminal and the facial nerves. (4) Visceral sensory fibers carry impulses from sense organs of taste (epiglottis) and from stretch receptors in the wall of the heart, superior vena cava, aorta, and the bifurcation of the common carotid, all of which regulate blood pressure and heart rate, and from stretch receptors in the lung, which regulate the rate and depth of respiration.

The vagus nerve gets its name from its long meandering course (*vagus*, "wandering"). The ganglion cells of the sensory part of the nerve are in two clusters that are located in the portion of the nerve in the jugular foramen.

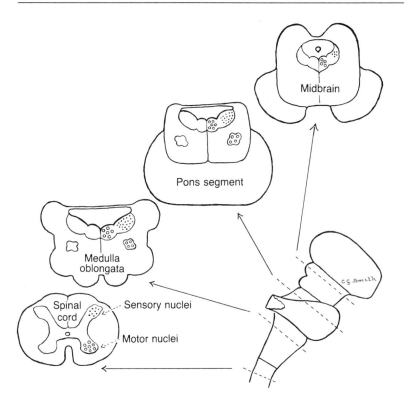

Figure 8-1. Location of the sensory and motor nuclei in cross sections of the central nervous system.

Nerve 11. The Accessory Nerve

The accessory nerve is a motor nerve that supplies striated muscles that are derived from the mesoderm of the most caudal of the branchial arches. Some of those muscles are in the wall of the pharynx and larynx, but two are superficial muscles of the neck: the sternomastoid, and the trapezius.

Nerve 12. The Hypoglossal Nerve

The hypoglossal nerve is a motor nerve that supplies striated muscles that are derived from the mesoderm of somites. It supplies the muscles of the tongue.

Location of Sensory and Motor Nuclei in a Cross Section of Each Segment of the Central Nervous System

In a section of the spinal cord (Fig. 8-1), the sensory nuclei are located in the posterior horn; the motor nuclei are located in the anterior horn. Serial sections of the transitional zone between the spinal cord and the medulla reveal that the irregular, rectangular band of gray matter formed by the posterior and anterior horns extends up into the brain. However, it rotates and shifts dorsally in the medulla to lie in the floor of the fourth ventricle. The motor nuclei (anterior horn gray matter) lie in the medial part of the floor, and the sensory nuclei (posterior horn gray matter) lie in the lateral part of the floor. Serial sections also reveal that the gray matter of the anterior horn divides as it extends into the medulla and a slender column of cells remains in a ventral location in line with the anterior horn of the spinal cord. That slender column of gray matter contains the motor nuclei of muscles derived from branchial arch mesoderm. The motor nuclei in the floor of the ventricle supply striated muscles also, but they are derived from the mesoderm of somites. Along with them are motor nuclei that send preganglionic fibers to autonomic ganglia.

In a section of the tegmentum of the pons, the locations of the motor and sensory nuclei are the same as in the medulla.

In the midbrain, the column of gray matter that contains the branchial motor nuclei has dropped out. However, the gray matter that contains somite motor nuclei, preganglionic motor nuclei, and sensory nuclei is still present. It lies ventral to the aqueduct and forms a part of the central gray matter.

Motor Nuclei of the Brain Stem

The three kinds of motor nuclei—somite, preganglionic (visceral), and branchial—are arranged in three columns, like strings of irregularly spaced beads (Fig. 8-2). The column of branchial motor nuclei reaches up to the middle of the pons. The other two columns reach the upper border of the midbrain. Each of the nuclei is cylindrical and may be long or short.

The three columns (that is, an extension of the gray matter of the anterior horn) are together at the caudal end of the medulla. The branchial column ascends in the central part of the reticular substance of the medulla and pons, but the other two shift to the midline and dorsally, to lie in the floor of the fourth ventricle in the hindbrain, ventral to the aqueduct in the midbrain. It is necessary to point out that recent work has shown that the shift of preganglionic cells is not complete; some cells remain behind to form part of the branchial column.

Somite Motor Nuclei

The motor nuclei of the somite column are nuclei of the twelfth (hypoglossal), sixth (abducens), fourth (trochlear), and third (oculomotor) nerves (Fig. 8-3).

Nucleus of the Hypoglossal Nerve

The nucleus of the hypoglossal nerve is almost as long as the medulla. It produces a ridge, called the *hypoglossal trigone*, in the floor of the ventricle next to the midline. The ridge has a pointed caudal end because the preganglionic nucleus of the vagus nerve is dorsal to it in the closed medulla and gradually shifts laterally in the open medulla to leave the hypoglossal nucleus uncovered.

The nerve fibers of the nucleus course ventrally, just lateral to the medial lemniscus to emerge as a series of rootlets between the pyramid and the olive.

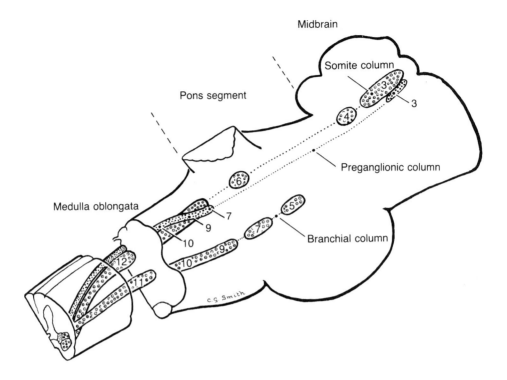

Figure 8-2. Columns of motor nuclei projected onto the lateral aspect of the brain stem.

Nucleus of the Abducens Nerve

The nucleus of the abducens nerve is a small cluster of cells. It is located in the caudal part of the pons segment and elevates the floor of the ventricle between the sulcus limitans and the midline. The mound-like elevation is called the *facial colliculus* because the facial nerve helps to produce it.

The nerve fibers of the nucleus course ventrally and caudally to avoid the thickest part of the pons and emerge between it and the pyramid.

Nucleus of the Trochlear Nerve

The nucleus of the trochlear nerve also is a small cluster of cells. It is located in the ventral part of the central gray matter of the midbrain at the level of the inferior colliculus.

The nerve fibers of that nucleus have a peculiar course. They course dorsally and caudally to cross the midline and emerge in the superior velum. Thus the trochlear nerve has its nucleus on the opposite side of the brain.

Somite Motor Nucleus of the Oculomotor Nerve

The somite motor nucleus of the oculomotor nerve is a cylindrical cluster of cells that extends from the trochlear nucleus to the upper border of the midbrain. It lies close to

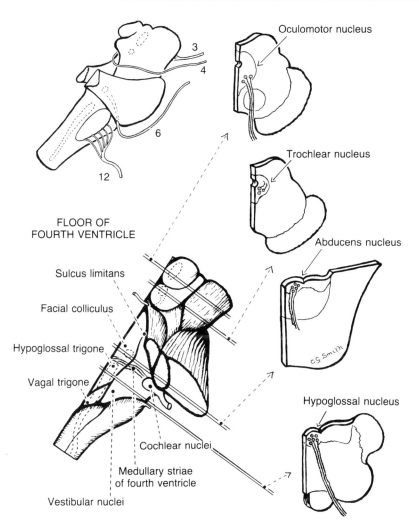

Figure 8-3. Motor nuclei that supply muscles derived from somites.

the midline in the ventral part of the central gray matter. Its cells are in five groups—one for each muscle it supplies.

The nerve fibers course ventrally through the red nucleus and emerge at the medial border of the crus cerebri. The fibers to the superior rectus muscle come from cells in the nucleus of the opposite side.

Preganglionic Nuclei

The motor nuclei of the preganglionic column are the tenth (vagus), ninth (glosso-pharyngeal), seventh (facial), and third (oculomotor) nerves (Fig. 8-4).

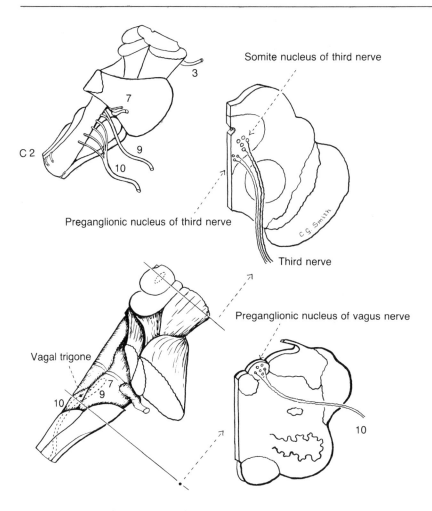

Somite nucleus of third nerve

Preganglionic nucleus of third nerve

Third nerve

3

7

C 2

9

10

Vagal trigone

Preganglionic nucleus of vagus nerve

7
9
10

10

Figure 8-4. Preganglionic, or visceral, motor nuclei.

Preganglionic Nuclei of the Vagus, Glossopharyngeal, and Facial Nerves
The preganglionic nuclei of the vagus, glossopharyngeal, and facial nerves form an un-interrupted cell column that extends the length of the medulla. In the caudal part of the medulla, that column is located at the midline dorsal to the hypoglossal nucleus. As it enters the open part of the medulla it is visible in the floor of the ventricle and forms the ridge known as the *vagal trigone*, or *ala cinerea*. That ridge grows narrower, tapering to a point toward the pons, because the cell column gradually shifts laterally to lie lateral to the hypoglossal nucleus and ventral to the vestibular nucleus.

A small rostral segment of that column sends its fibers into the facial nerve and is known as the *superior salivary nucleus*. The middle segment sends its fibers into the glossopharyngeal nerve and is known as the *inferior salivary nucleus*. The caudal, and the longest, portion sends its fibers into the vagus nerve and is called the *dorsal motor nucleus of the vagus*.

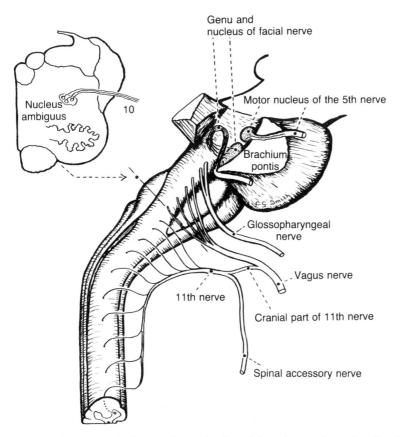

Figure 8-5. Motor nuclei that supply muscles derived from the mesoderm of the branchial arches.

The nerve fibers from each of those nuclei course laterally to emerge in thread-like rootlets along the dorsal border of the olive.

Preganglionic Nucleus of the Oculomotor Nerve

The preganglionic nucleus of the oculomotor nerve is a short, cylindrical cluster of cells that lies medial to the upper end of the somite motor nucleus of the oculomotor nerve. It is popularly known as the *nucleus of Edinger-Westphal.*

The nerve fibers of that nucleus join the other fibers of the third nerve and course with them in one bundle as far as the orbit. There they leave the other fibers to enter the ciliary ganglion.

Branchial Motor Nuclei

The motor nuclei of the branchial column are the eleventh (accessory), tenth (vagus), ninth (glossopharyngeal), seventh (facial), and fifth (trigeminal) nerves (Fig. 8-5).

The Branchial Motor Nuclei of the Accessory, Vagus, and Glossopharyngeal Nerves
The branchial motor nuclei of the accessory, vagus, and glossopharyngeal nerves form an uninterrupted column that extends the length of the medulla in the central part of the reticular substance. It is known as the *nucleus ambiguus* because its cells are widely spaced and its borders are irregular. The cells of the glossopharyngeal nucleus are located in a small rostral segment of the nucleus ambiguus. Caudal to that is a long segment that contains the cells of the vagus nerve fibers, and caudal to that, in turn, is the short segment for the accessory nerve. If the nucleus ambiguus is traced toward the spinal cord in serial sections, it is found to be continuous with a column of cells in the anterior horn that extends to the fifth cervical segment.

The nerve fibers of the cells at the rostral pole of the nucleus are joined by fibers of the inferior salivary nucleus and course laterally to emerge behind the olive in two or three rootlets that unite to form the ninth nerve. Similarly, the nerve fibers of the vagal portion of the nucleus ambiguus are joined by preganglionic fibers of the dorsal motor nucleus of the vagus and emerge behind the olive as three or four rootlets that unite to form the vagus nerve.

The nerve fibers of the cell column in the spinal cord that is continuous with the nucleus ambiguus leave the anterior horn and course laterally through the lateral funiculus to emerge in groups along a longitudinal line that is nearer the dorsal roots than the ventral roots. Those intermediate roots ascend alongside the spinal cord and join to form the spinal part of the accessory nerve. That nerve ascends in the subarachnoid space and enters the skull through the foramen magnum. Inside the skull, it picks up a few rootlets from the caudal part of the nucleus ambiguus. The nerve, having obtained all its fibers, leaves the skull again through the jugular foramen. In that foramen, its cranial and spinal fibers separate. The spinal fibers form an external branch that supplies the sternomastoid and the trapezius muscles. The cranial fibers join the vagus nerve and are distributed through its branches to help supply the striated muscles of the larynx and pharynx. The fibers of the nucleus ambiguus that form the cranial division of the accessory nerve are essentially vagal fibers that delay joining their fellows until the vagus nerve enters the jugular foramen.

Nucleus of the Facial Nerve
The nucleus of the facial nerve is a fusiform cluster of cells that is 2 or 3 mm long, located in the caudal part of the pons.

The fibers of that nucleus have a very unusual course. Instead of passing laterally and caudally a distance of 2 mm to the caudal border of the pons, where the facial nerve emerges, they take a circuitous route around the abducens nucleus (Fig. 8-5). The course of the facial nerve within the pons reveals, like a vapor trail, the course of migration of its nucleus during phylogenetic development. There is no satisfactory explanation for it. As it emerges at the caudal border of the pons, it is almost in line with the ninth and tenth nerve rootlets. It is just ventral to the attachment of the eighth nerve, separated from it only by a thread-like filament, known as the *nervus intermedius*. This is looked upon as the sensory root of the facial nerve, but it contains preganglionic fibers as well as sensory fibers.

Nucleus of the Trigeminal Nerve
The nucleus of the trigeminal nerve is about 2 mm long and is located in the middle of the pons segment in line with the facial nucleus.

The nerve fibers pass directly laterally in a bundle that penetrates the brachium pontis to emerge in line with the seventh, ninth, and tenth nerves. It is the motor root of the trigeminal nerve, but it is not ventral to the sensory root as might be expected (see Fig. 18-3).

Sensory Nuclei of the Brain Stem

Let us begin our study of the sensory nuclei by identifying those that can be seen in a section of the open medulla (Fig. 8-6). In such a section, the rectangular mass of sensory nuclei in the floor of the ventricle is divided into a dorsal and a ventral layer. The dorsal layer is the sensory nucleus of the vestibular nerve. The ventral layer is divided into a small medial and a large lateral part by a small bundle of fibers. The medial nucleus is that of the tractus solitarius (visceral sensory), and the lateral nucleus is that of the spinal tract of the fifth nerve. In Figure 8-7, those nuclei are represented as though they were projected onto the lateral surface to show how far those nuclei extend upward and downward in the brain stem. Beginning with the nucleus of the spinal tract of the fifth nerve, we see that it becomes very large in the caudal part of the medulla and extends to the spinal cord, where it forms the crest of the dorsal horn of the first cervical segment. That nucleus receives the terminals of all the pain and temperature fibers of the cranial nerves. The portion of the nucleus adjacent to the pons also receives terminals of touch fibers (Fig. 8-8). The nucleus of the spinal tract of the fifth nerve extends into the pons, where it joins the main sensory nucleus of the same nerve. That nucleus is a relay station for all the position sense fibers and some touch fibers of the cranial nerves. A third nucleus is a slender column that extends from the main sensory nucleus to the upper end of the midbrain. It is known as the mesencephalic nucleus of the fifth nerve, but its cells are comparable to sensory ganglion cells (Fig. 8-8).

Turning now to the nucleus of the tractus solitarius (visceral sensory), we see that it extends caudally into the lateral part of the posterior horn of the spinal cord. Traced upward, it ends at the junction of medulla and pons. That nucleus receives the visceral sensory fibers of the seventh, ninth, and tenth nerves. Those nerves penetrate the medulla to reach its lateral side and turn caudally to form the tractus solitarius. As the tract descends, it is surrounded partly by the cells of its nucleus.

The vestibular nucleus forms the width of the floor of the ventricle lateral to the sulcus limitans and extends laterally slightly beyond it (Fig. 8-6). That portion of the floor of the ventricle, and with it, the vestibular nucleus, tapers to a point (see Fig. 8-3) as the ventricle grows narrower rostrally and caudally. Laterally, the gray matter of the floor of the ventricle extends out onto the floor of the lateral recess. The lateral extension of the sensory gray matter is the nucleus of the cochlear division of the eighth nerve. It rests on the inferior cerebellar peduncle.

The remaining subdivisions of the sensory gray matter of the brain stem are the nuclei gracilis and cuneatus. They are displaced sensory nuclei of the spinal cord, because they receive the ascending branches of spinal sensory nerve fibers of touch and the sense of position. Each of those nuclei is a column of cells that begins close to the first cervical segment and extends to the vestibular nucleus. In serial sections of the medulla those nuclei are seen as parts of the cranial prolongation of the gray matter of the posterior horn.

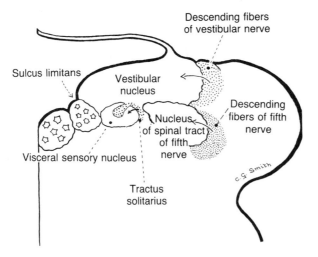

Figure 8-6. Cross section of the open medulla showing the subdivisions of the sensory columns of gray matter (the dorsal horn of the spinal cord). Plane of this section is shown in Figure 8-7.

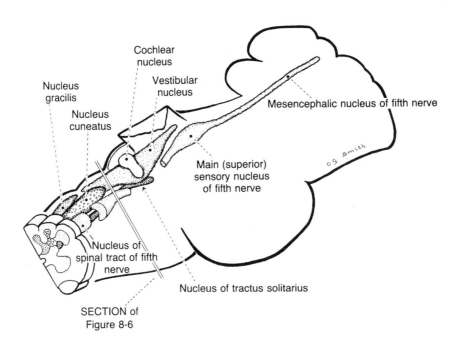

Figure 8-7. Subdivisions of the sensory column of gray matter projected onto the lateral aspect of the brain stem. Segments of the nucleus of the spinal tract of the fifth nerve have been removed.

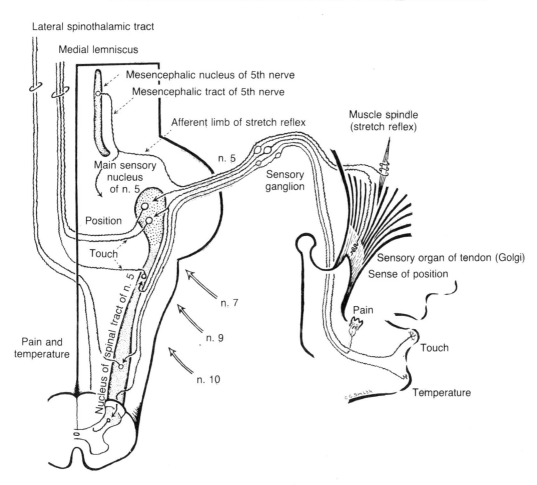

Lateral spinothalamic tract

Medial lemniscus

Mesencephalic nucleus of 5th nerve

Mesencephalic tract of 5th nerve

Afferent limb of stretch reflex

Muscle spindle (stretch reflex)

n. 5

Main sensory nucleus of n. 5

Sensory ganglion

Position

Touch

Sensory organ of tendon (Golgi)

Sense of position

Nucleus of spinal tract of n. 5

n. 7

Pain

n. 9

Touch

Pain and temperature

n. 10

Temperature

C.G.Smith

Figure 8-8. Column of gray matter made up of general sensory nuclei (pain, temperature, touch, and sense of position), showing its afferent fibers and the efferent fibers that ascend to the forebrain. Note that the general sensory fibers in nerves 7, 9, and 10 have the same connections as do the fibers in nerve 5.

Afferent and Efferent Fibers of the Three Parts of the Sensory Nucleus of the Fifth Nerve

The afferent fibers of the so-called sensory nuclei of the fifth nerve are fibers from sense organs of position, touch, pain, and temperature. Most of those sensory fibers enter the brain in the fifth cranial nerve, but some enter in nerves 7, 9, and 10; hence the nuclei are not only nuclei of the fifth nerve, as their designation would imply.

When the fifth nerve penetrates the middle cerebellar peduncle, it encounters the main sensory nucleus. The position sense fibers end at that point. The touch fibers, like those in spinal nerves, divide. One branch accompanies the position sense fibers and ends in the main sensory nucleus, and the other descends with the pain and temperature fibers to form the spinal tract of the fifth nerve; it ends with them in the nucleus of that tract.

Fibers of the main sensory nucleus cross the midline to ascend in the medial lemniscus with the position sense and touch pathways from the spinal cord. The fibers from the nucleus of the spinal tract of the trigeminal nerve (5) cross the midline to ascend in the lateral spinothalamic tract, but only after ascending to the upper end of the medulla (see Fig. 8-8). This explains why a lesion in the lateral part of the medulla does not cut the pain pathways from the opposite side of the head along with those from the opposite side of the body.

The enigma of the general sensory nuclei of the brain is the mesencephalic nucleus (Fig. 8-8), which is composed of cells that (unlike the cell bodies of other sensory nerve fibers, which form peripheral nerve ganglia, such as the posterior root ganglia of spinal nerves) migrate into the brain stem and ascend into the midbrain. From those cells, fibers can be traced caudally, within the midbrain, along the lateral border of the mesencephalic nucleus, where they form the mesencephalic tract of the fifth nerve, and then out into the fifth nerve to a stretch receptor in muscle, the *muscle spindle.* That forms the afferent limb of the exceptional reflex arc, called the *stretch reflex.* It is exceptional because it is a chain of only two nerve cells: the first cell has its cell body in the mesencephalic nucleus; the second, in the motor nucleus of the fifth nerve. The connection with the motor nucleus is indicated in Figure 8-8.

Afferent and Efferent Fibers of the Nucleus of the Tractus Solitarius

The afferent fibers of the nucleus of the tractus solitarius come from taste buds, heart, aorta, lungs, and alimentary tract and enter the brain through nerves 7, 9, and 10 (Fig. 8-9). Those fibers course medially to reach their nucleus and descend partly surrounded by its cells to form the tractus solitarius. Because that bundle is surrounded by gray matter, it stands out clearly in a section stained to show the fibers. It gets smaller caudally as fibers drop out to end in the nucleus.

Taste information is relayed by cells in the rostral part of the solitary nucleus along fibers that course in the central tegmental tract of the same side to the posterior medial part of the nucleus ventralis posterior of the thalamus. From that nucleus, fibers extend to the sensory taste area of the cortex. Reflex responses to taste stimuli are mediated by way of efferent fibers of the solitary nucleus to the reticular formation.

This description of the sensory taste pathway is based on the experimental findings of a study that was done on the pathway in monkeys. Clinically, the evidence supports a crossed pathway for taste.

Afferent and Efferent Fibers of the Cochlear and Vestibular Nuclei

The principal connections of the cochlear and vestibular nuclei are described in Chapter 5. In this section some additional features are considered.

A special feature of the auditory system is the orderly arrangement of the pathways that conduct impulses from the cochlea to the cerebral cortex. At all levels, pathways for each frequency, ranging from 16 cycles/sec (from the apical turn) to 20,000 cycles/sec (from the basal turn) can be identified. Conduction in those pathways is regulated by inhibitory and facilitative input at each relay station. The input may come from other sensory pathways or from higher levels of the central nervous system, including the cerebral

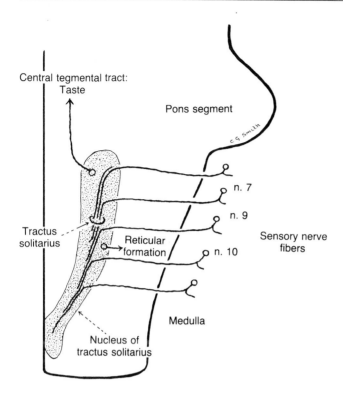

Central tegmental tract:
Taste

Pons segment

C.G.Smith

n. 7

n. 9

n. 10

Tractus
solitarius

Reticular
formation

Sensory nerve
fibers

Medulla

Nucleus of
tractus solitarius

Figure 8-9. Column of gray matter that is composed of visceral sensory nuclei—the nucleus of the tractus solitarius—showing its afferent and efferent fibers in the monkey.

cortex. In this way, attention may be given to a selected auditory input, for example, to hear someone speaking in a noisy room.

The interruption of the auditory pathways by synapses in the cochlear nuclei, superior olive, and inferior colliculi makes possible a dispersal of impulses to effect reflex responses. For example, some cells in the superior olive send fibers to the motor nuclei of the fifth and seventh nerves to excite the tensor tympani muscle and the stapedius muscle, respectively. The action of those muscles protects the delicate sense organs by dampening conduction from the eardrum when sounds are traumatically loud. Other auditory reflexes, such as head turning and the startle reaction, are mediated by means of the inferior colliculus and collateral branches to the reticular formation.

The reflex connections of the vestibular nuclei extend to the upper part of the brain stem and the entire length of the spinal cord. The fibers of ascending pathways form the medial longitudinal fasciculus; the corresponding descending fibers form the medial and lateral vestibulospinal tracts. The ascending fibers activate the motor neurons of the eye muscles; the descending fibers activate anterior horn cells and thus excite postural adjustments and maintain equilibrium.

Eye movements may be excited by way of direct connections between the vestibular nuclei and the motor nuclei of nerves 3, 4, and 6, as indicated earlier. However, for

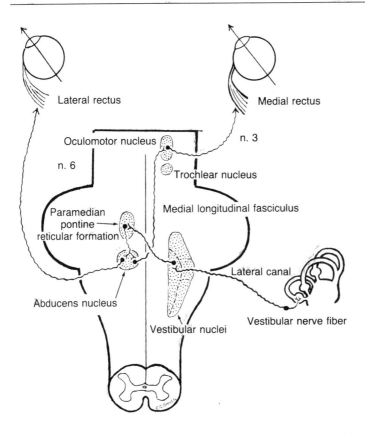

Figure 8-10. Vestibular reflex pathway for lateral conjugate movements of the eyes.

conjugate side-to-side movements, in response to head turning, a special indirect pathway is utilized (Fig. 8-10). When the head turns to one side, the eyes are reflexly directed to the opposite side as if to retain the visual field. If the head is turned to the right side, the sense organs of the right lateral semicircular canal are stimulated and the eyes turn to look to the left. Impulses are conveyed by the vestibular nerve to the medial vestibular nucleus, which sends its fibers across the midline to synapse with cells of a so-called gaze center for horizontal eye movements. That center is a small paramedian part of the pontine reticular formation (PPRF) that is close to the abducens nucleus. Fibers of the cells of the pontine reticular formation relay impulses to the abducens nucleus, which contains the motor cells of the sixth nerve but also internuncial cells. The internuncial cells send fibers across the midline to ascend in the medial longitudinal fasciculus to reach the nucleus of the third nerve. There they synapse with the cells that supply the medial rectus muscle. Turning the head to the left side would excite a corresponding pathway from the lateral semicircular canal of the left side.

A unilateral lesion of the medial longitudinal fasciculus, for example, on the right side, rostral to the abducens nucleus, results in an inability to look to the left with the right eye. The functional deficit is known as *anterior internuclear ophthalmoplegia.* In the example given, the medial rectus muscle can still be activated voluntarily by corticobulbar fibers when directing the eyes to a near point, because the motor nucleus of the third nerve is still functional. If there is a unilateral lesion of the pontine reticular formation or of the abducens nucleus, neither eye will be able to look to the side of the lesion. This condition is known as *paralysis of the lateral gaze.*

Review Questions (Answers Available on Pages Cited)

1. Where are the cell bodies of the sensory fibers of the olfactory nerve (p. 101)?
2. Where would you find the nuclei of the sensory nerves in a section of the medulla oblongata (p. 105)?
3. Why could a small lesion of cranial nerves 12, 6, or 3 also involve the pathway for voluntary movement (p. 107)?
4. Where are the cell bodies of the fibers of (a) the spinal tract of the fifth nerve (see Fig. 8-8); (b) the tractus solitarius (see Fig. 8-9)?
5. What purpose is served by the nuclei interpolated in the auditory sensory pathway to the cerebral cortex (p. 115)?
6. How can impulses from the right internal ear reach the lateral rectus of the left eye and the internal rectus of the right eye (p. 116)?

9

The Reticular Formation

The reticular formation makes up the core of the brain stem. It is composed of internuncial nerve cells in a meshwork of interweaving nerve fibers. Functionally, it integrates data from widespread sources, that is, from all sense organs of the body, the cerebral hemisphere, and the cerebellum. In lower vertebrates, it forms the major integrating part of the brain.

Some efferent fibers of the reticular formation descend into the spinal cord, where they modify motor activity as well as conduction in sensory pathways. Some ascend into the diencephalon as part of a pathway to the cerebral cortex, which influences the level of consciousness.

The reticular formation is the basic functional unit of the central nervous system.

Extent and Relationship Within the Brain Stem

The reticular formation is continuous, caudally, with the intermediate gray matter of the spinal cord. The transition between the closely crowded cells of the intermediate gray matter and the widely spaced cells of the reticular formation of the brain stem occurs just rostral to the decussation of the corticospinal tracts. At the midolivary level, the reticular formation increases in size and is enclosed by the medial lemniscus, the olive, the spinothalamic tracts, and the nuclei that form the floor of the fourth ventricle (Fig. 9-1).

In the pons, the reticular formation expands to the midline as the medial lemniscus shifts to lie ventral to it. Laterally, it is enclosed by the superior olive, the lateral lemniscus, and the spinothalamic tracts. Dorsal to the reticular formation is the gray matter in the floor of the fourth ventricle and the medial longitudinal fasciculus.

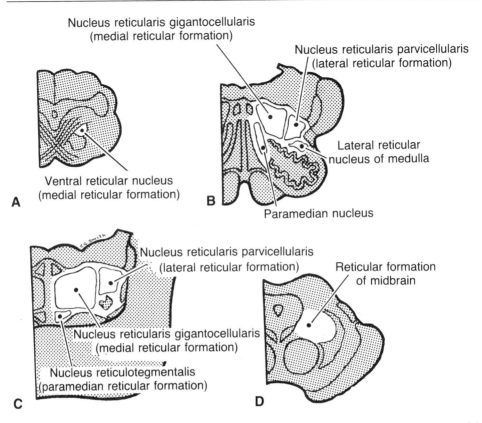

Figure 9-1. Cross sections of the brain stem, showing the location of the reticular formation: (A) caudal medulla; (B) medulla, midolivary level; (C) the pons segment; and (D) upper midbrain.

In the midbrain, the reticular formation is restricted to an area that is bounded dorsally by the tectum, ventrally by the red nucleus, medially by the medial longitudinal fasciculus, and laterally by the medial lemniscus, the spinothalamic tracts, and the brachium of the inferior colliculus. An attenuated portion extends into the diencephalon, where it is said to be represented by the zona incerta and the reticular and intralaminar nuclei of the thalamus.

Subdivisions of the Reticular Formation

On the basis of differences in cell types and of input and output, the reticular formation is divided grossly into paramedian, medial, and lateral portions. Subdivisions of those portions are known as *reticular nuclei*.

Nuclei of the Paramedian Portion

The paramedian nuclei of the medulla form a parasagittal lamina that is located immediately lateral to the medial longitudinal fasciculus and the medial lemniscus. In the pons segment, the paramedian portion of the reticular formation is a cluster of cells near the midline, called the *reticulotegmental nucleus*, which is located at the ventral border of the tegmentum. It appears to be a dorsal extension of the basilar pontine nucleus. Like the basilar pontine nucleus, the paramedian nuclei of the pons and the medulla receive fibers from the cerebral cortex and send fibers to the cerebellum.

Medial Reticular Nuclei

The medial reticular nuclei are the major part of the reticular formation; they extend from the spinal cord to the diencephalon. One of its nuclei, the nucleus reticularis gigantocellularis, is located partly in the medulla and partly in the pons. It has large cells and is readily identified. It has a role in regulation of respiration and the control of blood pressure.

The medial reticular nuclei receive input from sense organs, the cerebellum, and the cerebral cortex. They comprise the origin of long fibers that extend into the spinal cord and the diencephalon. Some of the long ascending and descending fibers are branches of the same axon, indicating there is a possibility for simultaneous activation of both higher and lower levels of the central nervous system.

Fibers that descend from the medulla exert an inhibitory influence over muscle tone and motor activity. They descend, widely dispersed, within the ventral part of the lateral funiculus and converge on the same cells of the intermediate gray matter as the corticospinal and vestibulospinal fibers.

Fibers that descend from the pons have an excitatory role in the control of muscle tone and motor activity. They descend in the anterior funiculus and mingle with the fibers of the spinothalamic and vestibulospinal fibers.

The ascending fibers of the medial reticular nuclei form part of the central tegmental tract. They pass through the subthalamus to end partly in the intralaminar nuclei of the thalamus and partly in the hypothalamus. When stimulated, those fibers, along with some fibers from the lateral reticular nuclei (see the following discussion), excite a behavioral arousal response and desynchronization of the cortical electroencephalogram.

Lateral Reticular Nuclei

The principal nucleus of the lateral reticular region is the nucleus reticularis parvicellularis. It forms the lateral third of the core of the medulla and the pons and serves as an association nucleus for the medial reticular nuclei. Secondary sensory fibers of the cranial nerve nuclei and spinoreticular fibers provide input from sense organs; input from the cerebral cortex is delivered by way of direct corticoreticular fibers. The efferent fibers of that lateral reticular nucleus end in the adjacent medial reticular nuclei and in motor nuclei of the cranial nerves.

Another nucleus in the lateral part of the reticular formation is the lateral reticular nucleus of the medulla. It is a short column of cells dorsal to the inferior olivary nucleus in the caudal half of the medulla. Its afferent fibers are corticoreticular fibers, spinoreticular fibers, and fibers from the red nucleus; its efferent fibers enter the cerebellum.

Dorsolateral to the parvicellular nucleus in the pons segment and just ventral to the mesencephalic nucleus of the fifth nerve is a cluster of pigmented cells, called the *locus ceruleus*. It is described here because, like some cells of the medial reticular nuclei, its fibers have a widespread distribution in the central nervous system. Its fibers reach all parts of the cerebral cortex and may have a role in the arousal response.

In summary, the reticular formation integrates data from all the sense organs of the body and from the cerebral hemisphere and the cerebellum. The paramedian nuclei and the lateral reticular nucleus of the medulla project to the cerebellum. Some cells in the lateral reticular nuclei project to cranial motor nuclei; cells in the parvicellular nucleus project to the medial reticular nuclei; and the medial nuclei project to all parts of the central nervous system.

Raphe Nuclei

The raphe nuclei are sometimes included in the paramedian portion of the reticular formation. They are described under a separate heading because their connections are different and because their neurons utilize serotonin as their transmitter substance. They are found immediately adjacent to the midline in the medulla, the pons, and the midbrain.

The raphe nuclei of the upper medulla oblongata give rise to fibers that inhibit conduction in sensory pathways for pain. Some of the raphe fibers extend to sensory nuclei of the hindbrain; others descend, bilaterally, in the spinal cord to end in laminae I and II and partly in laminae of the intermediate gray matter.

The raphe nuclei of the upper pons and the midbrain give rise to ascending fibers that course within the medial forebrain bundle to reach the intralaminar nuclei of the thalamus, the septal and olfactory regions of the hemisphere and broad areas of the neocortex. Raphe nuclei appear to have diverse roles, including a role as the neural mechanism of the sleep-waking cycle.

Review Questions (Answers Available on the Pages Cited)

1. Name the three general sources of input to the reticular formation (p. 119).
2. State three general functions of the efferent fibers of the reticular formation (p. 119).
3. What is the suggested representation of the reticular formation in the spinal cord (p. 119)?
4. What is the source of the data processed by the parvicellular nucleus of the lateral portion of the reticular formation (p. 121)?
5. What portion of the reticular formation is the origin of the reticulospinal tracts (p. 121)?
6. What do the efferent fibers of the locus ceruleus and the raphe nuclei have in common (pp. 121 and 122)?

10

The Cerebellum

The cerebellum is an accessory part of the brain, both anatomically and functionally. Anatomically, it develops as an outgrowth on the back of the hindbrain, and functionally, it modulates the flow of impulses to muscles that are activated by other parts of the central nervous system. Removal of the cerebellum does not impair sensation or result in muscle paralysis, but if its function is impaired by disease, the disturbance of muscle tone and voluntary movements may be completely disabling.

Form and Relationship to the Brain Stem

The cerebellum is a dumbbell-shaped mass set across the back of the pons segment (Fig. 10-1). It has a median constricted part, called the *vermis*, and right and left larger portions, called the *cerebellar hemispheres*. It forms the roof of the fourth ventricle between the superior and inferior velum and contains a short, midline, tent-like extension of a part of the ventricle, known as its *dorsal recess*. The lateral portions of the attachment of the cerebellum to the brain stem contain the large pedicles of afferent and efferent nerve fibers of the right and left halves of the cerebellum.

Gray and White Matter

The gray matter forms a thin layer, the cortex, on the outer surface of the cerebellum, and a cluster of small, centrally located nuclei. The white matter, made up of afferent and efferent fibers of the cerebellum, forms its core (Fig. 10-2).

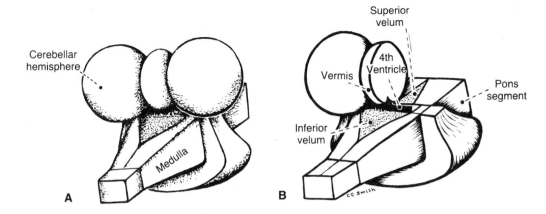

Figure 10-1.(A) Dorsolateral aspect of the hindbrain and the cerebellum. (B) The same view but with the right half of the cerebellum removed.

There are four nuclei, forming a medial-lateral series, in each half of the cerebellum; the medial one is in the vermis portion and the other three are in the hemisphere. They are embedded in the core of white matter close to the ventricle.

The outer aspect of the cerebellum has numerous transverse sulci. Sulci evolved to provide additional surface area to accommodate more cortex. The sulci all extend parallel to each other from side to side. The deeper ones demarcate lamella-like folds, called *lobules* (Fig. 10-3). The mass of white matter to which they are attached is the core proper of the cerebellum, which contains the central nuclei. The surface of each lobule is itself furrowed by transverse grooves. They vary in depth and cut into the lobule in such a way that, in a sagittal section, the branching pattern of the white matter resembles the branches of a tree. The smallest folds, called *folia,* are about 2 mm wide and are likened to leaves (*folium,* "a leaf").

Surfaces of the Cerebellum

The shape of the cerebellum and the contour of its surfaces conform to the space available in the posterior cranial fossa (Fig. 10-4). It has an anterior (ventral) surface that is molded around the hindbrain, a superior surface that is applied to the tentorium cerebelli (Fig. 10-5), and an inferior surface that is lodged in cup-like right and left halves of the posterior cranial fossa. The tentorial surface has right and left flattened portions that slope away from a median ridge. The inferior surface and the portion of the anterior surface that is applied to the medulla have right and left rounded hemisphere surfaces that are separated by a deep median depressed portion, which has the vermis for its floor.

The parts of the inferior surface that are unsupported above the foramen magnum may be pressed down into the foramen under certain conditions of increased intracranial pressure. When that happens the medulla is compressed, which impairs vital respiratory function.

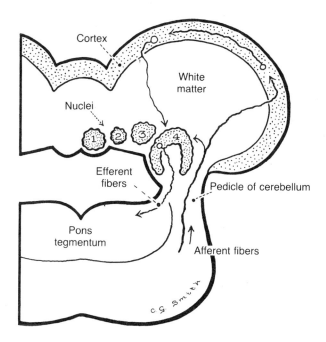

Figure 10-2. Cross section of the cerebellum, showing the location of its gray matter, the termination of its afferent fibers, and the origin of its efferent fibers.

Lobules of the Cerebellum

Deep fissures divide the cerebellum into a rostrocaudal series of lobules. Those lamella-like lobules extend right across the cerebellum but, in some cases, are markedly constricted at the junction of the hemisphere and the vermis. Figure 10-6 is a portrayal of the lobules in a diagram of the entire surface of the right half of the cerebellum. In that diagram, the worm-like vermis is represented as uncoiled to make all its lobules visible in a dorsal view. Similarly, the hemisphere portions of each of the lobules are pictured as lying on a flat surface. Each lobule has a named vermal portion and one or more named portions in the hemisphere. In Figure 10-6, the lobules are identified, using nomenclature of both human anatomy and comparative anatomy. In addition to the names, the subdivisions of the vermis are identified by number.

Three major subdivisions of the cerebellum are known as lobes. The anterior lobe is rostral to the primary fissure (Fig. 10-6A); the flocculonodular lobe is caudal to the posterolateral fissure; and the posterior lobe is between them. In Figure 10-6, the lobules of the anterior and flocculonodular lobes are stippled.

In Figure 10-7A, the striking resemblance of the uvula of the vermis to the uvula of the palate and the resemblance of the cerebellar tonsil to the palatine tonsil can be seen. Note that the tonsil is pressed against the inferior velum (Fig. 10-3) and lies above the foramen magnum. The paraflocculus is a tuft of three or four folia at the end of a slender band that is prolonged laterally from the tonsil.

The last of the rostrocaudal series of transverse lamellae is called the *flocculonodular*

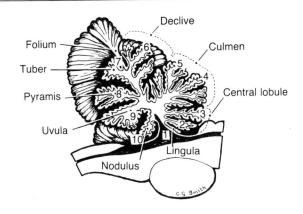

A

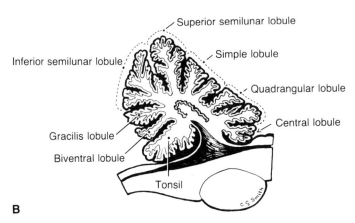

B

Figure 10-3.(A) Sagittal section of the vermis. (B) Sagittal section of the cerebellar hemisphere.

lobe. As its name implies, it has two parts: the nodule, in the vermis, and the flocculus, in the hemisphere. That very small portion of the cerebellum has the status of a major subdivision. It is, indeed, the original cerebellum. The posterolateral fissure, which separates it from the rest of the cerebellum, is the first fissure to appear in both embryologic and phylogenetic development. The nodule is a small mass of folia about the size of an orange seed; the flocculus, a tuft of four or five bud-like folia, is connected to the nodule by a delicate stalk of nerve fibers. As illustrated in Figure 10-7, the stalk has a U-shaped bend and gives attachment to the inferior velum. Some fibers of the stalk commonly take a shortcut from the nodule to the flocculus, traveling in the inferior velum to convert it into a medullary velum (one containing nerve fibers).

Core of the Cerebellum

The core of the cerebellum is the central mass of white matter that encloses the central nuclei; it gives attachment to the lobules. It has large right and left ovoid portions that are united at the midline by a thin band of crossing fibers. The entire superior surface

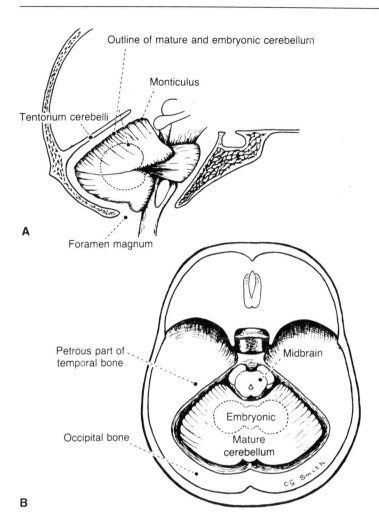

Outline of mature and embryonic cerebellum

Monticulus

Tentorium cerebelli

Foramen magnum

A

Petrous part of
temporal bone

Midbrain

Occipital bone

Embryonic

Mature
cerebellum

C.G. Smith

B

Figure 10-4. (A) The lateral aspect of the cerebellum and brain stem in a midsagittal section of the skull. (B) The superior aspect of the cerebellum and the caudal part of the brain stem fitted into the basal part of the skull.

and the posterior part of its inferior surface provide attachment for lobules. The anterior part of its inferior surface forms the roof of the fourth ventricle (Fig. 10-3).

Fibers of the Core

In Figure 10-8, the lobules have been detached, exposing the radiating fibers of the middle cerebellar peduncle. Those fibers course medially to reach the cortex of all lobules except the nodule. In Figure 10-9A, the middle cerebellar peduncle has been cut close to the brain stem, and its fibers have been removed from the core. This view exposes the inferior cerebellar peduncle, which makes a sharp turn dorsally, just rostral to the

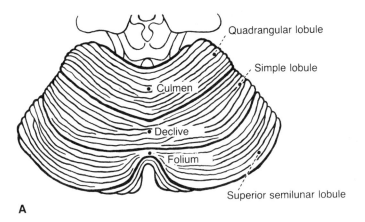

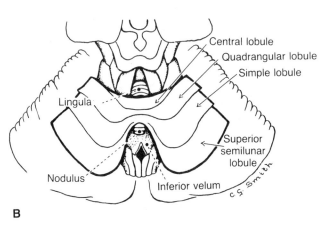

Figure 10-5. (A) *The superior surface of the cerebellum.* (B) *Lobules are detached to expose the core of white matter, the lingula, and the nodule.*

cochlear nuclei and enters the cerebellum between the middle and superior cerebellar peduncles. Its fibers fan out to form the middle layer of the core and reach the cortex of all the lobules of the cerebellum.

If the radiating superficial fibers of the inferior peduncle are teased away from the core, a few at a time, and are severed in the stalk of the cerebellum, a deep compact bundle, the uncinate fasciculus will be exposed (Fig. 10-9B). That bundle crosses the superior cerebellar peduncle superficially to enter the vermis. The fibers of the uncinate fasciculus are afferent and efferent fibers of the fastigial nucleus.

The removal of the fibers of the inferior cerebellar peduncle also exposes a thin layer of fibers that form a capsule for the central nuclei. These are axons of cells of the cerebellar cortex that end in the central nuclei.

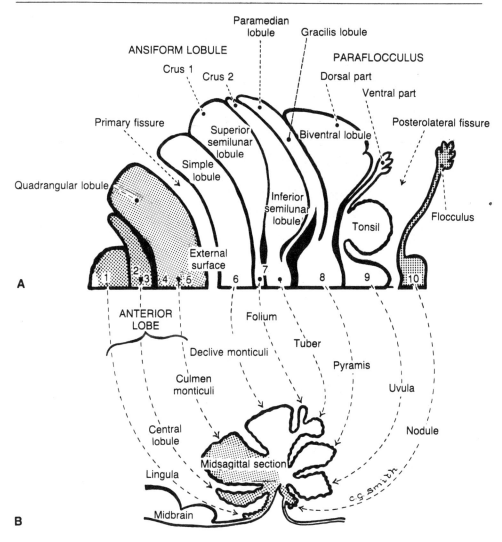

Figure 10-6. Lobules of the cerebellum. (A) The surface of the right half of the cerebellum. (B) A midsagittal section of the cerebellum. The lobules of the anterior and the flocculonodular lobe have been stippled.

Central Nuclei

Dentate Nucleus

The dentate nucleus is about 2 cm long and 1 cm wide and resembles the inferior olive in shape. It is sac-like, with a large opening directed medially and rostrally (Figs. 10-9B and 10-10). Its afferent fibers from the cerebellar cortex course along its surface and fill its deep sagittally oriented grooves. Efferent fibers form its core and emerge from its rostral open end to form the major part of the superior cerebellar peduncle.

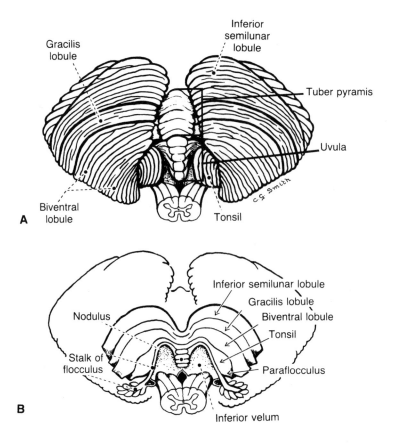

Figure 10-7. (A) *Inferior surface of the cerebellum.* (B) *Lobules are detached to expose the core of white matter and the flocculonodular lobe.*

Emboliform Nucleus

The stopper-shaped emboliform nucleus (*embolus,* "a stopper") extends along the medial border of the opening of the dentate nucleus (Figs. 10-10 and 10-11). Its efferent fibers form part of the superior cerebellar peduncle.

Globose Nucleus

The globose nucleus is divided into two or three clusters of cells medial to the emboliform nucleus (Figs. 10-10 and 10-11). Its efferent fibers form a small part of the superior cerebellar peduncle.

Fastigial Nucleus

The fastigial nucleus is the most medial of the four central nuclei (Figs. 10-10 and 10-11). It is located in the core of the vermis, adjacent to the roof of the fourth ventricle,

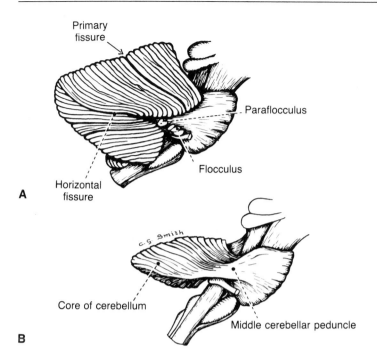

Labels on figure:
Primary fissure
Paraflocculus
Flocculus
Horizontal fissure
A
c. g. Smith
Core of cerebellum
Middle cerebellar peduncle
B

Figure 10-8. Steps in the dissection of the cerebellum. (A) The lateral aspect of the undissected cerebellum. (B) The lobules have been removed to show the contribution of middle cerebellar peduncle to the core.

and extends from the attachment of the lingula to the attachment of the pyramis. Many of its efferent fibers reach the brain stem in the uncinate fasciculus.

Structure and Organization of the Cerebellar Cortex

The cerebellar cortex is a superficial layer of gray matter, with cells arranged in layers. Its structure is the same in all parts of the cerebellum, and it has the same basic structure in all vertebrates. The cerebellar cortex developed early in phylogeny as an efficient modulator of motor activity.

The cerebellar cortex has three layers (Fig. 10-12A). The middle layer, one cell thick, contains the efferent cells of the cortex. Those large cone-shaped cells, known as *Purkinje cells*, have a single apical dendrite, with branches that extend in a sagittal plane (that is, in a plane across the folium) to the outer surface of the cortex. The dendrites and unmyelinated fibers that synapse with them form the almost cell-free molecular layer.

The deepest of the three layers of the cerebellar cortex is the thick layer of closely packed small cells that form the granular layer. Each cell has short dendrites, with brush-like branches that receive similar brush-like terminals of afferent fibers, known as *mossy fibers*. The axon of each granule cell extends into the molecular layer and divides into branches that extend medially and laterally along a folium for 1.5 mm in each direction.

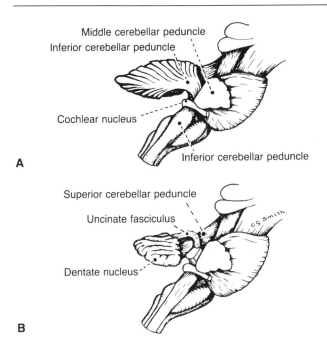

Figure 10-9. Steps in the dissection of the cerebellum. (A) The fibers of the middle cerebellar peduncle have been peeled off the core, revealing the fibers of the inferior cerebellar peduncle. (B) The fibers of the inferior cerebellar peduncle have been removed, exposing the dentate nucleus.

Those branches pass through the fan-shaped branching dendrites of many Purkinje cells, synapsing with each one in passing.

The cerebellar cortex receives two kinds of afferent fibers: mossy fibers and climbing fibers. Both types of fibers are excitatory. The mossy fibers synapse with granule cells; the climbing fibers, with Purkinje cells. The climbing fibers pass through the granule cell layer to climb, like a vine, along the long dendritic branches of Purkinje cells. The climbing fibers have collateral branches that synapse with other cells that resemble Purkinje cells but have axons that do not leave the cortex. Those cells, known as *basket cells*, are inhibitory cells (Fig. 10-12B). Their short axons extend across a folium, immediately above Purkinje cells, and give off collaterals that branch to form basket-like clusters around the bases of Purkinje cells. Their function is to cut short the excitation of the Purkinje cells and, in a sense, release them for the arrival of a later afferent input (Fig. 10-12B).

Subdivisions of the Cerebellum

The function of the cerebellum as a modulator of motor activity requires that it receive information from sense organs, but it also receives information from the cerebral cortex concerning projected voluntary movements. In a general way, those inputs determine both the anatomic and functional subdivisions of the cerebellum.

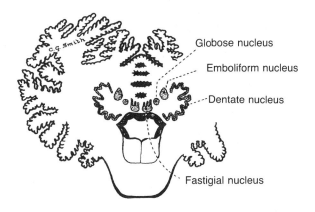

Globose nucleus

Emboliform nucleus

Dentate nucleus

Fastigial nucleus

Figure 10-10. Cross section of the cerebellum and pons segment, showing the cerebellar nuclei.

Phylogenetically, the oldest part of the cerebellum is the flocculonodular lobe, which is well developed in the fish. It receives its input from the sense organs of the vestibular nerve. With the development of limbs, the input from other sense organs increased and, as a result, the cerebellum enlarged. That occurrence led to the development of the corpus cerebelli—a rostral part of the cerebellum that is demarcated from the flocculonodular lobe by the posterolateral fissure. With the progressive enlargement of the corpus cerebelli, a deep transverse sulcus, the primary fissure, was acquired. The primary fissure divided the corpus cerebelli into anterior and posterior lobes.

With the development of the cerebral cortex, the cerebellum started to receive a cortical input, which led to the development of the cerebellar hemisphere. With its development, the portion that received the sensory input was crowded to the midline to form the vermis. Phylogenetically, therefore, the cerebellum may be described as being made up of an archicerebellum (the nodule and flocculus), a paleocerebellum (the remainder of the vermis), and the neocerebellum (the cerebellar hemispheres).

Representation of Parts of the Body in the Cerebellum

By stimulating different parts of the skin of monkeys and recording electrical changes in the cerebellar cortex, it was learned that a somatotopic representation of the parts of the body is created in the midline portion of the cerebellum. The lower trunk and hindlimbs project to the ipsilateral rostral part of the anterior lobe (vermis and a narrow paravermal sagittal band of hemispheric cortex); the upper trunk and forelimb project to the corresponding caudal parts of the anterior lobe. The head is represented in the declive and in an adjacent portion of the simple lobule.

In addition to the ipsilateral projection to the anterior lobe, a bilateral representation occurs in the posterior lobe. Impulses from the head, upper trunk and forelimb, and lower trunk and hindlimb are projected, in that order, to the pyramis and uvula, with their associated paravermal portions. In the monkey, the paravermal cortex forms the paramedian lobule.

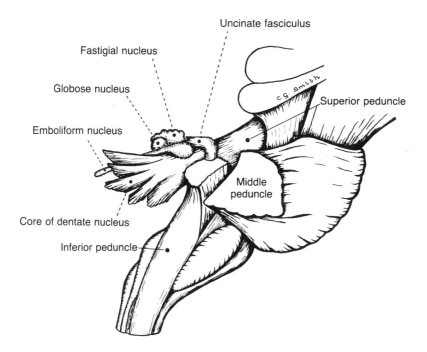

Uncinate fasciculus

Fastigial nucleus

Globose nucleus

Emboliform nucleus

Superior peduncle

Middle peduncle

Core of dentate nucleus

Inferior peduncle

Figure 10-11. Last step in the dissection of the cerebellum. The dentate nucleus has been removed.

Afferent Pathways of the Cerebellum

Pathways from the Spinal Cord (Sensory Input)

These four direct afferent pathways of the cerebellum are described with the spinal cord in Chapter 2. The posterior spinocerebellar and the cuneocerebellar pathways convey discriminative data from the leg and arm, respectively. The anterior and rostral spinocerebellar pathways convey less precise data from the leg and arm. Those pathways project somatotopically to the cerebellar cortex.

In addition, two indirect pathways reach the cerebellum from the spinal cord. They ascend in the anterior and lateral funiculus to relay stations in the accessory inferior olive and the lateral reticular nucleus of the medulla, respectively. Processed data from those nuclei are relayed to the cerebellum by means of the inferior cerebellar peduncle.

Pathways from the Sense Organs of the Vestibule and Semicircular Canals

Primary vestibular nerve fibers and fibers from cells in the vestibular nuclei reach the flocculonodular lobe by way of the inferior cerebellar peduncle.

Pathways from General Sense Organs of the Head

Fibers of cells in the nuclei of the trigeminal nerve and secondary fibers of the reticular formation convey impulses via the inferior cerebellar peduncle from general sense organs to the somatotopically organized anterior and posterior head areas of the cerebellar cortex.

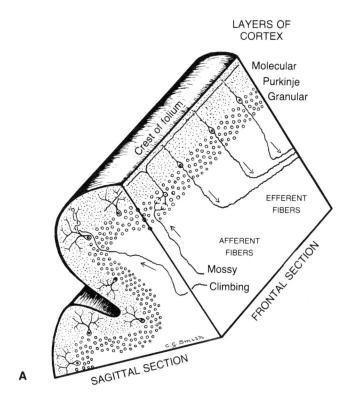

LAYERS OF
CORTEX

Molecular
Purkinje
Granular

Crest of folium

EFFERENT
FIBERS

AFFERENT
FIBERS

Mossy

Climbing

FRONTAL SECTION

C.S. Smith

A

SAGITTAL SECTION

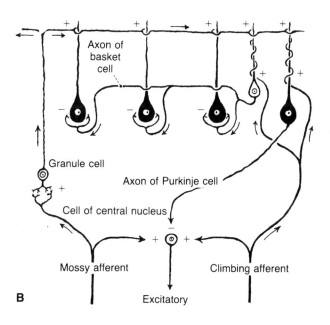

Axon of
basket
cell

Granule cell

Axon of Purkinje cell

Cell of central nucleus

Mossy afferent

Climbing afferent

B

Excitatory

Figure 10-12. (A) Wedge-shaped portion of two adjacent folia, showing the layers of cortex and the form of Purkinje cells in a frontal and sagittal section. (B) Basic connections of representative afferent and efferent fibers of cortical granule cells, Purkinje cells, basket cells, and cells of the central nuclei. The excitatory or inhibitory role of each cell is indicated by a plus or a minus sign.

Pathways from the Retina and the Cochlea

Impulses are conveyed to the cerebellum from the visual and auditory sense organs by indirect routes. They may reach the folium and tuber by way of the cerebral cortex as well as by way of the superior colliculus. In each case, there is a relay station in the pontine nuclei.

Pathways from the Cerebral Cortex

Most of the pathways from the cerebral cortex to the cerebellum originate in the motor cortex, but an appreciable number originate in other cortical areas. Those pathways have relay stations in the pontine and principal inferior olivary nuclei. Pontocerebellar fibers cross the midline to enter the cerebellum in the middle cerebellar peduncle. They end as mossy fibers in all parts of the hemisphere and all parts of the vermis except the nodulus. Their projection overlaps the sensory input to the vermis. As the pontocerebellar fibers enter the cerebellum, some give off collateral branches to the dentate, emboliform, and globose nuclei. Olivocerebellar fibers cross the midline to enter the cerebellum in the inferior cerebellar peduncle. Some of those fibers also give off collateral branches to the central nuclei, but they end in the cortex as climbing fibers.

Impulses can also reach the cerebellum by other pathways. One of those is a pathway with relay stations in the red nucleus and the inferior olive. The fibers reach the inferior olive from the red nucleus by way of the central tegmental tract.

Efferent Pathways of the Cerebellum

Corticonuclear Fibers

The efferent fibers of the cerebellar cortex are axons of Purkinje cells. None of them extend beyond the central nuclei, except for a small number from the vermis that reach the vestibular nuclei. The projection to the central nuclei is an orderly one. Purkinje cells, in each sagittal plane, project to cells located in the same plane. Thus cells of each half of the vermis project to the fastigial nucleus; cells of a paravermal band of hemispheric cortex project to the globose and emboliform nuclei; and the remaining large lateral portion of the cerebellar cortex projects to the dentate nucleus.

The orderly projection of Purkinje cells has suggested that the cortex is divided functionally into three portions: vermal, paravermal, and lateral hemisphere. Experimental and clinical studies have shown that the vermal subdivision of the cerebellum has a major role in maintaining equilibrium; the paravermal subdivision has a role in postural adjustments of the limbs on the same side; and the large lateral subdivision has an important role in skilled movements.

Efferent Fibers of the Central Nuclei

All the cells of the central nuclei convey excitatory impulses. The impulses they receive from the Purkinje cells are all inhibitory. This means that the cerebellar cortex has a role in modulating the flow of impulses to muscles by inhibiting selected cells of the central nuclei (Fig. 10-12B).

Efferent Fibers of the Fastigial Nucleus

Some fibers of the fastigial nucleus cross the midline and pass superficial to the superior cerebellar peduncle. Those fibers are derived from the uncinate fasciculus (Fig. 10-11) and end in the vestibular nuclei and the medial portion of the reticular formation. Other efferent fastigial fibers are uncrossed and reach the vestibular and reticular nuclei by coursing deep to the superior cerebellar peduncle and entering the medulla medial to the inferior cerebellar peduncle. Fibers of that efferent bundle are known as the *juxta-restiform body*. Impulses conveyed by those fastigial efferent fibers can influence motor activity of the trunk and limbs by way of the vestibulospinal and reticulospinal tracts.

The fastigial nucleus can also influence motor activity by way of a pathway that ascends to the origin of the corticospinal tracts. Fastigial efferent fibers ascend in the dorsolateral part of the brain stem to end in the ventral lateral thalamic nucleus. Impulses are relayed by that nucleus to the motor cortex.

Efferent Fibers of the Central Nuclei of the Cerebellar Hemisphere

Fibers of the globose, emboliform, and dentate nuclei ascend in the superior cerebellar peduncle, decussate in the midbrain, and are distributed to the red nucleus, the nuclei of the oculomotor nerve, and the ventral lateral nucleus of the thalamus. The latter nucleus relays impulses to the motor cortex of the cerebral hemisphere to influence motor activity of all parts of the body.

Review Questions (Answers Available on the Pages Cited)

1. What is the function of the cerebellum (p. 123)?
2. Name the central nuclei of the cerebellar hemisphere (pp. 129 and 130).
3. Account for the presence of sulci on the surface of the cerebellum (p. 124).
4. Name the fissures that delimit the posterior lobe of the cerebellum (p. 125).
5. Relate the fiber layers of the core of the cerebellum to the cerebellar peduncles (pp. 127 and 128).
6. What are the excitatory and inhibitory afferent fibers of the Purkinje cells (p. 132)?
7. How does the input of the vermis differ from the input of the cerebellar hemisphere (p. 133)?
8. What sensory data are projected (a) to the flocculonodular lobe; (b) to the folium and tuber (pp. 133 and 136)?
9. What functions have been attributed to the vermal, the paravermal, and to the hemisphere portion of the cerebellum (p. 136)?

11

The Cerebral Hemisphere: Part 1. Overview

The cerebral hemispheres have been acquired, in the course of phylogenetic development, to serve as dominant suprasegmental structures. Their function is to process data provided by all the sense organs, to record that data for future reference, and to initiate an appropriate response to sensory data and the data of past experience.

Structural Features of the Cerebral Hemisphere Explained by Its Development

A brief outline of the development of the cerebral hemisphere helps to explain its form, structure, and relationships.

Attachment of the Olfactory Bulb to the Cerebral Hemisphere

The primordium of the cerebral hemisphere, designed to provide the highest level of association in the central nervous system, is found in primitive vertebrates in the caudal part of the olfactory bulb. The bilateral olfactory bulbs are outpouchings of the lateral wall of the telencephalon (end brain) that receive terminals of the olfactory nerve fibers.

Figure 11-1A illustrates an early stage in the development of the hemisphere. In this diagram, the olfactory bulb is already divisible into two parts: the developing hemisphere and the smaller rostral portion—the original olfactory bulb. As development proceeds, the connection between the two becomes attenuated to form the olfactory tract. Thus, with the progressive enlargement of the cerebral hemisphere, the olfactory bulb becomes a small appendage of the cerebral hemisphere.

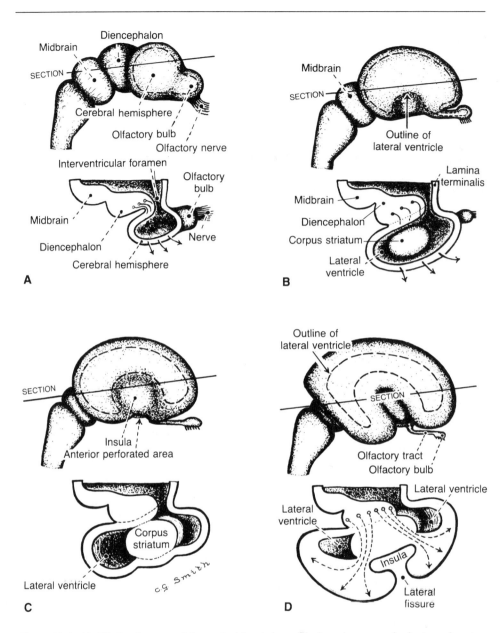

Figure 11-1. (A–D) Development of the cerebral hemisphere. The lateral aspect and a horizontal section of each of four specimens, illustrating stages in the development of the cerebral hemisphere.

Attachment of the Cerebral Hemisphere to the Entire Lateral Surface of the Diencephalon

As illustrated in the horizontal section of the forebrain in Figure 11-1A, all the fibers connecting the diencephalon with the cerebral hemisphere must pass through the caudal part of its tubular stalk. As the size of the hemisphere and the number of fibers connecting it with the brain stem increase, that portion of its stalk must grow progressively thicker. As a result, as illustrated in Figure 11-1B, the hemisphere extends its attachment to the entire lateral surface of the diencephalon.

Corpus Striatum and the Form of the Lateral Ventricle

In the course of development, the ovoid lateral ventricle is converted to a tubular C-shaped cavity by the development of an ovoid mass of gray matter, the corpus striatum, as illustrated in Figures 11-1B, C, and D. The horizontal section reveals a swelling in the middle of the floor of the lateral ventricle. That swelling is produced by a mass of cells and nerve fibers, called the *corpus striatum*. The developing corpus striatum becomes much larger and spreads across the floor to connect the inferior parts of the medial and lateral walls. In its final stage of development, the corpus striatum bulges upward to occupy all of the ventricle that is located lateral to the diencephalon. In so doing, it converts the lateral ventricle into a C-shaped tubular space that extends rostrocaudally around the corpus striatum.

A feature of the medial wall of the ventricle is the choroid membrane, which is a membranous band that contains the choroid plexus (Fig. 11-2). It extends the whole length of the ventricle adjacent to the attachment of the hemisphere to the diencephalon.

Insula and Lateral Fissure of the Cerebral Hemisphere

While the corpus striatum is developing, nerve cells are also accumulating on the external surface of the hemisphere to form a bark-like investment, called the *cerebral cortex*. The cerebral cortex covers the entire lateral surface and most of the ventral and medial surfaces of the hemisphere (Fig. 11-2C). The cortex, lateral to the corpus striatum, behaves as though its growth were inhibited by that adjacent mass of gray matter. At any rate, it fails to expand as rapidly as the surrounding cortex, and as the hemisphere enlarges, that area becomes the floor of an ever-deepening depression on the lateral surface of the hemisphere (Fig. 11-1C and 11-1D). The cortex in that depressed area is known as the *insula*. It is progressively overlapped by the expanding bordering parts of the hemisphere, and in the fully developed brain, the overhanging parts meet along a straight line to form the lateral fissure. The lateral fissure begins ventrally, lateral to the external surface of the corpus striatum, and extends to the middle of the lateral surface of the hemisphere.

Cerebral Commissures, Transverse Cerebral Fissure, and Septum Pellucidum

The fibers of the commissures that unite the right and left hemispheres course within the lamina terminalis to cross the midline. The enormous accumulation of fibers within that lamina forms a canopy-like structure that extends back above the diencephalon, separated from it by a space known as the *transverse cerebral fissure*. The steps in the development of that canopy are illustrated in Figure 11-3.

In Figure 11-3A, the part of the lamina terminalis that is just rostral to the roof of

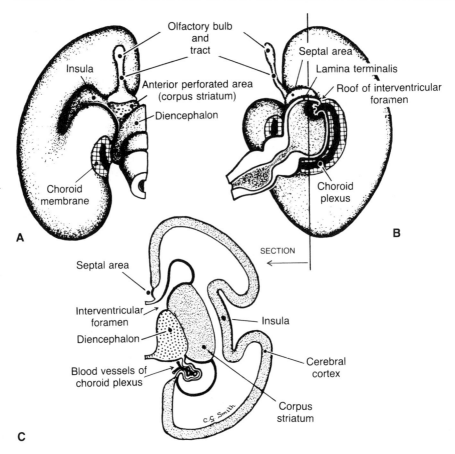

Figure 11-2. The right half of a fetal brain at 3½ months: (A) inferior aspect, (B) medial aspect, (C) horizontal section of the forebrain.

the interventricular foramen is beginning to increase in thickness. Initially, it is invaded by cells of a small portion of the surface of the hemisphere, adjacent to the lamina terminalis, called the *septal area* (Fig. 11-2). The cells of the septal area are in clusters, not in layers as in the cortex. It receives a direct pathway from the olfactory bulb.

The first commissural fibers that develop pass through the cellular thickening of the lamina terminalis. They unite the right and left olfactory bulbs. As the cerebral cortex matures, its commissural fibers are added, and the thickening of the lamina terminalis forms a dorsally projecting transverse ridge. As more fibers are added to the ridge, from the progressively more posterior parts of the hemisphere, the thickened portion of the lamina terminalis takes the form of a canopy for the diencephalon. It is attached laterally to the right and left hemispheres and retains its continuity with the rostral thin part of the lamina terminalis.

The cul-de-sac between the canopy and the diencephalon is the transverse cerebral fissure. Its lateral border is the thin choroid membrane in the medial wall of the lateral ventricle.

While the commissural band is growing to acquire the size and shape pictured in Figure

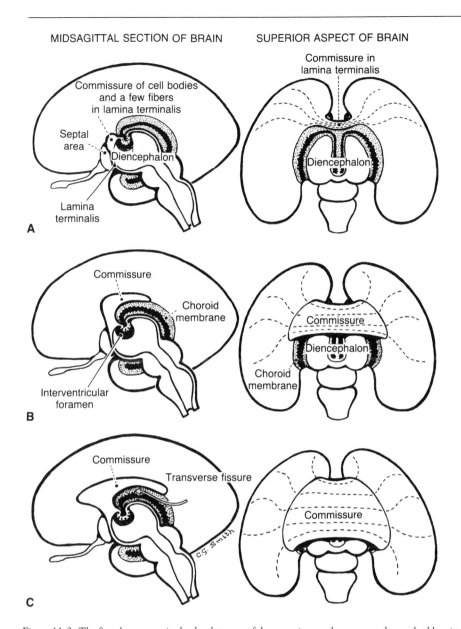

MIDSAGITTAL SECTION OF BRAIN   SUPERIOR ASPECT OF BRAIN

Figure 11-3. The first three stages in the development of the commissures that connect the cerebral hemisphere.

11-3C, the fibers it contains are grouping themselves to form three bundles, as shown in Figure 11-4. The largest of those bundles is the corpus callosum; the other two are the hippocampal commissure and the anterior commissure.

The corpus callosum forms a thick, compact layer on the outer aspect of the commissural band. Its fibers connect phylogenetically newer cortex that contains six layers of cells. It has four named parts: the body, splenium, genu, and rostrum (see Fig. 11-4).

The hippocampal commissure connects the relatively small areas of archicortex in the

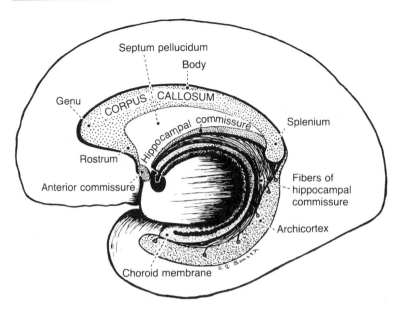

Figure 11-4. Medial aspect of the right cerebral hemisphere, showing the fourth and final stage in the development of its commissures.

two hemispheres. That phylogenetically older cortex contains only three layers of cells. It is located in the inferior parts of the hemispheres, and its commissural fibers form a very thin layer at the inferior border of the commissural band.

The anterior commissure is a compact bundle that is 2 or 3 mm in diameter, located just in front of the interventricular foramen, where the first fibers to unite the hemispheres crossed the midline. It contains some fibers that connect the right and left olfactory bulbs, but most of its fibers connect neocortical areas located in the inferior lateral portions of the hemispheres (the temporal lobes).

The separation of the fibers of the corpus callosum from those of the hippocampal commissure is associated with a medial extension of the lateral ventricle, as illustrated in Figure 11-5. As the cross-sectional diameter of the lateral ventricle increases, it extends to the midline, wedging apart the upper and lower commissural fibers. In that way, the ventricles are separated by a median translucent membrane—the septum pellucidum. It contains some nerve cells that are caught up from the septal region. In some otherwise normal brains, that septum may be perforated (8%), and then cerebrospinal fluid can flow from one ventricle to the other and be drained by either the right or the left interventricular foramen.

Form and Relationships

The cerebral hemispheres plus the diencephalon to which they are attached fill a chamber that has a spherical, dome-like roof and a terraced floor (Fig. 11-6). The anterior part of the floor is the roof of the orbit. The posterior part of the floor, formed by the middle

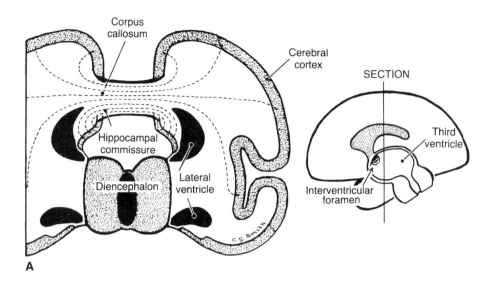

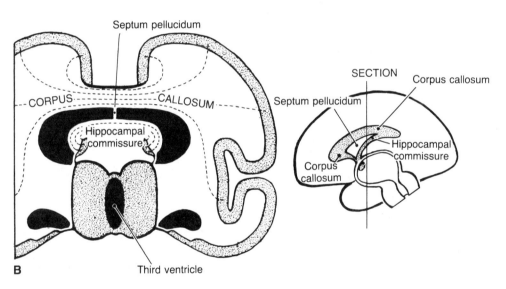

Figure 11-5. Frontal sections of the forebrain, showing how the commissural fiber band is split by the right and left lateral ventricles to form the corpus callosum, the hippocampal commissure, and the septum pellucidum.

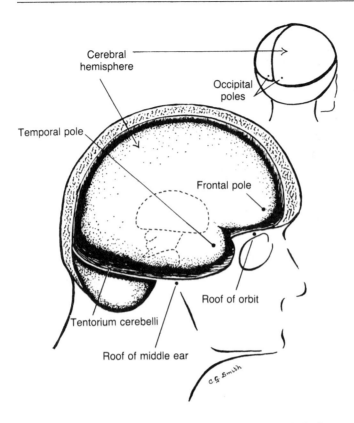

Cerebral
hemisphere

Occipital
poles

Temporal pole

Frontal pole

Roof of orbit

Tentorium cerebelli

Roof of middle ear

c.g. Smith

Figure 11-6. Right cerebral hemisphere, exposed within the skull, showing its lateral aspect and its chief relationships.

cranial fossa and the tentorium cerebelli, is at the level of the floor of the orbit. The two hemispheres occupy all the space available in that chamber. They project in front, above, and behind the diencephalon, extend medially to enclose it, and flatten out against each other at the midline. Thus each hemisphere acquires the shape of a quarter of a sphere with two notches—one for the diencephalon and one for the orbit. Its three surfaces face laterally, medially, and inferiorly.

Lateral Surface

The lateral surface is part of a sphere and has a superior semicircular border that extends from the frontal pole—the extremity above the orbit—to the occipital pole, its posterior extremity (Fig. 11-6). The inferior border completes the semicircular outline, but it is divided into a shorter anterior part above the roof of the orbit and a posterior part that is at the level of the floor of the orbit. The rounded, anterior end of the inferior portion of the hemisphere behind the orbit is the temporal pole.

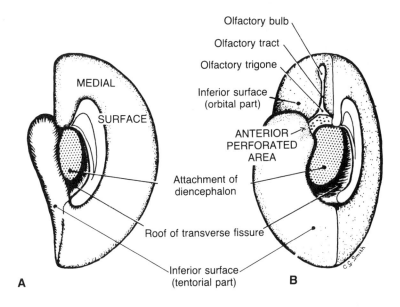

Olfactory bulb
Olfactory tract
Olfactory trigone
Inferior surface
(orbital part)
ANTERIOR
PERFORATED
AREA
MEDIAL
SURFACE
Attachment of
diencephalon
Roof of transverse fissure
Inferior surface
(tentorial part)

A

B

Figure 11-7. (A) Medial aspect of the cerebral hemisphere. (B) Inferior aspect of the cerebral hemisphere.

Medial Surface

The medial surface is flat and its outline is that of a semicircle (Fig. 11-7A). At the middle of its straight inferior border is the deep notch that is occupied by the diencephalon. The connection with the diencephalon is in the floor of that notch, and in a sense, it is a hilum of the hemisphere, because through it pass all the pathways that connect the hemisphere and the brain stem. The upper wall of this notch—for the diencephalon— is separated from the superior surface of the diencephalon by the transverse fissure. Above the notch is the arc-like sagittal section of the commissural band that connects the right and left cerebral hemispheres.

Inferior Surface

The inferior surface has a lateral border that is a semicircle, extending from the frontal pole to the occipital pole (Fig. 11-7). Its medial border completes the semicircular outline. At the middle of its straight medial border is the notch occupied by the diencephalon. The floor and walls of that notch were described with the medial surface. The anterior third of the inferior surface is in front of the notch for the diencephalon and rests on the orbit. The posterior two-thirds is on a lower level and is described as the tentorial surface, although part of it rests on the floor of the middle cranial fossa. Neither the orbital nor the tentorial surface is horizontal. The orbital surface faces laterally as well as inferiorly, and the tentorial surface faces medially as well as inferiorly. Hence the tentorial surface is usually described with the medial surface.

A feature of the inferior surface is the attachment of the olfactory bulb and the pathways leading from it to three parts of the hemisphere—the cerebral cortex, the anterior perforated substance (a derivative of the corpus striatum), and the septal region. The olfactory bulb is about the size of an orange seed and is connected to the hemisphere by a slender fiber bundle—the olfactory tract. That tract is attached to the apex of a small pyramidal mass on the inferior surface of the hemisphere, called the *olfactory trigone*. The olfactory trigone is located just in front of the anterior perforated area, that is, about 1 cm in front of the notch for the diencephalon and about 1 cm from the midline. The olfactory trigone serves as a distributing center for olfactory impulses. Pathways fan out into the anterior perforated substance and along its borders. The medial pathways course into the septal area; the lateral pathways course to the temporal pole. The fibers that follow the lateral border of the anterior perforated area are called the *lateral olfactory stria*. The stria is located on the surface of a band of gray matter, the lateral olfactory gyrus, which is at the ventral border of the insula.

Cerebral Cortex

General Characteristics

The cerebral cortex is a layer of gray matter that is 2 to 4 mm thick. It forms a bark-like covering for most of the hemisphere. In it occur the complex associations that constitute the function of the cerebral hemisphere. The only parts of the free surface that are not covered by cortex are the choroid membrane, which contains no nerve cells, the septal area, which contains cells in irregularly arranged clusters, and the anterior perforated area, which is a part of the corpus striatum.

Structurally, in addition to being a thin, superficial layer of gray matter, the cortex is peculiar in that its cells are arranged in three to six layers that are parallel to the surface. Functionally, it may be considered to consist of unit masses that are microscopic, elongated blocks that reach from its outer to its inner surface. Since the cell content of each of the three to six layers in a unit can only vary within relatively narrow limits, it follows that the length of a unit and hence the thickness of the cortex is also relatively constant. This explains why the thickness of the cortex in man is only a little greater than in the rat.

Because the cortex is made up of cylindrical units set side by side to form a superficial layer of gray matter, it follows that as more units are added, more surface must be provided. To provide the very large surface that is required to accommodate the cerebral cortex of the human brain, the surface of the hemisphere is wrinkled. Each furrow is called a *sulcus* and each ridge is called a *gyrus*.

Archicortex and Neocortex

Two very different kinds of cortex are found on the surface of the cerebral hemisphere— the archicortex, which has three layers, and the neocortex, which has six. The archicortex is present in reptiles and birds. In mammals, the need for a more efficient association mechanism led to the development of the six-layered neocortex. The neocortex has proved to be so useful that it and not the archicortex has increased in amount with the

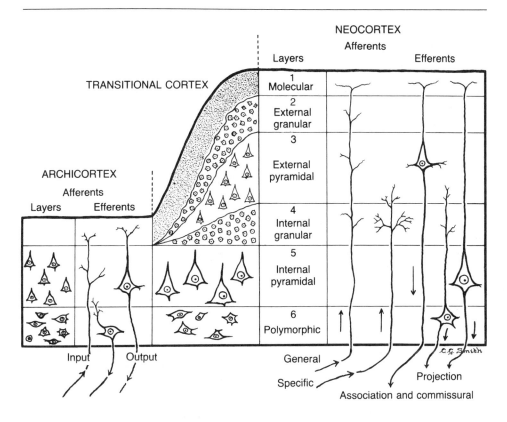

Figure 11-8. Diagram showing (1) the relationship of the layers of the neocortex to those of the archicortex, and (2) the termination of the afferent fibers and the origin of the efferent fibers in each.

need for a larger and more complex association mechanism. Hence, in man, the archi-cortex is only a small fraction of the total amount of cortex.

The histology of archicortex and neocortex is illustrated schematically in Figure 11-8. The simpler archicortex has a superficial, thin, almost acellular layer that receives the terminals of fibers that enter the cortex. Deep to it are two layers of cells. Those cells have fibers that convey impulses out of the cortex. Layer 1 of the archicortex is a layer of synapses. The afferent fibers of the cortex synapse there with the dendrites that extend into it from the cells in layers 2 and 3. In a histological preparation, the sections of dendrites and nerve fibers of layer 1 are visible as dust-like particles; hence layer 1 is called the *molecular layer*. Layer 2 is composed of pyramid-shaped cells. Each cell has a long apical strand of cytoplasm that ends, as already stated, in layer 1. Layer 3 is the polymorphic layer; its cells vary in size and shape and some have dendrites that end in layer 1. Both layers 2 and 3 contain some small cells whose axons do not leave the cortex. Those cells provide extra indirect connections between the afferent fibers of the cortex and the efferent cells of layers 2 and 3.

The neocortex is double the thickness of the archicortex. The increase in thickness is due to the addition of a layer of small pyramids sandwiched between two layers of small, round cells, called *granules*. Those three new layers are insinuated between the layer of large pyramids and the superficial molecular layer of archicortex. The afferent fibers come into the neocortex as in the archicortex and push through to reach the superficial molecular layer. The dendrites of the large pyramidal cells also lengthen to reach the surface. In that way, the molecular layer retains its superficial position. The afferent fibers of the cortex, however, have terminals that end not only in layer 1 but also in each of the new layers numbered 2, 3, and 4. In this way a large number of cells are interposed as indirect links between the afferent fibers and the efferent cells.

With the addition of more layers of cells in the superficial receiving portion of the cortical unit, the terminals of the sensory fibers (auditory, visual, touch, and so forth) become more complicated and end in bush-like tufts. Those endings distinguish them from other incoming fibers, for example, commissural, and they are called *specific afferent fibers*. The specific afferent fibers end chiefly in layer 4 but also in layer 3. The larger branches of the bushy tuft of each fiber are myelinated and, therefore, in a histological preparation stained for myelin, there is a thin layer of fine myelinated fibers in layer 4. In the visual area of the cortex, the myelinated branches are present in layer 4 in such numbers that they form a band that is visible, in an unstained section, as a white line— the *line of Gennari*.

The addition of three layers of cells to archicortex to form the neocortex provides the cortex with additional cells for the reception and dispersal of impulses. The dispersal of impulses to other units of the same and opposite hemisphere is one of the functions of the cells of the external pyramidal layer. A few cells with this function, however, have also been acquired by layers 5 and 6 of the neocortex.

In an attempt to summarize what has been said concerning the structure and function of the cortex, we may state that in a general way, impulses that come to the cortex are received in the superficial layers and impulses that leave the cortex do so from the deeper layers. The cells interposed between the terminals of the afferent fibers and the efferent cells are largely in layers 2, 3, and 4, but all layers have cells that serve that purpose. The processes of those cells do not leave the cortex. Their branching nerve fibers are so distributed that the cells of the cortex are linked to form self-exciting circuits, within which impulses may go around again and again. Offshoots of such a circuit may thus excite adjacent cells periodically. This is one explanation that has been offered for the rhythmic changes in surface potential of the brain at rest.

Subdivisions of the Cerebral Cortex

The cerebral cortex is a specialized association mechanism, but some parts of that thin shell of gray matter serve as receiving stations for the incoming sensory pathways, and one part serves as a dispatching center, that is, as a site of departure for the long pathways that carry messages to the muscles.

The receiving areas are the sensory projection areas. There are five of those—one for each of the known sensory pathways, namely, the optic, auditory, general sensory, taste, and olfactory. Those receiving stations are widely separated. Between them, and also at a site in front of all of them, we find the association areas proper. The association areas receive impulses from the sensory areas and do the essential work of processing the data from the environment. The willed response is initiated by impulses that spread from the association areas to the centrally located area of cortex called the *motor area*. It is connected with the motor nuclei of the brain and spinal cord. The descending pathways are the motor pathways. Of those, the corticobulbar and the corticospinal, already studied in the brain stem, extend directly to the motor nuclei or at least to their immediate vicinity.

The cortical areas, of course, all look alike from the surface and cannot be identified by their appearance. They do, however, differ somewhat in histological structure. Thus in sensory areas—the site of termination of large numbers of afferent fibers—there is an increase in the number of granular cells in layers 2 and 4 and a corresponding decrease in the number of medium and large pyramids in layers 3 and 5. The replacement of large cells by small granular cells leads to a marked reduction in the thickness of the cortex. The cortex of sensory areas is therefore thinner than that of other areas, and because of the increased number of granular cells, it is called *granular cortex*.

The histological changes in the motor area are the counterpart of those in the sensory area. The need is for pyramidal cells with long nerve fibers to carry impulses to the brain stem. Those cells take the place of many small granular cells, and the result is a much thicker cortex (about 4 mm). Because it has so few granular cells, it is described as *agranular cortex*. All other areas are association areas and have the type of structure described as typical of neocortex.

The small differences in histological structure are great enough to influence the location of the lines along which the cortex buckles as it spreads out to cover more surface. In some cases, it buckles at the margin of an area (general sensory area); in other cases, it buckles along a line across the middle of the area (visual area). Since the first parts of the cortex to be differentiated are the sensory and the motor areas, it follows that the first sulci to develop appear in their vicinity. Those sulci then proceed to deepen as the developing association cortex crowds those areas. Hence, although obscured by secondary foldings of the cortex, they can in most cases be identified by their depth. This is possible in the dissecting room and, by reference to the deepest sulci, the cortical areas can be charted.

Review Questions (Answers Available on the Pages Cited)

1. Account for the attachment of the olfactory nerve to an appendage of the cerebral hemisphere (p. 139).
2. Account for the attachment of the cerebral hemisphere to the lateral surface of the diencephalon (p. 141).
3. Account for the lateral fissure of the cerebral hemisphere (p. 142).
4. How do the right and left lateral ventricles come to be separated by a thin membrane, the septum pellucidum (p. 144)?
5. What is the functional unit of the cerebral cortex (p. 148)?
6. How does neocortex differ from archicortex (pp. 148 and 149)?
7. What are the functional subdivisions of the cortex? How do those areas differ in structure (pp. 150 and 151)?

12

The Cerebral Hemisphere: Part 2. Cortical Areas

The deep sulci of the cerebral hemisphere can be used to divide its surface into regions, called *lobes,* and to locate its functional areas.

Sulci Lobes and Gyri of the Lateral Surface

Sulci that Demarcate Lobes

The *lateral sulcus* is the deepest sulcus of the lateral surface (Fig. 12-1). It begins inferiorly at the lateral border of the anterior perforated area and extends posteriorly, parallel to the inferior border of the hemisphere, to end at the middle of the lateral surface.

The *central sulcus* ascends from the midpoint of the lateral sulcus to cut the superior border of the hemisphere just behind its midpoint.

The *parietooccipital sulcus* is one of the sulci of the medial surface that extends onto the lateral surface. It cuts the superior border of the hemisphere at a point in line with the lateral sulcus and extends toward it for about 2 cm.

By means of those three sulci, the hemisphere can be divided into lobes. They are given the names of the overlying bones of the cranium. The frontal lobe is in front of the central sulcus. The occipital lobe lies behind a line that extends from the parietooccipital sulcus to reach the inferior border about 5 cm from the occipital pole. The region between the frontal and occipital lobes is divided into upper and lower portions—the parietal lobe and the temporal lobe, respectively. They are separated by the lateral sulcus and a line that extends the sulcus to the occipital lobe.

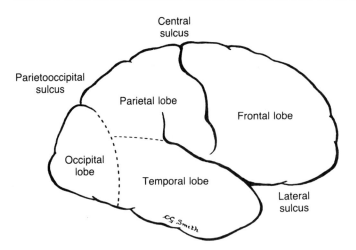

Figure 12-1. Lobes of the cerebral hemisphere.

Sulci and Gyri of the Frontal Lobe

The *precentral sulcus* is parallel to the central sulcus and about one finger's breadth in front of it. The gyrus between them is the *precentral gyrus*. The precentral sulcus is usually divided into upper and lower parts. The upper portion rarely cuts across the superior border of the hemisphere, but the lower portion may cut into the lateral sulcus.

A *superior* and an *inferior frontal sulcus* extend anteriorly from each portion of the precentral sulcus to end short of the frontal pole. Those sulci divide the anterior part of the frontal lobe into three portions: *superior, middle,* and *inferior frontal gyri.* The middle frontal gyrus may be divided into upper and lower parts by an intermediate sulcus, and the inferior frontal gyrus may be divided into three parts by sulci that cut into it from the lateral sulcus. The middle part is the pars triangularis, the orbital part is anterior to it, and the opercular part is posterior (Figs. 12-2 and 12-3A).

Sulci and Gyri of the Parietal Lobe

The *postcentral sulcus* is parallel to and a finger's breadth behind the central sulcus (Figs. 12-2 and 12-3A). It stops short of both the superior border of the hemisphere and the lateral sulcus. The *postcentral gyrus* is between the central and postcentral sulci. The *intraparietal sulcus* divides the large posterior part of the parietal lobe into superior and inferior parietal lobules. The inferior parietal lobule has an anterior portion around the end of the lateral sulcus. That is the *supramarginal gyrus.* Behind it is the *angular gyrus,* which caps the end of the superior temporal sulcus (see the following discussion).

Sulci and Gyri of the Temporal Lobes

The lateral surface of the temporal lobe has two sulci: the *superior* and *inferior temporal sulci.* They begin near the temporal pole and extend back, parallel to the lateral sulcus. The superior temporal sulcus ends in the inferior parietal lobule. They divide the lateral

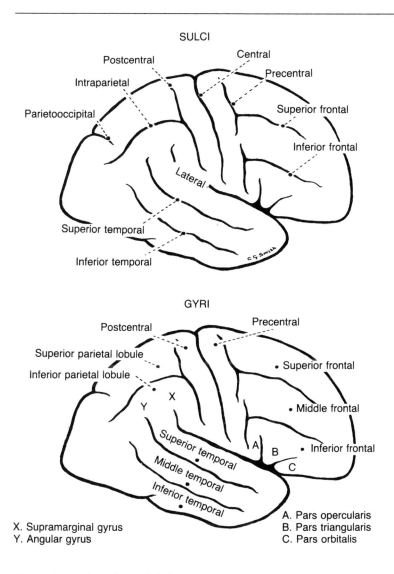

SULCI

Postcentral

Central

Precentral

Intraparietal

Superior frontal

Parietooccipital

Inferior frontal

Lateral

Superior temporal

Inferior temporal

C.G.Smith

GYRI

Postcentral

Precentral

Superior parietal lobule

Superior frontal

Inferior parietal lobule

X

Y

Middle frontal

Superior temporal

A

B

Inferior frontal

Middle temporal

C

Inferior temporal

X. Supramarginal gyrus
Y. Angular gyrus

A. Pars opercularis
B. Pars triangularis
C. Pars orbitalis

Figure 12-2. Sulci and gyri of the lateral surface of the cerebral hemisphere.

surface of the temporal lobe into three portions: the *superior, middle,* and *inferior temporal gyri* (Figs. 12-2 and 12-3A).

Sulci and Gyri of the Medial Surface of the Cerebral Hemisphere

The *sulcus cinguli* begins inferior to the rostrum of the corpus callosum and arches upward and backward about a finger's breadth from it as far as the splenium. It outlines the *cingulate gyrus.* The cingulate gyrus is separated from the corpus callosum by the *callosal*

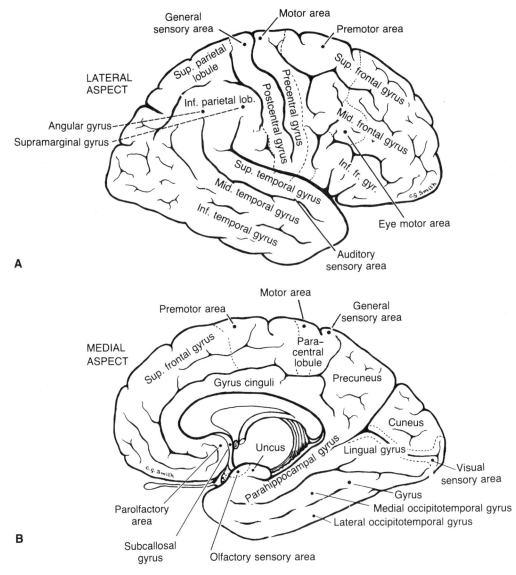

Figure 12-3. (A) *Lateral and* (B) *medial aspects of a cerebral hemisphere, showing the location of the principal motor and sensory areas.*

sulcus, except below the rostrum, where a narrow ridge of gray matter intervenes—the *subcallosal gyrus*. That gyrus is not a part of the cortex, and its cells are not in layers; it is a part of the septal area of the hemisphere described with the internal structure of the hemisphere in the following chapter. It tapers to a point toward the genu and is prolonged inferiorly along the anterior border of the lamina terminalis to end at the anterior perforated area. Anterior to the subcallosal gyrus is a narrow band of additional septal gray

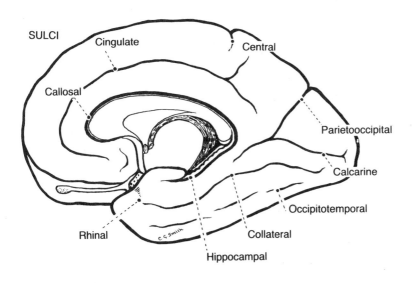

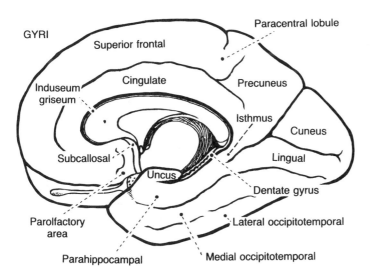

Figure 12-4. Sulci and gyri of the medial surface of the cerebral hemisphere.

matter, called the *parolfactory area*. It receives olfactory impulses and may or may not be limited anteriorly by a sulcus, as in Figure 12-3B.

The *calcarine sulcus* begins below the splenium, ascends about 1 cm onto the medial surface of the hemisphere, and turns back to the occipital pole (Figs. 12-3B and 12-4).

The *parietal-occipital sulcus* extends from the angular bend of the calcarine sulcus to cut the superior margin of the hemisphere about 5 cm from the occipital pole. The wedge of cortex between it and the posterior part of the calcarine sulcus is the *cuneus*. The cortex that surrounds the end of the central sulcus on the medial surface of the hemisphere is the *paracentral lobule,* and between it and the cuneus is the portion of the parietal lobe that is called the *precuneus* (Figs. 12-3B and 12-4B). The cortex anterior to the paracentral lobule and between the cingulate sulcus and the margin of the hemisphere is the medial aspect of the *superior frontal gyrus.*

Sulci and Gyri of the Inferior Surface of the Hemisphere

Orbital Surface

The sulci and gyri of the neocortex on the orbital part of the inferior surface are irregular. The features of that surface, as previously described, are the anterior perforated area and the attachment of the olfactory bulb.

Tentorial Surface

The deep sulci of the tentorial part of the inferior surface extend anteroposteriorly (Figs. 12-3B and 12-4). They divide the surface into three parts: a medial *parahippocampal gyrus,* a lateral *occipitotemporal gyrus,* and a middle portion, the medial *occipitotemporal gyrus.* The parahippocampal gyrus extends only as far posteriorly as the splenium of the corpus callosum, where it is directly continuous with the *lingual gyrus.* The lingual gyrus forms the lower border of the calcarine sulcus. The narrow fold of cortex that connects the parahippocampal and cingulate gyri behind the splenium is known as the *isthmus.* The parahippocampal gyrus ends anteriorly by bending medially and turning back on itself to form the *uncus.*

The most medial of the longitudinal sulci of the tentorial surface is the hippocampal sulcus (Figs. 12-4B and 12-5). It is located in the cleft between the parahippocampal gyrus and the diencephalon. The cortex in the wall of that sulcus is the *hippocampus.* It is archicortex. Extending along the floor of the hippocampal sulcus is a nodular band, called the *dentate gyrus.* It also is archicortex and, together with the hippocampus, makes up the hippocampal formation.

Posteriorly, the hippocampal sulcus is prolonged around the splenium to be continuous with the callosal sulcus. The dentate gyrus is also prolonged around the splenium to form the *induseum griseum*—a thin layer of gray matter on the upper surface of the corpus callosum. Anteriorly, the hippocampal sulcus is enclosed by the uncus.

The collateral sulcus intervenes between the parahippocampal gyrus and the medial occipitotemporal gyrus. It begins close to the occipital pole and ends about 3 cm from the temporal pole. A shallow groove, the rhinal sulcus, extends from it to form the outer border of the uncus. The occipitotemporal sulcus is the most lateral of the sulci of the tentorial surface. In most brains, it is represented by a series of short segments.

Cortical Areas

The cortex may be divided into areas on the basis of differences in histological structure. Fifty areas have been distinguished and each assigned a number. The number indicates the order in which the areas are encountered in a set of serial sections. Those areas (named Brodman's areas after the person who numbered them) have been found to have

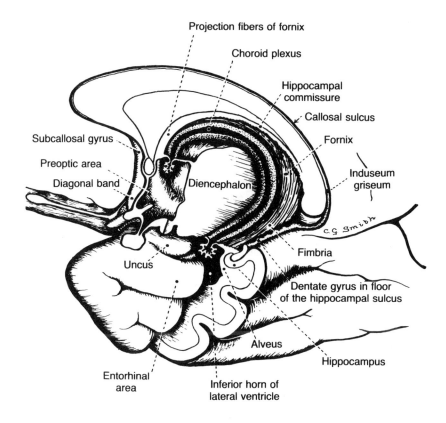

Figure 12-5. Medial aspect of the temporal lobe, with a segment removed to show the parts of the hippocampal formation and its efferent pathway, the fornix.

Labels in figure:
Projection fibers of fornix
Choroid plexus
Hippocampal commissure
Callosal sulcus
Subcallosal gyrus
Fornix
Preoptic area
Induseum griseum
Diagonal band
Diencephalon
C. G. Smith
Uncus
Fimbria
Dentate gyrus in floor of the hippocampal sulcus
Alveus
Hippocampus
Entorhinal area
Inferior horn of lateral ventricle

functional significance, and this labeling scheme has been used extensively by experimental workers.

Sensory Areas

Somesthetic Area (Areas 3, 1, 2)

The somesthetic, or general sensory, area is coextensive with Brodman's subdivisions of the cortex of the postcentral gyrus (Figs. 12-3A and 12-6). Area 3 is a narrow strip of cortex that stretches the length of the anterior part of the gyrus; area 2 is a similar posterior strip, and area 1 is between them. There is evidence that cutaneous tactile pathways end chiefly in area 3, and paths from muscles and joints end chiefly in area 2. Only a minor representation of pain or temperature sense exists in the postcentral gyrus. The postcentral gyrus is the terminus of fibers of the ventral posterior thalamic nucleus.

The parts of the body are represented in order along the length of the gyrus. Impulses

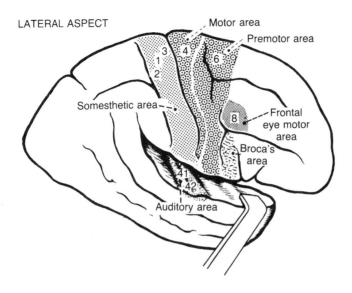

LATERAL ASPECT

Motor area

Premotor area

3 4 6

1

2

Somesthetic area

8 —Frontal eye motor area

Broca's area

41
42

Auditory area

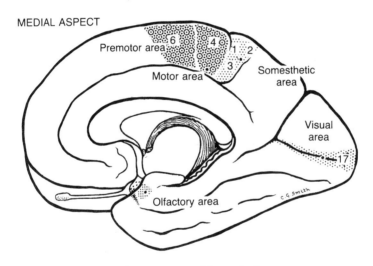

MEDIAL ASPECT

Premotor area 6 4 1 2

Motor area 3

Somesthetic area

Visual area

17

Olfactory area

C. G. Smith

Figure 12-6. Motor and sensory areas of the cerebral cortex.

from the foot are recorded in the paracentral lobule, and impulses from the head are recorded adjacent to the lateral sulcus. The extent of cortical representation of each part of the body is proportional to the density of its sensory innervation. The hand area, for example, is much larger than the rest of the upper limb.

Auditory Sensory Area (Areas 41 and 42)
The auditory sensory cortex is located in two transverse temporal gyri—an anterior and a posterior—that extend across the middle of the lower wall of the lateral sulcus. Impulses reach that area from both ears, but the larger input is from the opposite side. In unilateral

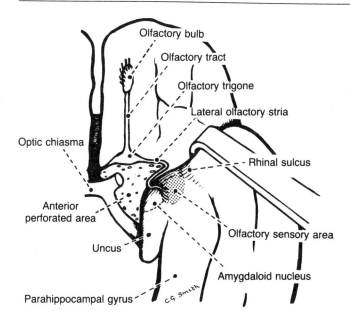

Figure 12-7. Pathway from the olfactory bulb to the olfactory sensory area of the cerebral cortex.

lesions, the major loss of hearing is contralateral. A tonotopic localization occurs along the length of the area: high frequencies are recorded near the insula; low frequencies, laterally. It is the terminus of fibers from the medial geniculate body (Figs. 12-3A and 12-6A).

Visual Sensory Area (Area 17)

The extent of the visual sensory area can be charted by a dissector because the cortex contains the line of Gennari, which is a white line formed by afferent fibers that divide the cortex into superficial and deep layers. That line is easily seen in unstained slices of the occipital lobe.

The visual area is located in the upper and lower walls of the posterior part of the calcarine sulcus (Figs. 12-3B and 12-6B). It plays the role of a television screen by recording changes in the contralateral half of the visual field. Pathways from the upper quarter of comparable parts of each retina project to the upper wall of the sulcus, and pathways from the lower retinal quarters project to the lower wall. The macula of the retina (central vision) has a large representation in that area adjacent to the occipital pole.

Olfactory Sensory Area

The olfactory sensory cortex is located on the anterior medial aspect of the uncus (Figs. 12-6B and 12-7). It is an area of paleocortex, phylogenetically older than the three-layered archicortex of the hippocampus. The sensory olfactory pathway extends from the olfactory bulb to its cortical area without entering the brain stem. Fibers leave the bulb in the olfactory tract, diverge laterally at the olfactory trigone as fibers of the lateral olfactory stria, and follow the lateral border of the anterior perforated area to the uncus.

There they enter the external surface of the sensory area instead of the deep surface, that is, unlike the afferent pathways of other sensory areas.

Sensory Area for Taste

The sensory area of the cortex for taste is adjacent to the general sensory area for the tongue. It is located in a prolongation of the postcentral gyrus, toward the insula, on the upper wall of the lateral fissure. It receives its impulses by means of fibers from the most medial part of the posterior ventral nucleus of the thalamus.

Motor Areas

Motor areas of the cortex are the origin of descending pathways to the skeletal muscles. The muscles they control can be excited by weak electrical cortical stimuli.

Primary Motor Area (Areas 4 and 6)

The primary motor area is now believed to include Brodman's area 4 and 6, that is, all of the precentral gyrus and a small portion of the adjacent cortex of the superior and middle frontal gyri (Figs. 12-3 and 12-6). Areas 4 and 6 are both areas of agranular cortex, but area 4 contains giant pyramidal cells, known as *Betz cells*. Those cells are the origin of the longest fibers of the corticospinal tract. According to earlier concepts, area 4 was considered to be the only origin of the more direct corticobulbar and corti- cospinal tracts and, therefore, the primary motor area. Area 6 was designated as the premotor area and was considered to be the origin of the multineuronal pathways, with relay stations in the corpus striatum and in the brain stem.

Because the multineuronal pathways were not included in the pyramid of the medulla they were grouped under the heading of extrapyramidal pathways. It is now known that both the direct and indirect pathways arise from cells in the same functional unit of cortex—that is, in a column of cells perpendicular to the external surface.

The motor cortex controls all the muscles of the opposite side of the body and also some muscles on the same side. Muscles that are controlled bilaterally are normally active together, such as the muscles of mastication. Muscles that move the eyes also work together, but they are controlled by a special area in the middle frontal gyrus (see the following discussion). The parts of the body are controlled, in order, by successive portions of the cortex along the length of the precentral gyrus—the muscles of the head, by cortex adjacent to the lateral sulcus, and the muscles of the foot, by cortex of the paracentral lobule. The size of the cortical area that controls a muscle group is proportional to the delicacy of the movements it controls.

Motor Areas that Excite Conjugate Movements of the Eyes

Frontal Lobe Area (Area 8). This frontal lobe area controls voluntary movements of the eyes (Figs. 12-3A and 12-6A). It is located in the posterior part of the middle frontal gyrus (Brodman's area 8). When stimulated electrically, the eyes turn to the opposite side and either up or down, depending on the precise location of the stimulating electrode. In unilateral head injuries involving that area, the eyes of an unconscious patient will be deviated to the opposite side if the area is irritated by the injury, or to the same side if it is traumatized.

Occipital Lobe (Area 17). Cortical area 17, the visual sensory area, is the origin of descending pathways to the superior colliculus and reticular formation, which excite automatic movements of the eyes that serve to keep a moving object in view (Figs. 12-3B and 12-6B). If the frontal eye area is destroyed, a patient can only move his eyes to read by following his finger across a page below the line of print.

Association Areas. Association areas of the neocortex may be classified as primary, secondary, and tertiary. *Primary association areas* are adjacent to the sensory areas. In each of those areas, data from the sensory area are integrated. For example, in areas around the visual area, characteristics of an object such as color, shape, and surface features can be associated as the initial steps in its identification.

Secondary association areas are located between the primary association areas and receive data from all of them. There the data from several sensory areas are associated as the last phase of the process of recognition. Secondary association areas are found in the occipital, temporal, and parietal lobes. Of those, the most central area is located in the inferior parietal lobule. Destruction of that region seriously impairs a person's ability to identify objects or recognize friends.

There is evidence that the functions of the association areas of the right and left hemisphere are not identical. They collaborate by means of the corpus callosum, but certain skills are delegated particularly to one hemisphere or the other. In general, in a right-handed person the left hemisphere is concerned with verbal skills (language), while nonverbal skills depend more on the right hemisphere. In short, one hemisphere in each case is dominant.

Disturbances of language function, known as *aphasia,* occur in lesions of the secondary association areas of the parietal and adjacent parts of the occipital and temporal lobes in the dominant hemisphere. That hemisphere is usually on the left side, even in many left-handed persons. Depending on the particular location of a lesion in the dominant hemisphere, relative to the sensory areas, the most evident finding may be the inability to understand the written word (word blindness) or the spoken word (word deafness). However, all aspects of language function are invariably impaired to some degree. In addition to so-called receptive aphasia, referred to in the previous discussion, expressive aphasia occurs in lesions of Broca's area (Fig. 12-6A). That is an area of cortex in the posterior part of the inferior frontal gyrus. When that area is destroyed, there is no muscle paralysis of the larynx, but the ability to speak is lost.

Tertiary association areas are located in the frontal lobe anterior to the motor areas and receive projections from secondary association areas. The development of that cortex, designated prefrontal cortex, is one of the characteristic features of the human brain. A lower animal, such as the cat, has only a small amount of prefrontal cortex. Therefore, its motor area is closer to the frontal pole.

Tertiary association cortex is utilized in the highest levels of intellectual activity, as in solving problems. Removal of prefrontal cortex bilaterally is associated with a major loss of initiative and mental ability. The ability to recognize objects, speak, write, or read is not impaired.

The association areas of the phylogenetically older cortex are located in the anterior part of the parahippocampal gyrus, known as the *entorhinal area* (area 28), and in the hippocampus and the dentate gyrus.

The cortex of the entorhinal area represents a transitional stage in the development of neocortex. It is located immediately behind the olfactory sensory area and receives fibers from it. Its major input, however, is from the adjacent neocortex of the tentorial surface and from the cortex of the cingulate gyrus. The medial border of the entorhinal

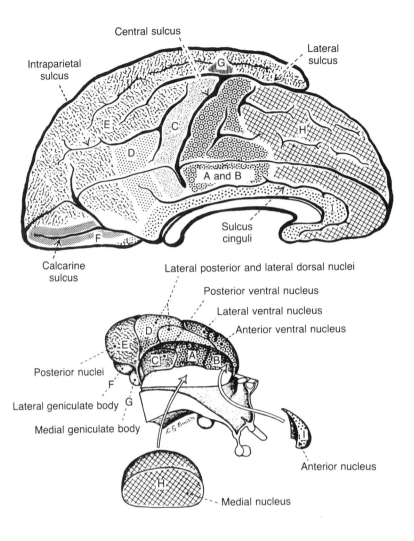

Figure 12-8. Cortical area connected with each of the nuclei of the diencephalon. The medial and anterior thalamic nuclei are displaced to expose nuclei of the lateral thalamus.

cortex is in the wall of the hippocampal sulcus, where it is directly continuous with the typical archicortex of the hippocampus.

Cortical Areas in Terms of Their Thalamic and Metathalamic Connections

Before the neocortex was acquired, in the process of phylogenetic development, the nuclei of the diencephalon served as the highest level of association in the central nervous system. With the development of the neocortex, that role was largely assumed by the cortex, and the diencephalic nuclei acquired connections, in some cases two-way connections, with a particular area. Thus data were relayed to the cortex, and the nucleus of the diencephalon was relegated to a junior partner in the association process.

Figure 12-8 shows the nuclei of the diencephalon that are thus related to the areas of neocortex of the lateral and medial surfaces of the hemisphere. The connections of those nuclei have been identified in detail using the neuroanatomical pathway tracing techniques (described in Chapter 2) in experimental animals.

Review Questions (Answers Available on the Pages Cited)

1. How can you distinguish the central sulcus from the precentral sulcus (pp. 153 and 154)?
2. Locate the supramarginal gyrus (p. 154).
3. What lies along the floor of the hippocampal sulcus (p. 158)?
4. Describe the sensory loss when the paracentral cortex is destroyed (p. 160).
5. What is the function of the fibers of the line of Gennari (p. 161)?
6. Locate the cortical area that excites voluntary movement of both eyes to look to the left (p. 162).
7. How does the function of the association areas of the parietal lobe differ from that of the frontal lobe association areas (p. 163)?
8. Name the nucleus of the thalamus that sends fibers to end in (a) the postcentral gyrus; (b) the precentral gyrus (see Fig. 12-8).

13

The Cerebral Hemisphere: Part 3. Internal Structure

The disposition of the structures contained in the cerebral hemisphere is revealed in a frontal section (Fig. 13-1). In a central location, lateral to the diencephalon, are the cell masses that comprise the corpus striatum. The tubular C-shaped lateral ventricle curves around the corpus striatum in a sagittal plane and is cut twice; its medial wall contains the paper-thin choroid membrane. The white matter forms the massive core of the cerebral hemisphere that intervenes between the gray matter of the cerebral cortex and that of the corpus striatum.

White Matter

Three kinds of interweaving fibers make up the white matter of the cerebral hemisphere: association, commissural, and projection fibers. The association fibers are the axons of cells in the cortex that connect cortical areas located in the same hemisphere. The longest of those axons extend anteroposteriorly and form compact bundles that are cut across in a frontal section (Fig. 13-1A). The commissural fibers connect areas of cortex in the right and left hemispheres. They converge to form two compact layers, the corpus callosum and the hippocampal commissure, seen in Figure 13-1A, and a small bundle, the anterior commissure, that crosses the midline in the lamina terminalis. The projection fibers (Fig. 13-1B) connect the cortex with the corpus striatum, the brain stem, and the spinal cord. They are afferent and efferent fibers of the cortex. Projection fibers of the neocortex form the internal capsule for the lentiform nucleus as they pass through the corpus striatum. Projection fibers of the archicortex form the fornix. Its fringe-like part, along the border of the hippocampus, is called the *fimbria.*

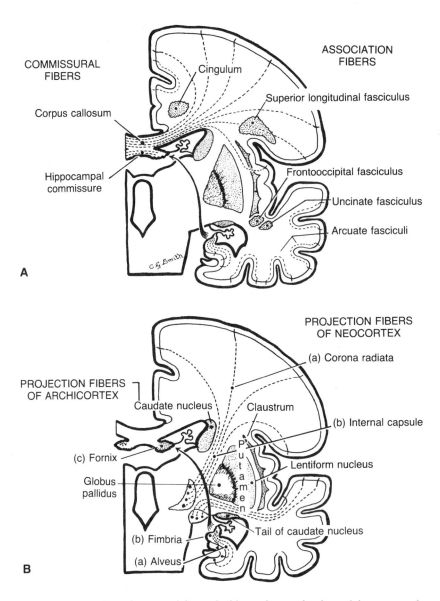

Figure 13-1. (A) *Frontal section of the cerebral hemisphere in the plane of the postcentral gyrus, showing the location of the association and commissural fibers.* (B) *Same frontal section, showing the location of representative projection fibers, that is, neocortical afferent fibers entering through the internal capsule and archicortical efferent fibers leaving through the fornix.*

The Cerebral Hemisphere: Part 3. Internal Structure

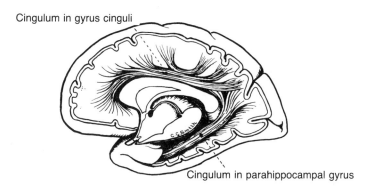

Cingulum in gyrus cinguli

Cingulum in parahippocampal gyrus

Figure 13-2. Dissection of the medial aspect of the cerebral hemisphere, exposing the cingulum.

Association Fibers

Arcuate Fibers
The arcuate fibers connect adjacent gyri and form U-shaped bands just deep to the cortex. They are illustrated connecting adjacent temporal gyri in Figure 13-1A.

Bundles of Long Association Fibers
The bundles of long association fibers extend between the frontal lobe anteriorly and the remaining lobes posteriorly (Fig. 13-1A). They are located deep to the short arcuate fibers. One of the bundles, the cingulum, connects areas of cortex of the medial aspect of the hemisphere. The other two, the superior and inferior longitudinal fasciculi, connect cortical areas of the lateral part of the hemisphere.

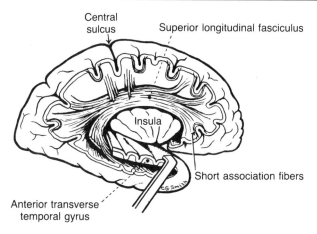

Central sulcus

Superior longitudinal fasciculus

Insula

Short association fibers

Anterior transverse temporal gyrus

Figure 13-3. Dissection of the lateral aspect of the cerebral hemisphere, exposing the superior longitudinal fasciculus.

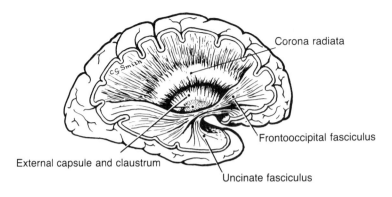

Corona radiata

Frontooccipital fasciculus

External capsule and claustrum

Uncinate fasciculus

Figure 13-4. Dissection of the lateral aspect of the cerebral hemisphere, exposing the long association fibers coursing deep to the inferior angle of the insula.

The Cingulum. The cingulum extends within the core of the cingulate gyrus, the isthmus, and the parahippocampal gyrus (Fig. 13-2). Fibers enter and leave it to connect areas of cortex along its length.

The Superior Longitudinal Fasciculus. The long fibers that course anteroposteriorly in the lateral portion of the hemisphere are crowded into an upper and a lower bundle to pass above and below the insula (Fig. 13-1A). The superior bundle, the superior longitudinal fasciculus, is about 2 cm in cross section, where it bends around the end of the lateral sulcus in the parietal lobe (Fig. 13-3). The dissector should look for it there. Its fibers connect the association areas of the temporal, occipital, parietal, and frontal lobes. If that bundle is interrupted in the dominant hemisphere, speech is seriously impaired.

The Inferior Longitudinal Fasciculus. The inferior longitudinal fasciculus forms a compact bundle as it courses deep to the inferior angle of the insula (Fig. 13-4). Its long upper frontooccipital fibers extend from the frontal lobe to the temporal, parietal, and occipital lobes. The shorter lower fibers form an uncinate fasciculus—a hook-like bundle that connects the cortex of the temporal lobe with the cortex of the orbital surface of the frontal lobe.

Commissural Fibers Are Grouped to Form Three Bundles

Corpus Callosum
The corpus callosum connects areas of neocortex. Its fibers form the upper and anterior part of a canopy-like structure that is attached to the lamina terminalis and arches back above the diencephalon to within 5 cm of the occipital pole. Its subdivisions, as seen in a midsagittal section, are the rostrum, genu, body, and splenium (Fig. 13-5).

In a frontal section (Fig. 13-1A), the fibers of the body of the corpus callosum can be seen to fan out to reach the cortex of the medial, superior, and lateral surfaces above the lateral sulcus. The deepest fibers continue laterally, in the roof of the lateral ventricle, and turn down, lateral to it, to form part of the external capsule of the lentiform nucleus and end in the insula.

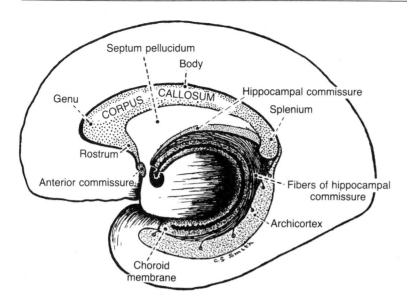

Figure 13-5. Medial aspect of the cerebral hemisphere, showing the parts of the corpus callosum and the course of the fibers of the hippocampal commissure.

The radiating fibers of the genu and the splenium can be demonstrated by dissection. The shorter anterior fibers curve medially, within the frontal lobe, to form the forceps minor. The longer fibers of the splenium form the forceps major (Fig. 13-6).

Fibers of the posterior part of the body of the corpus callosum descend behind the insula to form the tapetum, which is a thin layer of fibers in the lateral wall of the inferior and posterior horns.

Anterior Commissure
The anterior commissure is, phylogenetically, the oldest commissure of the cerebral hemisphere. In lower animals, its fibers connect the olfactory bulbs. In man, a few of those fibers are retained, but most of its fibers connect areas of neocortex in the temporal lobes. The fibers are crowded into a bundle that is 2 mm in diameter, which crosses the midline in the lamina terminalis just in front of the fornix (Fig. 13-6B). Traced from the midline into the hemisphere, the bundle pierces the corpus striatum below the anterior limb of the internal capsule to fan out in the anterior part of the temporal lobe.

Hippocampal Commissure
Commissural fibers leave the deep surface of the hippocampal cortex, where they form a thin layer of white matter, the alveus, on its ventricular aspect (Figs. 13-6 and 13-7). From there they follow the medial border of the hippocampus in a fringe-like bundle (the fimbria) as far as the splenium. At the midline, they cross to the other side in the inferior border of the septum pellucidum and reach the contralateral hippocampus by way of its fimbria and alveus.

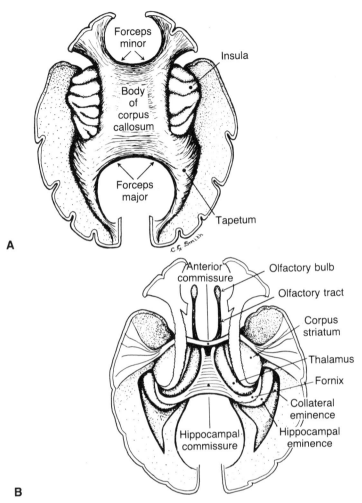

Figure 13-6.(A) Dissection of the superior aspect of the two cerebral hemispheres, showing the fibers of the corpus callosum. (B) Same preparation after removing the fibers of the corpus callosum and exposing the anterior and hippocampal commissures.

Bundles of Projection Fibers

Projection Fibers of Neocortex

Projection fibers are present in "pure culture" in the internal capsule. In a frontal section of the hemisphere (Fig. 13-1B), they form two diverging bands within the corpus striatum: upper and lower. Those bands are sections of the posterior and sublenticular limbs, respectively. Fibers of the posterior limb fan out above the insula; those of the sublenticular limb fan out below it. As they course to the cortex, they pass through the commissural and association fibers. If the association fibers of the superior and inferior longitudinal fasciculus are removed, the projection fibers, radiating deep to them in a sagittal plane,

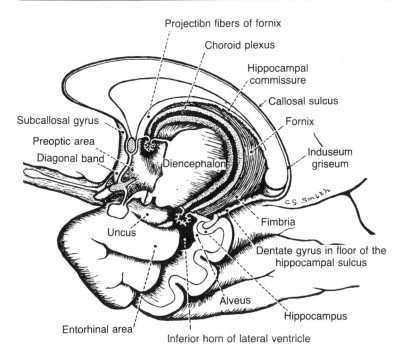

Figure 13-7. Medial aspect of the temporal lobe, with a segment removed, showing the parts of the hippocampal formation and its efferent pathway, the fornix.

can be followed to the cortex. The radiating fibers that are exposed in such a preparation form the corona radiata (Fig. 13-8).

Projection Fibers of the Archicortex

The projection fibers of the archicortex—that is, the hippocampal formation—together with its commissural fibers, form the fornix (Fig. 13-7). They emerge from the ventricular aspect of the hippocampus with the commissural fibers and course with them in the alveus and the fimbria of the fornix to the inferior border of the septum pellucidum. There the commissural fibers cross the midline, but the projection fibers follow the inferior border of the septum to the anterior commissure, where they enter the diencephalon, just in front of the interventricular foramen.

Gray Matter

The gray matter of the cerebral hemisphere forms (1) a thin outer layer, the cortex, (2) a centrally located collection of nuclei, the corpus striatum, and (3) a small portion of the medial wall of the lateral ventricle, the septal gray matter. The cerebral cortex has been described.

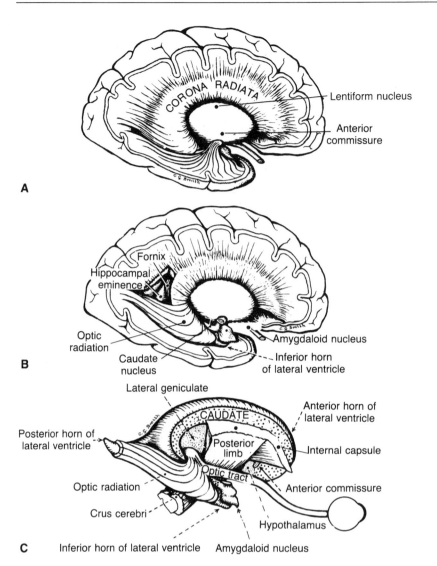

A

B

C

Figure 13-8. Serial dissections of the lateral aspect of the cerebral hemisphere. (A) Association fibers removed. (B) Anterior commissure removed and a window-like opening made in the lateral wall of the ventricle. (C) All of the optic pathway exposed.

Corpus Striatum

The term *corpus striatum* is used to identify the central cell mass that develops in the ventral wall of the embryonic cerebral hemisphere (described in Chapter 11). As development proceeds, that cell mass acquires subdivisions, and the term *corpus striatum* comes to be restricted to the portion penetrated by the internal capsule. The corpus striatum includes two subdivisions: the lentiform and caudate nuclei. The remaining subdivisions are the claustrum and the amygdaloid nucleus.

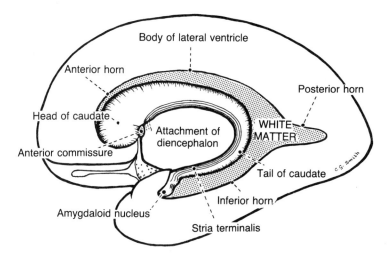

Figure 13-9. Structures in the lateral wall of the lateral ventricle.

The caudate nucleus is a thick ribbon-like, tapered, semicircular band of gray matter that extends along the length of the lateral wall of the ventricle (Fig. 13-9). It is helpful to think of it as a marginal part of the putamen of the lentiform nucleus that has been detached by fibers of the internal capsule (Figs. 13-10 and 13-11). Structurally and functionally, the caudate nucleus and the putamen are much alike and are treated as a functional unit known as the *striatum*.

The large anterior part of the caudate nucleus, the head, is medial to the anterior limb of the internal capsule (Fig. 13-12A) and is joined to the lentiform nucleus inferior to it (Fig. 13-12B). The body of the caudate nucleus is lateral to the superior border of the thalamus, and the attenuated tail is lateral to its inferior border (Fig. 13-12B). The tip of the tail is continuous with the amygdaloid nucleus.

The amygdaloid nucleus ("an almond") is a flattened ovoid mass about the size and shape of an almond. It lies partly in the roof of the ventricle and extends anterior to it to form a part of the external surface of the uncus, medial to the olfactory sensory area. Its upper surface abuts the putamen of the lentiform nucleus just anterior to the sublenticular limb of the internal capsule (Fig. 13-11).

The amygdaloid nucleus has two efferent fiber bundles that extend to the hypothalamus, the stria terminalis, and the diagonal band. The stria terminalis (Fig. 13-9) is a small bundle, about 2 mm in diameter, that leaves the ventricular aspect of the amygdaloid nucleus to course in the groove between the caudate nucleus and the diencephalon. It enters the hypothalamus with the fornix at the interventricular foramen.

The diagonal band (Fig. 13-13) is a bundle of loosely disposed fibers that leave the anterior surface of the amygdaloid nucleus and course medially along the posterior border of the anterior perforated area to reach the hypothalamus.

The lentiform nucleus has three parts: the globus pallidus, the putamen, and the anterior perforated substance. The putamen and globus pallidus are described with the diencephalon. They influence motor activity by way of their thalamic connections.

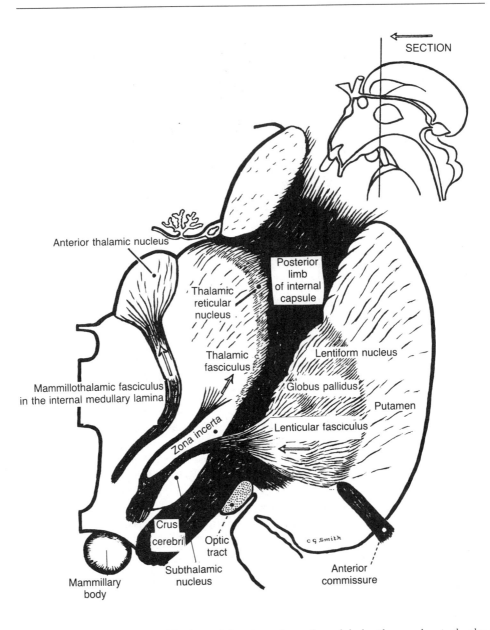

Anterior thalamic nucleus

Thalamic
reticular
nucleus

Posterior
limb
of internal
capsule

Thalamic
fasciculus

Lentiform nucleus

Mammillothalamic fasciculus
in the internal medullary lamina

Globus pallidus

Putamen

Lenticular fasciculus

Zona incerta

c g smith

Crus
cerebri

Optic
tract

Subthalamic
nucleus

Anterior
commissure

Mammillary
body

Figure 13-10. Frontal section of the diencephalon, internal capsule, and the lentiform nucleus in the plane
shown in the upper diagram.

SECTION

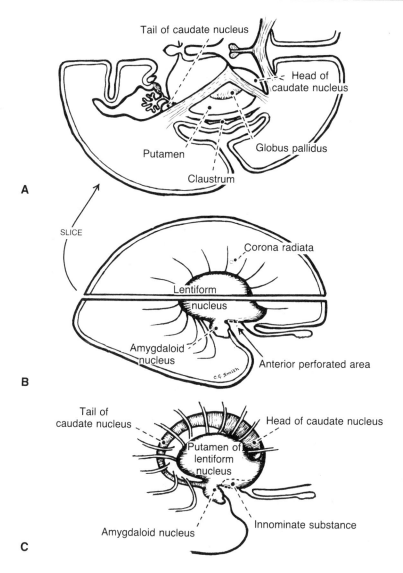

Tail of caudate nucleus

Head of caudate nucleus

Putamen

Globus pallidus

Claustrum

A

SLICE

Corona radiata

Lentiform nucleus

Amygdaloid nucleus

Anterior perforated area

B

Tail of caudate nucleus

Head of caudate nucleus

Putamen of lentiform nucleus

Amygdaloid nucleus

Innominate substance

C

Figure 13-11. Subdivisions of the central gray matter of the cerebral hemisphere. (A) Horizontal section of the cerebral hemisphere in the plane indicated in B. (B) Lentiform and amygdaloid nuclei exposed in a dissection of the lateral aspect of the cerebral hemisphere. (C) Lateral aspect of the isolated lentiform, amygdaloid, and caudate nuclei, with representative fibers of the internal capsule left in place.

The anterior perforated substance, located above the anterior perforated area and lateral to the hypothalamus, is involved in visceral responses. It receives fibers of the olfactory tract and has connections with the septal gray matter and the hypothalamus.

The claustrum ("a barrier") is a thin shell-like layer of gray matter that is separated from the outer surface of the lentiform nucleus by an external capsule, which is composed of afferent and efferent fibers of the overlying insular cortex. The inferior border of the

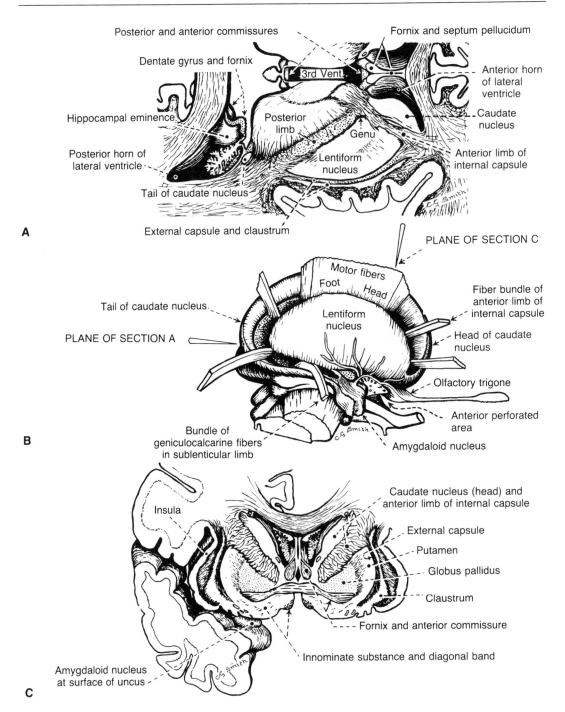

A

B

C

Figure 13-12. The corpus striatum: (A) As seen in a horizontal section of the hemisphere at the level of the interventricular foramen. (B) As revealed by dissection. (C) As seen in a frontal section at the level of the anterior commissure.

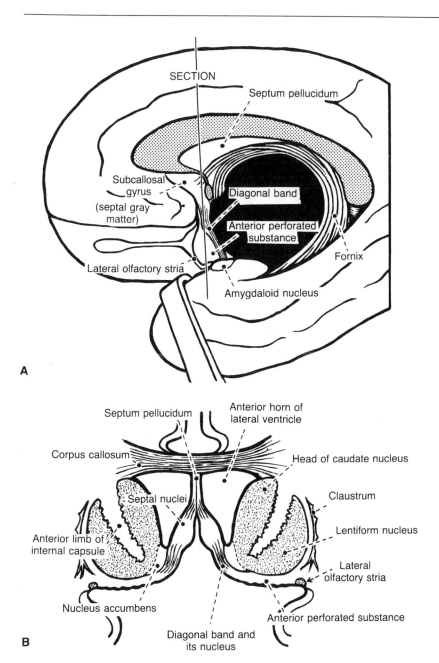

A

B

Figure 13-13. Position of the septal gray matter. (A) Medial aspect of the cerebral hemisphere. (B) Frontal section of the cerebral hemisphere at the level indicated in A.

claustrum abuts the amygdaloid nucleus. Superiorly, it tapers to a thin edge at the upper border of the insula (Figs. 13-12A and 13-12C).

Septal Gray Matter

The septal gray matter forms the medial wall of the anterior horn of the lateral ventricle. It is described as septal because its superior part forms the septum pellucidum, which separates the right and left lateral ventricles (Fig. 13-13).

The superior part contains no nerve cells and only a few nerve fibers. The inferior part of the septal gray matter contains a number of nuclei that form a thick layer between the ependymal lining of the ventricle and the medial surface of the hemisphere, where it forms the ridge-like elevation known as the *subcallosal gyrus*. One of its nuclei is a cluster of cells within the diagonal band. That nucleus extends inferiorly as far as the anterior perforated substance. The nucleus accumbens is closely associated with the inferior part of the septal gray matter. It is located in the floor of the anterior horn, adjacent to the head of the caudate nucleus, but it is believed to be a part of the striatum.

The septal gray matter, though small in amount, has input from many sources, including the anterior perforated substance, the amygdaloid nucleus, the hippocampus, and the hypothalamus. Its efferent fibers extend back to most of those structures, but they also reach the habenular nuclei by way of the stria medullaris thalami (see Fig. 14-2).

Functionally, the septal gray matter has a role in many behavioral responses, such as sexual behavior, feeding, and emotional expression. Lesions in the septal gray matter lead to a reduction in aggressive behavior. It also contains a so-called rewarding center. Patients and animals that have electrodes implanted, permitting self-stimulation, apparently find stimulation of the septal nuclei and some hypothalamic nuclei to be a pleasurable experience.

Lateral Ventricle

Form and Subdivisions

The lateral ventricle is a **C**-shaped tubular space. It has an anterior horn in front of the interventricular foramen, a body in the parietal lobe, an inferior horn in the temporal lobe, and a posterior horn in the occipital lobe. The pouch-like posterior horn is acquired later in development due to the encroachment on the cavity of the hemisphere by the development of the white matter. That extension of the ventricle into the occipital lobe may be almost obliterated in some brains.

Structures in the Walls of the Lateral Ventricle

The structures in the walls of the lateral ventricle are shown in a series of representative frontal sections in Figure 13-14. To locate those structures, it is convenient to describe the lateral ventricle as having a medial and lateral wall. In Figure 13-9, the medial portion of the hemisphere was dissected away to expose the structures in its lateral wall. They are the caudate nucleus, the amygdaloid nucleus, and the white matter of the hemisphere's core. The efferent fiber bundle of the amygdaloid nucleus can be seen,

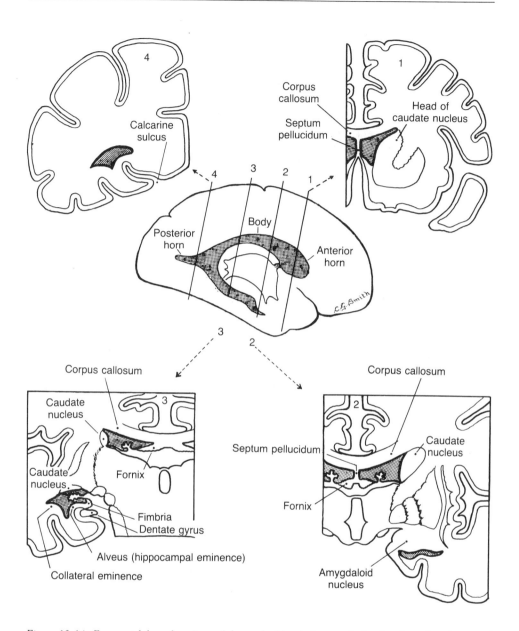

Figure 13-14. Four serial frontal sections of the cerebral hemisphere at the levels indicated in the central diagram, showing the structures in the walls of the lateral ventricle.

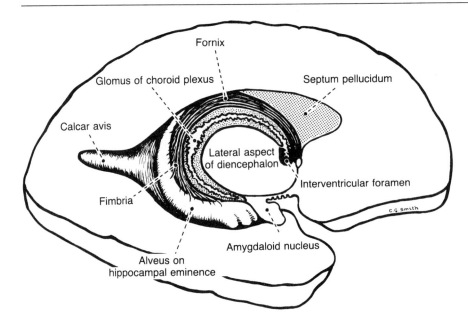

Figure 13-15. Dissection of the cerebral hemisphere, showing the structures in the medial wall of the lateral ventricle.

covered only by ependyma, extending to the interventricular foramen along the inner border of the caudate nucleus.

In Figure 13-15, the structures in the medial wall have been exposed by dissecting away the lateral portion of the hemisphere. The conspicuous feature in the medial wall is the hippocampal eminence, which extends the length of the inferior horn. It is a rounded ridge that is produced by the deep hippocampal sulcus on the tentorial surface. Extending along the medial border of the eminence is the fimbria portion of the fornix, which picks up fibers as it approaches the midline. The hippocampal eminence tapers to a point at the midline, and the fornix courses anteriorly in the inferior border of the septum pellucidum to enter the diencephalon, just in front of the interventricular foramen.

The long cleft-like interval between the fornix and the lateral border of the diencephalon is bridged by the choroid membrane, which is a layer of ependyma overlaid externally by pia mater. It contains the choroid plexus of the lateral ventricle. A feature of the choroid plexus is a large mass of veins, called the *glomus*, located in the roomiest part of the ventricle at the junction of the inferior and posterior horns. It commonly contains cysts, masses of caseous material, and may be calcified. If calcified, it provides a useful reference point for the radiologist.

The medial wall of the posterior horn also contains a ridge, the calcar avis. It is produced by the deep calcarine sulcus on the medial surface of the occipital lobe. Occasionally, additional parallel ridges are present. They contain fibers of the corpus callosum.

Review Questions (Answers Available on the Pages Cited)

1. Distinguish between commissural and association fibers of the cerebral hemisphere (p. 167).
2. What is the relationship of the superior and the inferior longitudinal fasciculi to the insula (p. 170)?
3. What portions of the cortex of the two hemispheres are connected by the anterior commissure (p. 171 and Fig. 13-6)?
4. In the mature brain, what cell masses form (a) the corpus striatum; (b) the striatum (pp. 174 and 175)?
5. Where does the amygdaloid nucleus reach the external surface of the hemisphere (p. 175)?
6. Explain why the gray matter in the medial wall of the anterior horn of the lateral ventricle is called *septal gray matter* (p. 180).
7. Account for the presence of the calcar avis and the hippocampal eminence on the medial wall of the lateral ventricle (p. 182).

14

The Limbic Lobe, Limbic System, and Olfactory Pathways

Limbic Lobe

The medial aspect of the cerebral hemisphere has a subdivision known as the *limbic lobe* (*limbus*, "edge"). It includes the cortex of the cingulate gyrus, the isthmus, the parahippocampal gyrus, the uncus, and the cortex of the hippocampal formation.

The cortex of the hippocampal formation has the typical three layers of archicortex; the cortex of the rest of the limbic lobe has additional layers but lacks the full complement of neocortex and is described as transitional.

The limbic lobe originally was believed to be associated with the integration of olfactory data and was treated as a part of the "nose brain," or rhinencephalon. It is now known to receive its major input from other sources and to be intimately associated with subcortical structures involved in the basic control of adaptive behavior required for the preservation of self and species.

Afferent and Efferent Fibers of the Limbic Lobe

The afferent fibers of the portion of the limbic lobe that is formed by the cingulate gyrus enter it by way of association fibers from adjacent neocortical areas of the frontal, parietal, occipital, and temporal lobes. It also receives afferent fibers from the anterior nucleus of the thalamus, which relays impulses from the hypothalamus. Efferent fibers of the cingulate gyrus extend into the core of the parahippocampal gyrus to reach the hippocampus (Fig. 14-1).

The parahippocampal gyrus receives input from the neocortex of the temporal lobe and from the prefrontal orbital cortex by way of the uncinate fasciculus. It also receives

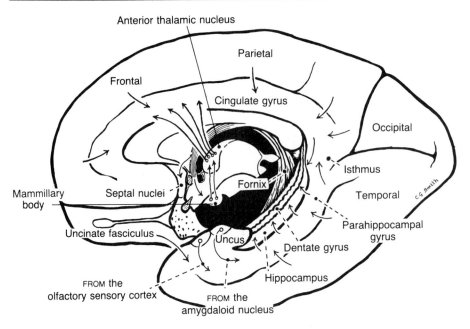

Figure 14-1. *Afferent and efferent fibers of the cortex of the limbic lobe.*

fibers from the olfactory sensory area and from the amygdaloid nucleus. Efferent fibers of the parahippocampal cortex (the entorhinal area, area 28) along with those of the cingulate gyrus enter the hippocampal formation all along its length. They provide the hippocampal formation with processed data from all the sense organs of the body.

The efferent fiber bundle of the hippocampal formation is the fornix. Some of its fibers reach the septal nuclei, in front of the anterior commissure; the rest enter the hypothalamus behind the commissure, where they form the anterior wall of the interventricular foramen. They extend to the mammillary body.

Limbic System

The term *limbic system* has been applied to the neural mechanism, which includes the cortex of the limbic lobe, the amygdaloid and septal nuclei of the cerebral hemisphere, their interconnecting pathways and pathways that descend to the hypothalamus, and the reticular formation. The hypothalamus, the origin of descending visceral and emotional effector pathways, is the major output of the limbic system.

The function of the limbic system, as revealed by the stimulation or ablation of each of its parts, is the control of emotional expression and the control of adaptive behavior required for the preservation of the individual and the species, such as obtaining food, self-defense, mating, and care of the young. In addition to those functions, it would appear to be a part of the neural mechanism of memory. Bilateral removal of the temporal

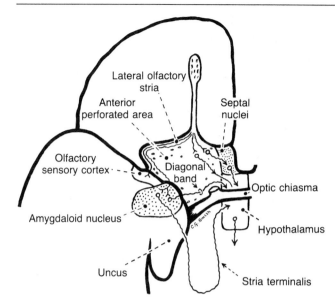

Figure 14-2. Olfactory pathways to the hypothalamus by way of the anterior perforated substance, the septal nuclei, and the amygdaloid nucleus.

pole region of the hemisphere that includes portions of the hippocampus and the amygdaloid nucleus results in a loss of the ability to recall recent events.

Olfactory Pathways

The Olfactory Sensory Pathway

The sensory pathway for smell has already been traced from the olfactory bulb, by way of the lateral olfactory stria, to the sensory cortex on the uncus (see Fig. 12-7).

Olfactory Reflex Pathways

Pathways that mediate reflex responses bypass the cortex. As described in the following discussion, they utilize subcortical reflex stations of the cerebral hemisphere to reach the hypothalamus and the reticular formation.

Pathways through the Amygdaloid Nucleus

Fibers that mediate olfactory reflex responses form part of the lateral olfactory stria. They accompany the fibers of the sensory pathway as far as the uncus, where the fibers of the reflex pathway penetrate the external surface of the amygdaloid nucleus. (Fig. 14-2) The amygdaloid nucleus processes data from the olfactory bulb, integrating them with data it receives from many other sources, including some from the neocortex of the frontal and temporal lobes by way of the uncinate fasciculus, some from the medial nuclei of

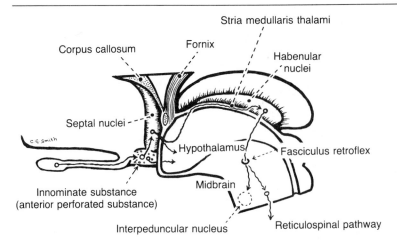

Figure 14-3. Olfactory pathway to the midbrain by way of the habenular nuclei and a pathway to the hypothalamus.

the thalamus through the inferior thalamic peduncle, and some from the hypothalamus through the diagonal band.

The efferent fibers of the amygdaloid nucleus leave it in two bundles to end chiefly in the hypothalamus, the origin of descending visceral and emotional effector pathways.

The Stria Terminalis. Fibers of the stria terminalis course along the medial border of the tail and body of the caudate nucleus to enter the anterior superior part of the hypothalamus just behind the interventricular foramen (Figs. 14-2 and 13-9).

The Diagonal Band. Fibers of the diagonal band course superficially along the caudal border of the anterior perforated area to enter the anterior inferior part of the hypothalamus (Fig. 14-2).

Pathways through the Anterior Perforated Substance

Some fibers of the olfactory tract synapse with cells in the anterior perforated substance (innominate substance), which relay impulses to the hypothalamus (Fig. 14-1).

The anterior perforated substance has both direct and indirect pathways to both the hypothalamus and the reticular formation of the brain stem (Fig. 14-3). Major indirect pathways have relay stations in the septal nuclei (the nucleus of the diagonal band). Fibers from the inferior septal area enter the anterior part of the hypothalamus. At that point some turn dorsally to reach the habenular nuclei by way of the stria medullaris thalami. Efferent fibers of the habenular nuclei form the fasciculus retroflex that ends partly in the interpeduncular nucleus and partly in nearby nuclei of the midbrain, which have direct connections with reticulospinal neurons.

Review Questions (Answers Available on the Pages Cited)

1. What parts of the cerebral hemisphere form the limbic lobe (p. 185)?
2. What kinds of cortex are present in the limbic lobe (p. 185)?
3. List the immediate sources of impulses received by the limbic lobe (p. 185).

4. What is the major efferent fiber bundle of the cortex of the limbic lobe (p. 186)?
5. What is included in the limbic system (p. 186)?
6. What basic functional changes may be expected as a result of lesions of the limbic system (p. 186)?
7. Name the nuclei of the cerebral hemisphere that relay olfactory impulses to the brain stem to excite olfactory reflex responses (pp. 187 and 188).

15

The Sensory, Motor, and Emotional Pathways

Sensory Pathways

Sensory pathways are chains of neurons that extend from sense organs to the cerebral cortex and convey impulses that excite awareness—that is, sensation. Pathways from those sense organs that have the same function come together, within the central nervous system, to form a cable. Each of those pathways has nuclei, positioned at intervals along its length, that serve as relay stations. In previous chapters those cables have been located, in each of the successive subdivisions of the central nervous system, on their way to specific areas of cerebral cortex. As a review, each sensory cable is now referred to as a pathway and is traced from its origin to its termination, noting significant relationships along its length.

Pain and Temperature Pathways

Pathways for pain and temperature sense enter the central nervous system in all the spinal nerves and in cranial nerves 5, 7, 9, and 10. The peripheral sensory nerve fibers have a small diameter. Some are unmyelinated; others have a thin myelin sheath. The myelinated pain fibers conduct more rapidly than the unmyelinated variety and are responsible for the well-localized immediate response to a pin prick. Impulses conveyed by the unmyelinated fibers excite a so-called second pain response that is slightly delayed and poorly localized (Fig. 15-1).

The cell bodies of the sensory nerve fibers are located in the dorsal root ganglia and in the ganglia of those cranial nerves that contain sensory fibers. Each dorsal root ganglion cell has a centrally directed fiber that enters the spinal cord to synapse with cells of the

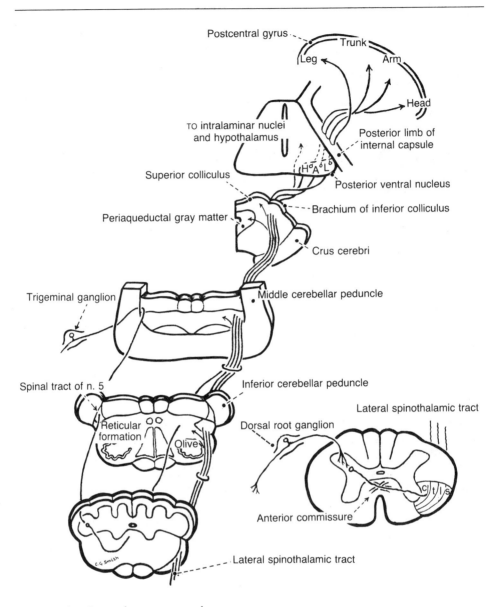

Figure 15-1. Pain and temperature pathways.

dorsal horn. The fibers of those cells and of cells activated indirectly by way of internuncials ascend obliquely to cross the midline as part of the anterior commissure in the segment immediately above. They add themselves to the medial side of the pain and temperature fibers ascending from lower levels in the anterior half of the lateral funiculus of the spinal cord to form the lateral spinothalamic tract. As a result, the deepest fibers of that tract, in the uppermost part of the spinal cord, are from cervical segments, and the thoracic, lumbar, and sacral fibers are progressively more superficial. Knowing this, the neurosurgeon, in cutting this tract, must adjust the depth of the incision to attain the required level of analgesia in the opposite side of the body. In this operation, some fibers of the spinocerebellar tract are severed but, fortunately, no significant loss of coordination occurs.

As fibers cross the midline in the anterior commissure, they may be interrupted by a degenerative disease of the gray matter around the central canal, known as *syringomyelia*. That disease severs the crossing fibers of the right and left halves of the segments involved in the disease process, resulting in a selective loss of pain and temperature in a belt-like band that encircles the body. Sensation above and below that analgesic band is unaffected.

As the lateral spinothalamic tract enters the medulla, it is crowded dorsally by the inferior olivary nucleus to lie deep to the depression on the lateral surface, between the olive and the inferior cerebellar peduncle. If the tract is cut in this location, pain and temperature sensation are lost below the head on the opposite side of the body. It happens that this tract and the spinal tract of the fifth nerve are included in the region supplied by the posterior inferior cerebellar artery. Hence when it is occluded, such as by thrombus or emboli, pain and temperature sensations are lost on the opposite side of the body and also on the same side of the head.

In the pons, the lateral spinothalamic tract passes deep to the middle cerebellar peduncle. There it is joined by fibers that convey impulses from pain and temperature sense organs of the opposite side of the head. Those fibers ascend obliquely from the nucleus of the spinal tract of the fifth nerve, which is located in the caudal part of the medulla. Thus cutting the lateral spinothalamic tract above the level of the pons will relieve pain on the entire opposite side of the head *and* body. That may be accomplished surgically by cutting the tract where it ascends deep to the brachium of the inferior colliculus in the midbrain. Severing the brachium does not significantly impair hearing, because pathways from each ear ascend in both the right and left brachia.

It is significant that a marked reduction occurs in the number of fibers in the lateral spinothalamic tract as it ascends within the brain stem. This happens because many of its fibers end in the reticular formation (spinoreticular), while others end in the superior colliculus (spinotectal) and in the pariaqueductal gray matter. The latter fibers terminate in nuclei that, when stimulated, inhibit conduction in pain pathways.

When the lateral spinothalamic tract enters the diencephalon, most of its fibers end in the nucleus ventralis posterior of the thalamus, which projects to the general sensory areas 3, 1, and 2 of the postcentral gyrus by way of the posterior limb of the internal capsule. Some fibers of the lateral spinothalamic tract bypass the nucleus ventralis posterior and join fibers from the reticular formation to end in the intralaminar nuclei. Stimulation of the latter nuclei excite a diffuse change in the electroencephalogram, known as the *alerting response*.

Touch Pathways

Nerve impulses that are excited by touching the skin are conveyed to the sensory cortex of the postcentral gyrus by way of two pathways. In the spinal cord, one of those pathways ascends as part of the posterior funiculus; the other crosses the midline to ascend as part of the anterior spinothalamic tract. Cutting one of those pathways does not reduce the sensitivity to touch, significantly, but some impairment of *touch discrimination* occurs if the uncrosssd pathway is cut. That problem is revealed as a lesser ability to recognize two contacts, as separate stimuli, that are closely related spatially (two-point discrimination) or to recognize individual, closely related successive stimuli (temporal discrimination). Temporal discrimination is tested by applying the stem of a vibrating tuning fork to the patient.

Uncrossed Touch Pathway of the Spinal Cord

Branches of sensory nerve fibers, with cell bodies in posterior root ganglia, ascend in the posterior funiculus. Fibers that ascend from segments caudal to the midthoracic level form the fasciculus gracilis; fibers entering, at higher levels, form the fasciculus cuneatus. Some of those ascending fibers extend all the way to the nuclei of these fasciculi in the medulla. Others end in the spinal cord and synapse with cells of the posterior horn, which relay impulses along fibers that ascend either in the posterior funiculus or in the dorsal part of the lateral funiculus. They end in the appropriate nucleus gracilis or cuneatus, depending on the level of their origin. When the clinician finds impaired discrimination in disease, primarily involving the posterior funiculus, the loss of function is explained as a spread of the lesion to include the extra pathways ascending in the dorsal part of the lateral funiculus.

The topographic grouping of pathways of the posterior funiculus is continued in the medial lemniscus. The fibers from the nucleus gracilis (lower limb and trunk) cross and ascend close to the midline, dorsal to the pyramid. Those from the nucleus cuneatus then cross and ascend, dorsal to the gracilis fibers. In the pons segment, the medial lemniscus spirals on to the ventral surface of the tegmentum and then lateral to it to course alongside the fibers of the anterior spinothalamic tract. Also at the level of the pons, touch pathways of the head region cross the midline, from the main sensory nucleus of the fifth cranial nerve, to form the ventral trigeminothalamic tract, which joins with the medial lemniscus. The smaller dorsal trigeminothalamic tract is composed of uncrossed fibers of the principal sensory nucleus. Those fibers ascend through the dorsal part of the reticular formation to end in the posterior ventral nucleus of the thalamus, which relays impulses to the postcentral gyrus of the hemisphere on the same side.

As the medial lemniscus, which includes the crossed fibers of the ventral trigeminothalamic tract, ascends on the lateral surface of the tegmentum of the midbrain, the pathways from the head, the arm, and the leg form its ventral, middle, and dorsal parts, respectively. When the medial lemniscus reaches the posterior ventral nucleus of the thalamus, the pathways from the head relay in its medial part; those from the arm, in its middle part; and those from the leg, in its lateral part. Fibers of the posterior ventral nucleus ascend in the posterior limb of the internal capsule to end in orderly fashion along the length of the postcentral gyrus, as indicated in Figure 15-2.

Crossed Touch Pathway of the Spinal Cord

Posterior root fibers synapse with cells in the posterior horn that relay impulses to cells in deeper laminae (V, VI, VII, and VIII), which give origin to the fibers of the anterior spinothalamic tract. Those fibers cross the midline, in the white commissure, along with the pain and temperature fibers, but unlike the pain and temperature fibers, they ascend in the anterior funiculus. As they ascend, they are crowded anteriorly and laterally by fibers crossing at higher levels.

As the anterior spinothalamic tract enters the medulla it courses dorsal to the olive, where its fibers mingle with those of the lateral spinothalamic tract. The bundle, so formed, is called the *spinal lemniscus*. In the upper part of the medulla, and the caudal part of the pons, the fibers of the anterior spinothalamic tract are joined by fibers of the

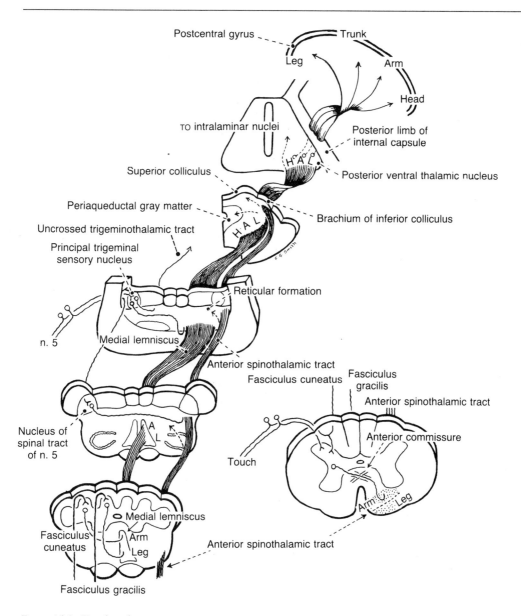

Figure 15-2. *Touch pathways.*

Within the figure, the following labels appear:

Postcentral gyrus — Trunk
Leg Arm
Head
TO intralaminar nuclei
Posterior limb of internal capsule
Superior colliculus
Posterior ventral thalamic nucleus
Periaqueductal gray matter
Uncrossed trigeminothalamic tract
Brachium of inferior colliculus
Principal trigeminal sensory nucleus
Reticular formation
n. 5
Medial lemniscus
Anterior spinothalamic tract
Fasciculus cuneatus
Fasciculus gracilis
Anterior spinothalamic tract
Nucleus of spinal tract of n. 5
Anterior commissure
Touch
Arm Leg
Medial lemniscus
Fasciculus cuneatus
Arm
Leg
Anterior spinothalamic tract
Fasciculus gracilis

rostral part of the nucleus of the spinal tract of the fifth nerve. That nucleus may relay less discriminatory touch data than that relayed by the principal sensory nucleus, suggesting an analogy with the two touch pathways of the spinal nerves, which relay in the nuclei of the posterior funiculus and in the gray matter of the spinal cord. As the anterior spinothalamic tract ascends through the pons segment, it courses deep to the middle cerebellar peduncle and is crowded dorsally by the medial lemniscus.

The Sensory, Motor, and Emotional Pathways   195

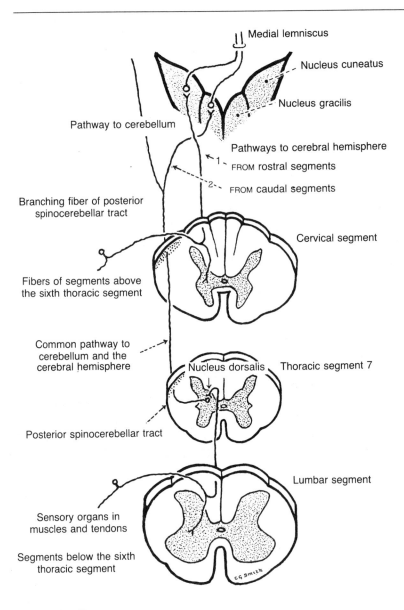

Medial lemniscus

Nucleus cuneatus

Nucleus gracilis

Pathway to cerebellum

Pathways to cerebral hemisphere

1 FROM rostral segments

2 FROM caudal segments

Branching fiber of posterior
spinocerebellar tract

Cervical segment

Fibers of segments above
the sixth thoracic segment

Common pathway to
cerebellum and the
cerebral hemisphere

Nucleus dorsalis   Thoracic segment 7

Posterior spinocerebellar tract

Lumbar segment

Sensory organs in
muscles and tendons

Segments below the sixth
thoracic segment

Figure 15-3. Position sense.

In the midbrain, the spinal lemniscus courses deep to the brachium of the inferior colliculus to reach the diencephalon. Most of its fibers end, topographically, along with those of the medial lemniscus in the posterior ventral thalamic nucleus, which relays impulses to the postcentral gyrus.

The anterior spinothalamic tract, like the lateral spinothalamic tract, contains some fibers that end in the reticular formation.

Position Sense Pathways

The position sense pathways convey impulses from sense organs in muscles, tendons, and joints but also from sense organs that are located in the skin near joints (Fig. 15-3). Those impulses provide awareness of the relative position of the parts of the body. A person lacking this sense has difficulty walking in the dark, because he is unaware of the position of his lower limbs.

The pathways ascend, uncrossed, in the spinal cord and relay in the nuclei gracilis (lower limb) and cuneatus (upper limb), which also serve as relay stations for the uncrossed touch pathways of the spinal cord. The position sense nerve fibers are myelinated and their cell bodies are located in the posterior root ganglia. The central processes of those cells, in segments above the sixth thoracic, ascend in the fasciculus cuneatus to end in the nucleus cuneatus. The central processes of position sense fibers of the lower segments of the body do not extend all the way to the medulla and, furthermore, convey impulses destined for both the cerebral cortex and the cerebellar cortex. They ascend about eight segments and synapse with cells in the nucleus dorsalis. Fibers of those cells ascend on the surface of the posterior half of the lateral funiculus, where they form the posterior spinocerebellar tract. As the spinocerebellar tract enters the medulla, some of its fibers enter the cerebellum; the others end in the rostral part of the nucleus gracilis. Some cells of the nucleus gracilis and the nucleus cuneatus serve as relay stations of position sense pathways. Fibers that ascend from those nuclei form the medial lemniscus and ascend to the posterior ventral nucleus of the thalamus, which relays impulses to the postcentral gyrus.

Most, if not all, of the position sense nerve fibers of the cranial nerves are believed to enter the brain in the fifth cranial nerve. Some of those fibers have their cell bodies in the trigeminal ganglion; others, in the mesencephalic nucleus of the fifth nerve. The fibers of cells in the trigeminal ganglion end in the principal sensory nucleus of the fifth nerve, which relays impulses along fibers that cross the midline to ascend in the medial lemniscus. The fibers of cells in the mesencephalic nucleus extend to the motor nucleus of the fifth nerve to complete a two-neuron stretch reflex pathway. Ascending pathways, to the postcentral gyrus from the mesencephalic nucleus, have not, as yet, been revealed experimentally.

Olfactory Sensory Pathway

The cell bodies of the olfactory nerve fibers, unlike the cell bodies of typical sensory nerves, are in a vulnerable location, within the epithelium of the nasal cavity. Dendritic processes of those cells form cilia-like, superficial, sensory endings (Fig. 15-4).

The sensory epithelium forms part of the roof of the nasal cavity and an area 1-cm square on its adjacent lateral and medial walls. That area may, however, be much smaller than normal, because inflammatory processes can involve that area and be severe enough to destroy the nerve cells. Whether they can regenerate in humans remains open to question.

The olfactory nerve fibers form thread-like bundles that pass through the foramina of the cribriform plate to end in the olfactory bulb, like the bristles of a brush. In the bulb, the impulses, which come from many nerve fibers, are conveyed to each of the large cells whose fibers form the olfactory tract. When the olfactory tract enters the hemisphere at the anterior border of the perforated area, the fibers of the olfactory sensory pathway

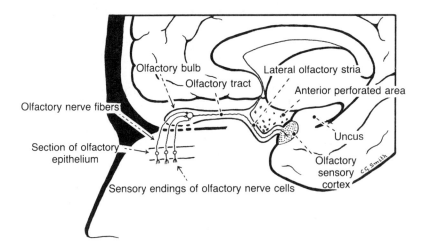

Figure 15-4. *Olfactory sensory pathway.*

follow its lateral border, in the lateral olfactory stria, to reach the olfactory sensory cortex in the anterior part of the uncus. That area is known as *paleocortex*. It is phylogenetically older than the three-layered archicortex of the hippocampus.

Sensory Pathways for Taste

Taste comprises the sensations of sweet, salt, sour, and bitter that are evoked by stimulation of specialized sensory epithelial cells of the tongue (Fig. 15-5). Impulses are conveyed from the anterior two-thirds of the tongue by sensory fibers of the seventh nerve and from the posterior third by fibers of the ninth and tenth nerves. Fibers of those nerves penetrate the medulla, dorsal to the olive, to reach the nucleus solitarius, which is a slender column of cells that extends the length of the medulla, lateral to the preganglionic cell column, in the gray matter of the floor of the fourth ventricle.

As the fibers reach the nucleus solitarius, they descend short distances to form the tractus solitarius. That tract descends partly within the nucleus; the taste fibers end in its rostral part. Axons of the cells of the nucleus ascend ipsilaterally in the central tegmental tract to end in the medial part of the posterior ventral nucleus of the thalamus. Fibers of that nucleus ascend in the posterior limb of the internal capsule to reach the cortical sensory area for taste. This area is adjacent to the general sensory area for the tongue, in an extension of the cortex of the postcentral gyrus on the upper lip of the lateral sulcus, adjacent to the insula.

The sensory pathway for taste has not been traced in the human brain, but clinical findings indicate that the pathway crosses the midline to end in the cortical taste area of the opposite side. Patients who experience brain injuries that involve the area in one cerebral hemisphere lose taste sensation on the opposite side of the tongue.

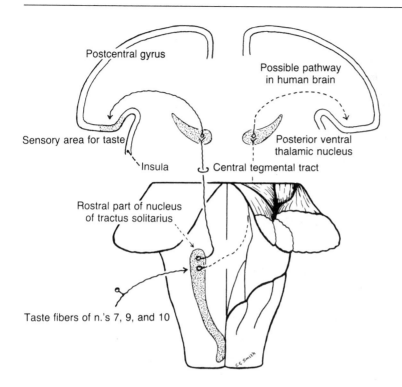

Figure 15-5. *Ipsilateral pathway illustrated here has been clearly demonstrated experimentally in the monkey. A contralateral cortical representation of taste has been demonstrated clinically in the human brain.*

Auditory Sensory Pathway

Features of the auditory sensory pathway are described in Chapters 5 and 8 and are summarized in this section.

Pathways extend from the auditory sense organs of each ear to both cerebral hemispheres, so that cutting the sensory pathway on one side of the brain at or above the level of midbrain does not significantly impair hearing in either ear (Fig. 15-6). Auditory nerve fibers divide as they enter the brain to end in dorsal and ventral cochlear nuclei. Fibers of each of those nuclei cross the midline to ascend to the inferior colliculus as fibers of the lateral lemniscus. From the inferior colliculus, impulses are relayed through the brachium of the inferior colliculus to the medial geniculate body and, from there, through the sublenticular limb of the internal capsule to the cortex of the transverse temporal gyrus. The ascending chain of neurons is tonotopically organized, so impulses from the laterally directed apical turn of the coiled cochlear duct (sensitive to low frquencies) reach the lateral end of the transverse temporal gyrus, and those from the more medial basal turn (sensitive to high frequencies) reach its medial part.

The fibers of the dorsal cochlear nucleus all cross in the dorsal part of the tegmentum. The fibers of the ventral cochlear nucleus cross in the ventral border of the tegmentum of the pons segment, where they form a strap-like band, the trapezoid body. Some of

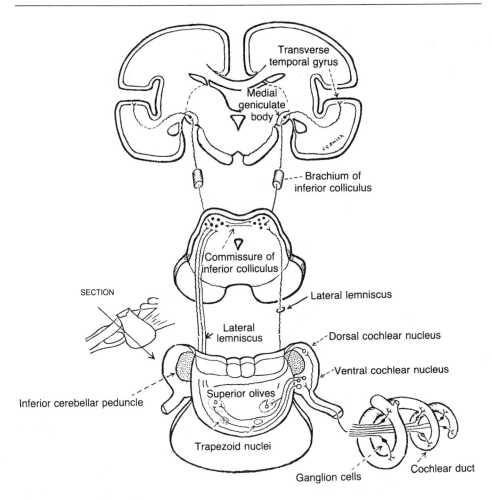

Figure 15-6. Auditory pathway.

those fibers end in the superior olive; others, in the ventrally located trapezoid nucleus. The trapezoid nucleus projects to the superior olive, which sends fibers, as part of the lateral lemniscus, to the inferior colliculus. Thus the ventral cochlear nucleus is an origin of pathways that reach the inferior colliculus of the opposite side, either directly or by way of relay nuclei in the pons.

The pathway from the ear to the hemisphere, on the same side, is provided by fibers of the ventral cochlear nucleus that synapse with cells of the ipsilateral superior olive. Fibers of that nucleus accompany the fibers from the opposite side that ascend in the lateral lemniscus to reach the inferior colliculus. Thus impulses from the sense organs of both ears are relayed by fibers of the brachium of the inferior colliculus to the medial geniculate body and, from there, to the auditory sensory cortex.

The nuclei of the auditory pathways have a variety of functions. An important one is the modulation of the flow of impulses to the cerebral cortex. Each relay station in the auditory pathway receives input from various levels of the central nervous system, including the cerebral cortex. Those inputs can inhibit conduction at the synapses. Certain nuclei, notably the superior olive, which receives input from both ears, may be involved in localization of sounds in space. Last, the relay nuclei of the pons and midbrain also relay impulses along reflex pathways, some to motor neurons, subserving orienting movements, and some to motor neurons of muscles that dampen the transmission of vibration to the sense organ for hearing.

Visual Sensory Pathway

The visual sensory pathway originates in the retina. Developmentally, this is an evaginated portion of the wall of the third ventricle, so it is actually a part of the brain. As such, it contains not only the layer of light-sensitive cells (rods and cones) whose cell bodies are comparable with those of typical sensory nerve ganglia, but also two other layers of nerve cells. Impulses are relayed from the rods and cones to bipolar nerve cells in the second layer and, from them, to larger cells whose axons form the optic nerve. Cells of those layers are interconnected by association neurons, so some association of data occurs within the retina.

The retina may be likened to a photographic film. In humans, the right and left retinae have overlapping visual fields (Fig. 15-7), except for small lateral portions. You may verify this fact by closing one eye at a time and noting the similarity in the two fields. If an object is located to the left of the head, when the eyes are directed straight ahead, an image of it is projected onto the right half of the retina of both eyes. The pathways from those *corresponding* sites in the retinae of the two eyes reach the *same* site in the visual cortex, in this case, of the right hemisphere, so that only one image is seen and not two. If, however, the right eye is forced out of alignment by pressing on it with a finger, the image received by the right eye will be shifted to a different part of the retina. Because the pathways excited in the right and left eyes now reach different parts of the cortex, two images are seen.

The optic nerves are attached to the anterior part of the floor of the third ventricle (Fig. 15-8), where pathways in each nerve, destined for the opposite hemisphere, cross the midline to form the chiasma. The cable of fibers that extends posteriorly from the chiasma is the optic tract. It is composed of the pairs of corresponding pathways from both eyes and extends superficial to the crus cerebri to reach the lateral geniculate body on the underside of the pulvinar. Fibers of the optic tract synapse with cells in the lateral geniculate body, which relay impulses along fibers that enter the hemisphere in the sublenticular limb of the internal capsule. After looping toward the temporal pole (Meyer's loop) in the lateral wall of the ventricle, the fibers turn back to reach the visual cortex, which is located in the walls of the calcarine sulcus.

The visual cortex of each hemisphere receives the projection of one-half of the visual field of each eye. The visual cortex of the right hemisphere receives the projection of the left half of the field of each eye and vice versa (Fig. 15-7). Thus destruction of the visual cortex of the right hemisphere will result in a loss of the left half of the visual field of both eyes. This condition is designated as a *left homonymous hemianopia*.

The retina has a point-to-point relationship with certain parts of the lateral geniculate body, and those parts, in turn, project to specific points in the visual cortex. The pathways from corresponding points in the retina of both eyes course alongside each other to enter the cortex together, so there is a point-to-point projection of the retina onto the visual

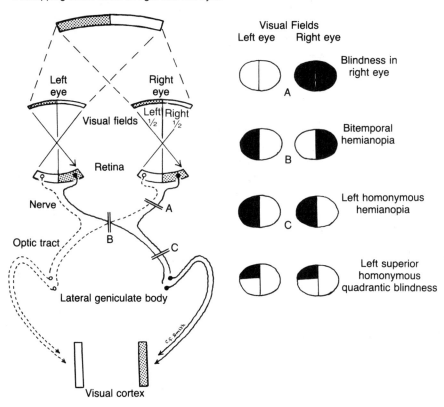

Overlapping visual fields of right and left eyes

Visual Fields
Left eye   Right eye

A   Blindness in right eye

B   Bitemporal hemianopia

C   Left homonymous hemianopia

Left superior homonymous quadrantic blindness

Left eye   Right eye

Visual fields   Left 1/2   Right 1/2

Retina

Nerve

Optic tract   B   A   C

Lateral geniculate body

Visual cortex

Figure 15-7. Visual sensory pathway; field defects.

cortex. The upper portions of the retina (the lower portions of the visual field) project to the upper half of the visual cortex; the lower portions of the retina (upper portions of the visual field) project to the lower half of the visual cortex. The macula (central vision) projects to the posterior portion, and peripheral parts of the retina project progressively more anteriorly.

The visual pathway may be severed at different levels along its length, in each case resulting in a characteristic loss of vision (Fig. 15-7). Where the fibers from the nasal half of each retina cross in the chiasma, they may be interrupted by an enlarging pituitary tumor (Fig. 15-8). That occurrence leads to a loss of the temporal half of the visual field of each eye, known as *bitemporal hemianopia*. Cutting the right optic tract, like destruction of the right visual cortex, as explained previously, leads to a loss of the left half of the visual field—that is, a left homonymous hemianopia. An injury to the temporal pole of the right hemisphere may lead to a partial loss of vision in the left half of the visual field of each eye. That happens because the fibers of pathways from the lower quadrants of the retina are in the lower part of the optic radiation and loop close to the temporal

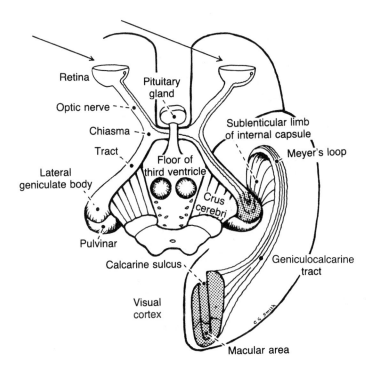

Figure 15-8. Visual sensory pathway.

pole. The visual deficit is known as *left superior quadrantic homonymous anopia* (blindness) (see Fig. 15-7).

Pupillary Reflex Pathways

Pupillary Light Reflex Pathway

A pencil of light directed onto either the medial or lateral half of the retina of each eye will excite constriction of the pupils of both eyes (Fig. 15-9). The impulses from the lateral half of the retina are conveyed by fibers of the optic nerve that course within the optic tract to reach the pretectum on the same side. The impulses from the medial half of the retina are conveyed to the pretectum on the opposite side by fibers of the optic nerve that cross in the chiasma. As the fibers leave the optic tract to enter the pretectum, they course medial to the corticotectal fibers, which form the brachium of the superior colliculus. The pretectum is a transition zone between the tectum of the midbrain and the thalamus. Impulses are relayed from the pretectum to the preganglionic nuclei of the oculomotor nerves on both the right and left side. The crossing fibers are in the posterior commissure. Fibers of the preganglionic nuclei form part of the oculomotor nerve. They extend to the ciliary ganglion in the orbit, where impulses are relayed by short ciliary nerves to the sphincter of the pupil.

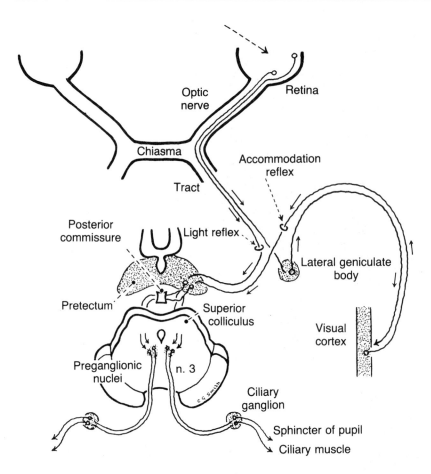

Figure 15-9. Pupillary reflex pathway.

Pathways that Mediate Pupillary Constriction Associated with Accommodation

The accommodation of the eye for near vision involves contraction of the ciliary muscle to reduce the tension of the suspensory ligament of the lens, allowing it to increase its curvature. As part of the accommodation process, impulses are conveyed to the sphincter of the pupil, which, by reducing the spherical aberration, sharpens the image for near vision. The stimulus that excites accommodation is a blurred image on the retina, which is projected to the visual cortex (Fig. 15-9). To sharpen the image, impulses are conveyed from cells of lamina V of the visual cortex by fibers that descend alongside the fibers of the afferent geniculocalcarine tract. As they reach the diencephalon, those efferent fibers bypass the lateral geniculate body and end in the pretectal region. Impulses are relayed from here, bilaterally, to cells of the preganglionic nuclei of the oculomotor nerves. Fibers of those nerves extend to the ciliary ganglion, which relays impulses to the sphincter of the pupil and to the ciliary muscle.

Motor Pathways

Pathways for Voluntary Movement

Voluntary movement is initiated by motor pathways that descend from the cerebral cortex to motor nuclei. Impulses that leave the cortex in those motor pathways are modulated by feedback pathways from the corpus striatum and the cerebellum. The latter structures receive input from the cortex and also from other parts of the brain and project back to the origin of the motor pathways.

The pyramidal pathway is the essential motor pathway for voluntary movement. If it is interrupted, muscles can still be activated reflexly, but useful voluntary control is lost. Fibers of cells in the cerebral cortex descend to motor nuclei to synapse with cells either directly or by way of internuncial cells. Fibers that descend to motor nuclei of the brain stem are known as *corticobulbar fibers*; fibers that descend to motor nuclei of spinal nerves form the corticospinal tracts. Other auxiliary motor pathways relay in the red nucleus or in the reticular formation of the brain stem. They have a role in regulating the level of excitability of the motor neurons of the brain stem and the spinal cord.

Most of the fibers of the corticobulbar and corticospinal tracts originate in the precentral gyrus, but some have cell bodies in adjacent anterior and posterior cortical areas. This becomes evident because electrical stimulation of the postcentral gyrus, which receives sensory pathways, can excite motor reponses. The cell bodies of the corticospinal and corticobulbar fibers are located in lamina V of the cerebral cortex. Cell bodies of the longest fibers (Betz cells) are among the largest nerve cells in the central nervous system and are a characteristic of area 4 within the motor area of the precentral gyrus.

Corticospinal Tract

Fibers from the trunk and limb areas of the cerebral cortex descend in the posterior limb of the internal capsule and continue into the crus cerebri of the midbrain. As they pass through the pontine nuclei of the basilar part of the pons, the fibers are grouped into small bundles that come together as they enter the medulla to form the pyramid. At the junction of the medulla and the spinal cord, most of the fibers cross the midline to form the lateral corticospinal tract. That tract is located in the lateral funiculus, between the posterior spinocerebellar tract and the posterior horn. Fibers drop out in each segment to complete a pathway to all cells of lamina IX, either directly or indirectly by means of internuncial neurons. Thus the motor cortex of each hemisphere controls all the skeletal muscles on the opposite side of the body.

The fibers of the pyramid that do not cross as they enter the spinal cord descend in the wall of the anterior median fissure to form the anterior corticospinal tract (Fig. 15-10). Fibers of that bundle drop out in successive segments to relay impulses, directly or indirectly, to the motor neurons of the muscles of the trunk and the muscles of the proximal parts of the limbs, that is, to the motor neurons of the axial muscles. Those motor neurons also receive terminals of the lateral corticospinal tract from the hemisphere of the opposite side, so a hemorrhage or another lesion involving the internal capsule will only sever the pathway from one cerebral hemisphere to the axial muscles and therefore *they* will *not be paralyzed*. The same lesion will sever the only pathway to the *distal* limb muscles on the opposite side, so *they will be paralyzed*.

As the fibers of the corticospinal tract descend through the brain stem, they pass immediately lateral to the emerging third nerve in the midbrain, are penetrated by the

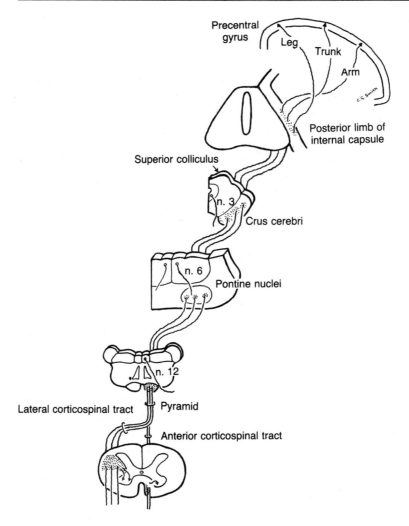

Figure 15-10. *Corticospinal tract.*

sixth nerve in the pons segment, and course medial to the rootlets of the twelfth nerve in the medulla. One of those cranial nerves may be involved with a lesion of the corticospinal fiber bundle, in which case the paralysis of the muscles supplied by the cranial nerve involved will be on the side of the lesion, and the paralysis of muscles supplied by the spinal nerves will be on the opposite side.

Corticobulbar Tract
Corticobulbar fibers descend from the cortex of the head area of the precentral gyrus and from area 8, located in the middle frontal gyrus, and accompany the corticospinal fibers in their course within the brain stem. At the level of each of the motor cranial nerves, some corticobulbar fibers cross the midline to convey impulses by means of internuncial

cells to the motor nucleus of the nerve on the opposite side. In addition to supplying all the motor nuclei in the opposite side, fibers of the corticobulbar tract supply most of the motor nuclei on the same side. The muscles that are supplied only by pathways from the opposite hemisphere are muscles of the lips and the tongue. A patient with a lesion in the right cerebral hemisphere is not able to voluntarily retract the left angle of the mouth when asked to smile; when asked to protrude the tongue, the tongue will deviate to the left side due to the unopposed action of the unparalyzed muscles of the right half of the tongue. Bilateral supply of all other muscles of the head ensures a normal function of these muscles after a unilateral cerebral lesion.

Corticorubrospinal Pathway

The cell bodies of the corticorubral fibers are in the same cortical áreas as the cells that give rise to the corticospinal tracts. They accompany them as far as the midbrain before ending in the red nucleus of the same side. Impulses are relayed by the axons of the cells of the red nucleus that cross the midline in the ventral tegmental decussation and descend in the lateral portion of the tegmentum of the pons. They continue dorsal to the inferior olive of the medulla and then descend in the spinal cord, mingling with the fibers of the lateral corticospinal tract. Some fibers end in the anterior horn of each segment. The function of that pathway is believed to have a secondary role in the control of voluntary movement.

Corticoreticular Pathways

The corticoreticular pathways are not somatotopically organized. They originate in the precentral gyrus and descend in the posterior limb of the internal capsule. They continue within the crus cerebri to the pons segment, where they enter the tegmentum and end bilaterally in the portions of the reticular formation of the pons and the medulla that are the origin of fibers of the reticulospinal tracts. Those tracts descend in the ventral part of the lateral funiculus and in the ventral funiculus to end directly on the motor cells or on internuncial cells of the intermediate gray matter that relay impulses to the motor cells of the anterior horn.

Fibers that descend in the ventral funiculus originate in the pontine reticular formation and have an excitatory action. Fibers that descend from the reticular formation of the medulla have a predominantly inhibitory influence on motor activity.

Cortical Feedback Pathways of the Corpus Striatum

Pathways from the corpus striatum to the motor cortex of the cerebral hemisphere are considered to be feedback pathways, because one of the major inputs of the corpus striatum is from the motor cortex (Fig. 15-11).

Fibers from the motor areas of the cortex converge on the putamen of the lentiform nucleus and, less extensively, on the caudate nucleus, along with fibers from the intralaminar nuclei of the thalamus and the substantia nigra. Processed data are relayed to the globus pallidus, which in its turn receives input from the subthalamic nucleus. The output of the globus pallidus is through the lenticular fasciculus and the ansa lenticularis to the nuclei ventralis, anterior and lateralis. Those thalamic nuclei also receive input from the cerebellum and the processed data from all the sources mentioned are relayed through the posterior limb of the internal capsule to the origin of the cortical motor pathways.

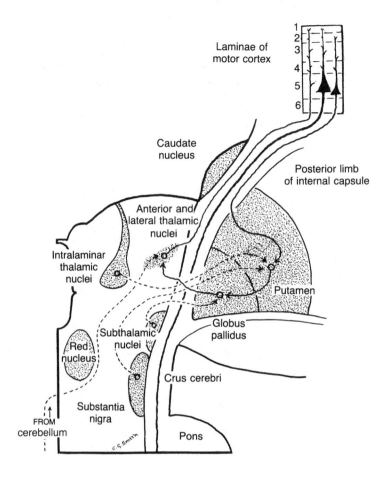

Figure 15-11. Cortical feedback pathway of the corpus striatum.

The fibers that project impulses from the substantia nigra to the corpus striatum use dopamine as a neurotransmitter. Lesions of the nigra lead to a reduction in the dopamine input to the striatum. That permits overaction of the striatum and a consequent excessive discharge of impulses, which, on reaching the cortex, excite an abnormal sustained contraction of flexors and extensors that is known as *muscle rigidity*. That rigidity and an associated tremor, characteristically present at rest, are features of the parkinsonian syndrome. Relief may be obtained by making up the dopamine deficiency by proper drug administration. In some cases, the condition may require surgical destruction of the nucleus ventralis anterior, which eliminates the feedback of impulses to the motor cortex.

This operation is also effective in relieving the violent contralateral, uncontrolled movements that are a feature of a lesion of the subthalamic nucleus. That nucleus apparently exerts a modulating influence on the output of the globus pallidus.

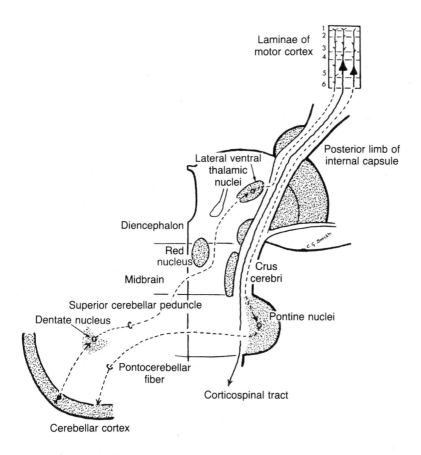

Figure 15-12. Cortical feedback pathway of the cerebellum.

Cortical Feedback Pathways of the Cerebellum

The smoothly executed movements initiated by motor pathways of the cerebral cortex require the collaboration of the cerebellum (Fig. 15-12). To ensure that collaboration, the corticopontocerebellar pathway conveys data, concerning movements, to the cerebellum. The major portion of that pathway originates in the motor areas of the cortex, but a significant part originates in the association areas of the parietal, temporal, and frontal lobes.

Because the cerebral hemisphere controls the muscles on the opposite side of the body, whereas each cerebellar hemisphere coordinates the muscles on its own side, it follows that the corticopontocerebellar pathway must cross the midline to reach the appropriate half of the cerebellum. Corticopontine fibers accompany corticospinal fibers as far as the pons, where they synapse with cells of the pontine nuclei. Those nuclei relay impulses along fibers that cross the midline to end in the cerebellar cortex. Data processed by the cerebellar cortex are, in turn, relayed by Purkinje cells to the dentate nucleus. Fibers of that nucleus leave the cerebellum in the superior cerebellar peduncle, cross the midline in the midbrain, and sweep around the red nucleus to reach the ventral lateral nucleus of the thalamus. That nucleus relays impulses by way of the posterior limb of the internal capsule to the motor cortex of the precentral gyrus. A lesion of that feedback pathway is associated with an intention tremor that appears with active movement.

Special Features of Cortical Efferent Pathways that Control Eye Movements

Movements of the eyes may be initiated voluntarily by one group of cortical efferent fibers and reflexly by another group. A voluntary movement selects a point of fixation in the visual field, and the reflex mechanism automatically retains it when the point of fixation moves or as the head moves. The pathway for voluntary movement originates in area 8 of the cortex of the frontal lobe. The efferent limb of the reflex pathway originates in the primary visual sensory area 17 and the adjacent cortex of the occipital lobe.

Because the eyes are functionally yoked together and cannot be moved separately, the efferent pathways of each hemisphere that control eye movements must project to special cell groups, or "centers," that coordinate the muscles of both eyes. Those cell groups have not been defined, but experimental and clinical evidence indicate the nodal regions for control of conjugate movements are located (1) in the reticular formation of the pons, adjacent to the abducens nucleus, and (2) in the rostral part of the midbrain. The pontine reticular center (see Fig. 8-10) is concerned chiefly with conjugate, side-to-side movements; the midbrain reticular center is concerned with vertical conjugate movements. Clinically, vertical movements are impaired by the pressure of pineal tumors.

Electrical stimulation of area 8 of the cortex of the frontal lobe excites movements of both eyes to look toward the opposite side and upward or downward, depending on the positioning of the stimulating electrode. In an unconscious patient who has a head injury involving the frontal area of one hemisphere, the eyes deviate to the uninjured side if the area is stimulated by the injury and to the side of the injury if area 8 is destroyed. The cortical efferent fibers of the frontal eye area that control those eye movements form part of the corticobulbar tract.

The pathways that descend from the occipital cortex are excited by a shift of the image on the retina, with a consequent shift of excitation in the visual area. The efferent fibers of the cortex have cell bodies in lamina V of the visual area and course alongside the geniculocalcarine tract to reach the diencephalon. They bypass the lateral geniculate body and reach the superior colliculus as part of its brachium. Stimulation of the superior colliculus excites conjugate movements of the eyes, presumably by way of its efferent fibers to the reticular formation.

Emotional Pathways

Emotions may be excited by any of the senses of the body or by recalling events of past experience. The integration of data that excite an emotional feeling occurs in extensive portions of the highest levels of association cortex and in some subcortical cell masses of the hemisphere. The cortical gray matter includes portions of the temporal, prefrontal,

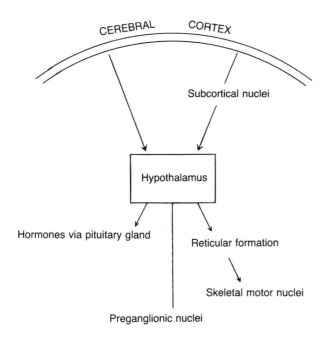

CEREBRAL   CORTEX

Subcortical nuclei

Hypothalamus

Hormones via pituitary gland

Reticular formation

Skeletal motor nuclei

Preganglionic nuclei

Figure 15-13. Emotional pathways.

and cingulate cortex and the hippocampus. The subcortical cell masses involved include the septal gray matter and the amygdaloid nuclei (Fig. 15-13).

Emotional responses are excited by pathways to the hypothalamus, which is responsible for the integration of the response to be made, whether it is laughter, sorrow, rage, or terror. The pathways to the hypothalamus are not included in the internal capsule and are therefore still capable of exciting, for example, muscles of expression, which may not be activated voluntarily following a capsular lesion (stroke).

The hypothalamus is well suited for its role in emotional responses, because it is the integrator of the neural mechanisms that maintain an optimal internal environment. Those responses involve neural, autonomic, and somatic effector pathways and the elaboration and release of hormones through the pituitary gland. The autonomic neural pathways descend to the preganglionic nuclei; the somatic motor pathways relay in the reticular formation to reach the motor nuclei.

Review Questions (Answers Available on the Pages Cited)

1. Why does the pain tract have to be cut at least one segment above the level of analgesia required (p. 192)?
2. Explain why occlusion of the posterior inferior cerebellar artery can cause a loss of pain on the same side of the head and on the opposite side of the body (p. 193).

3. Locate and describe the loss of sensation when the right fasciculus cuneatus is cut (pp. 193 and 197).
4. At what level of the brain stem do the touch pathways of the medial lemniscus and the anterior spinothalamic tract come together (p. 194)?
5. Name the fiber tracts that make up the spinal lemniscus (p. 194).
6. Why may position sense in the leg be retained when the fasciculus gracilis is cut in the cervical region (p. 197)?
7. Locate the cell bodies of the position sense fibers of the trigeminal cranial nerve 5 (p. 197).
8. Describe a homolateral pathway for hearing (p. 200).
9. What loss of vision would result if the right optic tract were cut (p. 203)?
10. Explain why both pupils contract when a light is flashed into one eye after the optic chiasm is cut (p. 203).
11. If the visual sensory cortex is stimulated, the pupils of both eyes contract. Explain (p. 204).
12. Why are the muscles of the shoulder not paralyzed by a lesion of the internal capsule (p. 205)?
13. Locate the lesion that causes the muscles of the left hand to be paralyzed and the right eye unable to be abducted (p. 206).
14. How may impulses from the motor cortex reach the anterior horn cells if the corticospinal tract is cut in the medulla (p. 207)?
15. How does the lentiform nucleus exert its influence on voluntary movement (p. 207)?
16. How may the cerebellum regulate the output of the motor cortex of the cerebral hemisphere (p. 209)?
17. Explain why a lesion of the internal capsule impairs the ability to smile voluntarily, but an emotional smile is still possible (p. 210).

16

Blood Supply of the Brain and Spinal Cord

Blood is brought to each side of the brain by two vessels, the vertebral and the internal carotid arteries (Fig. 16-1). Those two arteries enter the cranial cavity at opposite ends of the brain stem, course toward each other on its ventral surface, and anastomose to form an arterial trunk. A branch of that trunk descends onto the ventral surface of the spinal cord to form the upper end of an arterial trunk for the cord.

The longitudinal arterial trunks of the brain, a right and a left, anastomose with each other in front of the pons to form a median vessel and in front of the lamina terminalis, where they are connected by a short, transverse branch. Side branches of those trunks course medially and laterally on the surface of the brain and those branches, particularly the ones that extend onto the cerebral hemisphere and onto the cerebellum, anastomose freely. Thus the brain is enclosed in a network of vessels through which arterial blood may reach any part of its surface.

The nutrient vessels of the brain are branches of the vascular tunic. They are fine, thread-like branches that penetrate the brain at right angles to its surface. Each vessel is the core of a cylindrical or cone-shaped portion of nervous tissue, which it nourishes. Its capillaries anastomose with those of adjacent nutrient arteries, but that anastomosis is not free enough to permit one vessel to supply the capillary bed of its neighbor.

Parts of the Arterial Trunk of the Brain

The vertebral artery enters the skull through the foramen magnum at the side of the junction of the spinal cord and medulla and ascends to join its fellow of the opposite side at the midline at the lower border of the pons (Fig. 16-2). The common vessel so

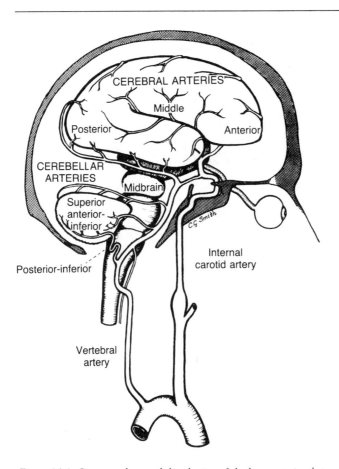

Figure 16-1. Source and general distribution of the large arteries that enter the skull to supply the brain.

formed is the basilar artery. A median septum is occasionally seen in the basilar artery as evidence of its formation from right and left parallel vessels. The basilar artery is as long as the pons segment. It ends by dividing into right and left branches that are called the *stems of the posterior cerebral arteries*. Those parts of the right and left ventral arterial trunks are so named because they carry most of the blood that is distributed by the posterior cerebral arteries. They ascend at the borders of the interpeduncular fossa as far as the diencephalon. There the slender posterior communicating artery, the diencephalic portion of the longitudinal arterial trunk, leaves the end of the stem of the posterior cerebral artery to connect it with the internal carotid artery. The part of the posterior cerebral artery that extends laterally from this site is an enlargement of a side branch of the ventral trunk. It courses laterally around the side of the brain stem. In atypical cases, the posterior cerebral artery receives most of its blood from the internal carotid artery instead of the basilar artery. In such cases, the diameter of the posterior communicating artery is correspondingly large and serves as the stem of the posterior cerebral artery.

The internal carotid artery, which delivers blood into the upper end of the arterial trunk, enters the base of the skull on the lateral side of the pharynx and then courses

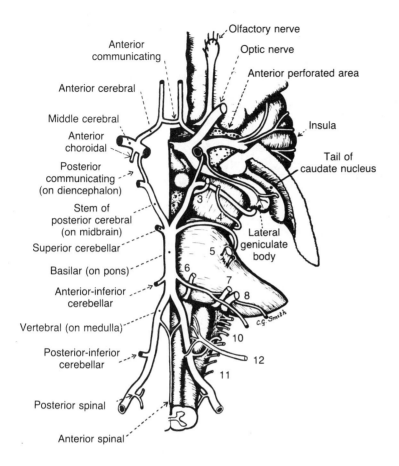

Figure 16-2. Right and the left ventral arterial trunks of the brain, their anastomoses with each other, and their large branches.

The following labels appear in the figure:

Olfactory nerve
Optic nerve
Anterior perforated area
Anterior communicating
Anterior cerebral
Middle cerebral
Anterior choroidal
Posterior communicating (on diencephalon)
Stem of posterior cerebral (on midbrain)
Superior cerebellar
Basilar (on pons)
Anterior-inferior cerebellar
Vertebral (on medulla)
Posterior-inferior cerebellar
Posterior spinal
Anterior spinal
Insula
Tail of caudate nucleus
Lateral geniculate body
c.g. Smith

medially in the bony roof of the pharynx, that is, in the temporal bone, to reach the foramen lacerum. Through that foramen, it ascends into the posterior end of the cavernous sinus at a point just lateral to the dorsum sellae (Fig. 16-1). It courses forward on the floor of the sinus to its anterior wall. There it makes a right-angled turn and ascends to pierce the dural roof of the sinus and strike the underside of the optic nerve just behind the optic foramen. The optic nerve deflects it, causing it to turn posteriorly and laterally, to the side of the optic chiasma, where it is able to continue its ascent to the anterior perforated area (Fig. 16-2). There it divides into its terminal branches, the anterior and middle cerebral arteries. The anterior cerebral artery courses forward and medially above the optic nerve toward the midline, just in front of the lamina terminalis. The middle cerebral artery courses laterally and posteriorly onto the insula.

The parts of the internal carotid artery that lie, respectively, on the floor, the anterior wall, and on the roof of the cavernous sinus are considered by the radiologist to be a unit. This unit is called the *carotid siphon.*

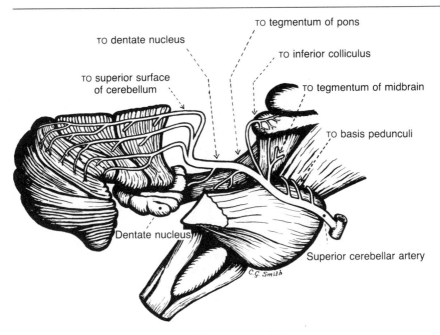

TO dentate nucleus

TO tegmentum of pons

TO superior surface of cerebellum

TO inferior colliculus

TO tegmentum of midbrain

TO basis pedunculi

Dentate nucleus

C.G. Smith

Superior cerebellar artery

Figure 16-3. Course and distribution of the superior cerebellar artery.

Branches of the Ventral Arterial Trunk

The Cerebellar Arteries

The cerebellar arteries are named according to the surfaces of the cerebellum that receive them. There is one for the superior surface and two for the inferior surface: anterior and posterior.

Superior Cerebellar Artery

The superior cerebellar artery arises from the basilar artery at the upper border of the pons and passes laterally and dorsally, hugging the isthmus region of the pons segment (Figs. 16-2 and 16-3). On the dorsal surface of the pons segment, where it is overlapped by the cerebellum, it gives off its cortical branches—two to four of them. Those branches bend around the anterior border of the tentorial surface of the cerebellum and course backward in the sagittal plane. They reach as far as the inferior semilunar lobule, where they anastomose with the terminal branches of the inferior cerebellar arteries.

In addition to its terminal branches, the artery has important collateral branches. Near its origin, it gives off very fine branches that sweep laterally and penetrate and supply the basis pedunculi, where that fiber bundle enters the pons. At the dorsolateral border of the basis pedunculi and beyond that point, it gives off additional fine branches, some of which penetrate the brachium conjunctivum to supply it and the tegmentum of the pons. Others penetrate the lateral lemniscus and supply the tegmentum of the midbrain. One or two relatively large branches accompany the brachium conjunctivum into the core of the cerebellum to supply the dentate nucleus. Another relatively large branch courses onto the inferior colliculus to supply that part of the tectum of the midbrain.

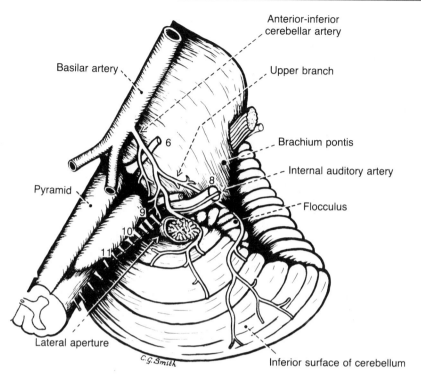

Figure 16-4. Course and distribution of the anterior-inferior cerebellar artery.

Anterior-Inferior Cerebellar Artery

The anterior-inferior cerebellar artery arises from the basilar artery close to the inferior border of the pons segment (Fig. 16-4). It courses laterally toward the flocculus, usually in front of nerve 6 so as to press it against the pons. Before reaching the flocculus, it divides into two branches—upper and lower. The upper branch follows the brachium pontis and turns onto the inferior surface of the cerebellum lateral to the flocculus. The inferior branch usually passes laterally below and in contact with the seventh and eighth nerves to reach the inferior surface of the cerebellum medial to the flocculus. As it crosses the eighth nerve, it usually gives off the internal auditory artery that follows that nerve to the sense organs for hearing and position in the internal ear. The internal auditory artery may come directly from the basilar artery.

The noncortical branches of the anterior-inferior cerebellar artery are (1) the internal auditory, (2) nutrient branches that pierce the caudal part of the pons and the brachium pontis, and (3) the nutrient branches that enter the medulla along the caudal border of the pons, lateral to the pyramid. Those nutrient vessels to the pons and medulla penetrate as far as the floor of the fourth ventricle.

Posterior-Inferior Cerebellar Artery

The posterior-inferior cerebellar artery does not come from the basilar artery as it should but from the vertebral artery (Figs. 16-2 and 16-5). Moreover, it leaves the vertebral

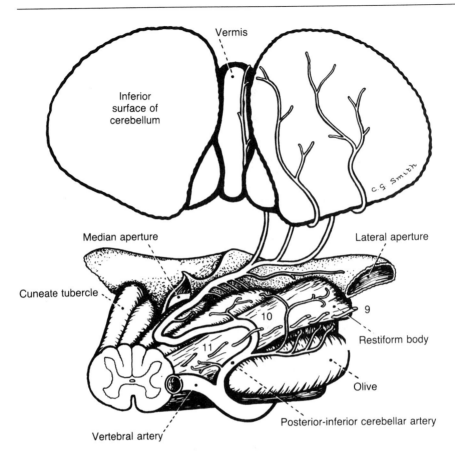

Figure 16-5. *Course and distribution of the posterior-inferior cerebellar artery.*

artery near the caudal end of the medulla. One would expect this artery to reach the cerebellum along its stalk and it does, but only after it has executed a preliminary, S-shaped bend to supply nutrient branches to the lateral and dorsal aspects of the medulla.

As Figure 16-5 shows, the artery turns around the caudal end of the olive to ascend ventral to the rootlets of nerves 11 and 10. It does that to deliver a leash of fine vessels that enter the medulla between the olive and the restiform body. The posterior-inferior cerebellar artery then turns dorsally, usually about the middle of the olive, passing through the rootlets of nerves 11 or 10 to reach the cuneate tubercle. Here it turns caudally and gives off fine branches that enter the cuneate tubercle. It descends to a level below the inferior velum, then makes a hairpin turn and ascends on the medulla and skirts the side of the inferior aperture to course up onto the roof of the fourth ventricle. In that part of its course, it give off a series of very fine vessels, closely spaced like the teeth of a comb, that penetrate the medulla, along the attachment of the inferior velum. Fine twigs also pass directly to the choroid plexus of the fourth ventricle.

When the artery approaches the stalk of the cerebellum, it divides into two terminal cortical branches—a medial one for the inferior surface of the vermis and a lateral one for the medial part of the inferior surface of the cerebellar hemisphere. Those branches sweep backward, clinging to the cerebellum, and reach as far as the tuber and the inferior semilunar lobule, respectively.

The course of the artery, as given, conforms to this description in about 70 percent of cases. In about 10 percent, the anterior-inferior cerebellar artery enlarges its distribution to supply the whole inferior surfaces. In some cases, the posterior-inferior cerebellar artery passes almost directly backward from the vertebral artery omitting its ascent on the side of the medulla. In such cases, the lateral side of the medulla plus the upper ends of the restiform body and the cuneate tubercle are supplied by a series of side branches of the vertebral artery.

Cerebral Arteries

The cerebral hemisphere, like each cerebellar hemisphere, is supplied by three arteries. The cerebral arteries are named *anterior, middle,* and *posterior*.

Anterior Cerebral Artery

The anterior cerebral artery leaves the internal carotid artery as it ascends lateral to the chiasma (Fig. 16-6). It courses medially and anteriorly between the optic nerve below and the anterior perforated area above, to follow the medial olfactory stria onto the medial surface of the hemisphere. That brings the right and left anterior cerebral arteries to within 1 or 2 mm of each other, and at that site they are connected by the short, stout anterior communicating artery, not labeled in Figure 16-6.

On the medial surface of the hemisphere, the anterior cerebral artery courses directly to the genu of the corpus callosum and then clings to the corpus callosum as far back as the splenium. Its cortical branches, some as large as the parent vessel, come off at irregular intervals after it passes onto the medial surface of the hemisphere. Those branches extend obliquely toward the margin of the hemisphere and continue around it onto the orbital surface and onto the lateral surface. They supply the cortex of the medial surface to within 1 cm of the parietooccipital fissure, and on the orbital and lateral surfaces they supply an adjacent marginal band of cortex that is about 3 cm wide. That marginal band extends back to within 1 cm of the occipital lobe.

The stem of the anterior cerebral artery gives off fine nutrient vessels throughout its course. Close to its origin, it sends branches to the optic chiasma and to the preoptic region of the hypothalamus. As it approaches the medial border of the hemisphere, it sends branches through the anterior perforated area to supply the head of the caudate, the anterior pole of the lentiform nucleus, and the anterior limb and genu of the internal capsule. Those are the striate branches of the anterior cerebral artery. One of those branches is much larger than the rest, and it delivers most of the blood to the above portion of the striate region. It begins close to the anterior communicating artery at the medial border of the hemisphere and courses back to reach the base of the olfactory trigone. That artery was first described by Heubner and commonly is referred to by his name. It divides into three or four smaller vessels that enter foramina located behind the lateral part of the base of the olfactory trigone. In Figure 16-6 a part of the septal region of the medial wall of the hemisphere has been removed to show the striate vessels within the head of the caudate nucleus.

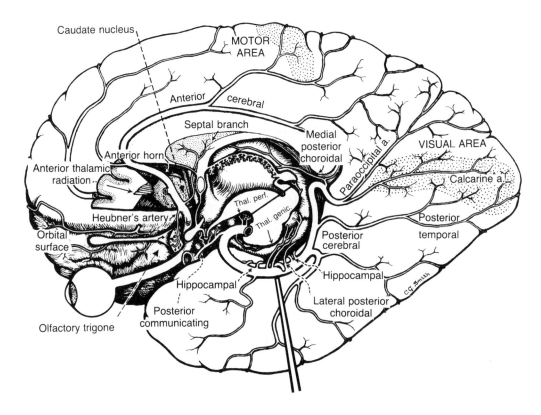

Figure 16-6. Course and distribution of the anterior and the posterior cerebral arteries. The head of the caudate nucleus has been exposed to show the course of the striate branches of the anterior cerebral artery.

As the anterior cerebral artery begins its course on the medial surface, it gives off branches that supply the septal area, including the septum pellucidum. As it lies on the corpus callosum, it gives off a series of fine nutrient vessels that supply all but the splenium (supplied by the posterior cerebral artery).

From a practical standpoint, the distribution of the anterior cerebral artery has the following significant features: (1) It supplies the cortex of the motor area of the lower limb and the motor pathway to the head and arm in the internal capsule. (2) It supplies the septal region, where small lesions may induce a prolonged state of unconsciousness. (3) It supplies the corpus callosum, which has in it the significant pathway from the dominant hemisphere to the motor area of the nondominant hemisphere. The functional deficit that follows the interruption of this pathway is known as *apraxia*.

Middle Cerebral Artery
The middle cerebral artery begins lateral to the chiasma (Fig. 16-7). It is one of the two terminal branches of the internal carotid artery. It courses laterally below the anterior perforated area to the limen insulae. As it approaches the insula, it begins to divide into a leash of cortical branches. Those fan out on the insula and then pass onto the deep

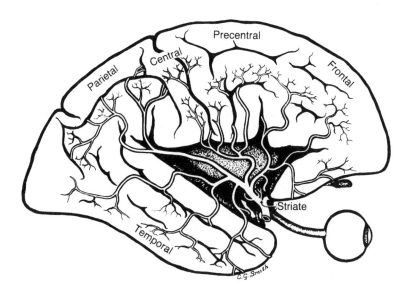

Figure 16-7. Course and distribution of the middle cerebral artery. The opercula are pulled apart to expose the striate branches and the beginning of each of the cortical branches on the insula.

surface of its opercula to reach the borders of the lateral fissure. From the lateral fissure, the branches extend to within 3 cm of the superior margin, to within 1 cm of the inferior margin of the temporal lobe, and as far back as the occipital lobe. They also extend onto the lateral two-thirds of the orbital surface and onto the temporal pole but not to the uncus, which is supplied by the anterior choroidal artery. The vessels are shown in Figure 16-7 as they were seen in one injected specimen. Note that one of those arteries enters the central sulcus to supply the portion of the motor area and the portion of the general sensory area of the upper half of the body.

The stem of the middle cerebral artery gives off nutrient vessels that enter the brain through the anterior perforated area. They comprise the striate branches of the middle cerebral artery. The largest branches are crowded together in the lateral part of the perforated area, where they find their way into the lower edge of the external capsule. They fan out within this lamina, clinging at first to the lateral aspect of the lentiform nucleus, but gradually penetrating it. The largest of those vessels can be followed by dissection (see Fig. 16-9). They supply (1) all the putamen and all the caudate, except in each case the frontal ends, which are supplied by the anterior cerebral artery; (2) the lateral part of the globus pallidus; (3) all that part of the anterior limb, the genu, and the posterior limb, which lies adjacent to the putamen.

The crowding of the nutrient vessels into the lateral angle of the perforated area is due to the buckling of its lateral border as a result of the growth forward of the elongating temporal lobe.

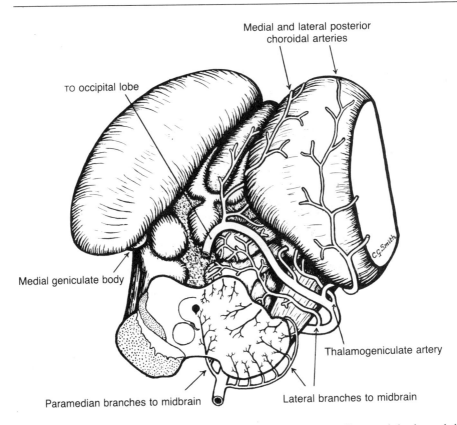

Medial and lateral posterior
choroidal arteries

TO occipital lobe

Medial geniculate body

Thalamogeniculate artery

Paramedian branches to midbrain

Lateral branches to midbrain

C.G.Smith.

Figure 16-8. Branches of the posterior cerebral artery that supply the midbrain and the diencephalon.

Posterior Cerebral Artery

The right and left posterior cerebral arteries are the terminal branches of the basilar artery (Figs. 16-6 and 16-8). Each one ascends at the border of the interpeduncular fossa medial to the third nerve and then turns laterally around it as around a marker buoy (Fig. 16-2). As it courses laterally (Fig. 16-6), it lies in the cleft between the parahippocampal gyrus and the brain stem. That conducts it to a point just below the splenium, where it makes a right-angled turn and crosses the end of the parahippocampal gyrus to enter the end of the calcarine sulcus. Its terminal branches lie in the parietooccipital and the posterior calcarine sulci, respectively. The calcarine branch usually supplies all the visual cortex, except the lower macular projection. Branches of the parietooccipital artery supply the rest of the cuneus, plus a strip of cortex 1 cm wide along the anterior border of the parietooccipital fissure, and they cross the superior border to help supply the lateral surface of the occipital lobe.

The other cortical branches of the posterior cerebral artery are collateral branches that leave it as it courses along the medial border of the parahippocampal gyrus. There are two sets—one set for the neocortex and one for the archicortex of the hippocampal formation.

The arteries to the neocortex, three or four of them, are large and course laterally across the parahippocampal gyrus, fanning out on the tentorial surface of the temporal and the occipital lobes. At the inferolateral border of the hemisphere, they turn onto the lateral surface and supply the inferior temporal gyrus and the lower part of the occipital lobe.

The branches that supply the cortex of the hippocampal formation are short and slender. They pass to the medial surface of the parahippocampal gyrus, and at the hippocampal sulcus they turn to run along the free surface of the dentate gyrus. In the specimen illustrated in Figure 16-6, two hippocampal arteries entered the uncal portion of the hippocampal fissure and two entered the fissure near its midpoint. As those arteries course along the hippocampal sulcus, they give off nutrient vessels to the dentate gyrus and other longer, penetrating vessels that reach the hippocampus proper in the hippocampal eminence of the lateral ventricle. It is the longer vessels to the hippocampus that are most likely to be occluded by pressure caused by a herniation (protrusion) of the hippocampal gyrus into the interval between the midbrain and the free edge of the tentorium. Hence the hippocampus is damaged more than the dentate gyrus in such a condition. The pathologist calls the vulnerable part of the cross section of the hippocampal formation *Sommer's sector*.

The noncortical branches of the posterior cerebral artery supply the choroid plexus of the lateral ventricle, the choroid plexus of the third ventricle, the diencephalon, and the midbrain.

A lateral posterior choroidal artery leaves the posterior cerebral artery opposite the lateral geniculate body (Figs. 16-6 and 16-8). It courses forward into the lateral part of the transverse fissure on the lateral part of the thalamus as far as the anterior tubercle. It sends some branches to the choroid plexus of the lateral ventricle. Others cling to the lateral part of the thalamus to supply it through its dorsal surface. A medial posterior choroidal artery leaves the posterior cerebral artery near the midline just below the splenium. It courses forward into the transverse fissure also (but close to the midline), and its branches supply the choroid plexus of the third ventricle, the epithalamus, and the medial part of the thalamus through its dorsal surface.

The posterior cerebral artery, as we shall see, supplies most of the diencephalon. It supplies all the dorsal portion of the diencephalon through branches of its choroidal arteries. It supplies most of the inferior portion of the diencephalon by direct branches that enter its inferior surface. Of those branches, three or four, called the *thalamogeniculate arteries*, leave the posterior cerebral artery lateral to the basis pedunculi and enter the diencephalon through the metathalamus (Fig. 16-8). An additional cluster of perforating vessels, called the *thalamoperforating vessels*, enters the diencephalon just behind the mammillary bodies—that is, through the subthalamus (Fig. 16-6).

Since the stem of the posterior cerebral artery is, developmentally, the midbrain portion of the ventral arterial trunk, it follows that it should supply the midbrain, and it does. The branches to the midbrain are side branches that extend medially and laterally. The medial ones enter the midbrain through the posterior perforated area. Those paramedian vessels are relatively large and long. They penetrate as far as the aqueduct, supplying in turn the medial part of the basis pedunculi, the medial parts of the brachium conjunctivum and red nucleus, and the motor nuclei of the third and the fourth nerves (Fig. 16-8).

The lateral branches of the posterior cerebral artery to the midbrain extend across the basis pedunculi toward the dorsal surface of the midbrain. Usually only one vessel reaches the tectum. It branches to supply the superior and inferior colliculi. All those vessels give off branches that penetrate the basis pedunculi or the lemnisci or the brachium of

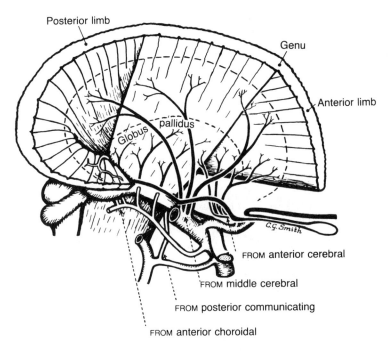

Posterior limb

Genu

Anterior limb

Globus pallidus

C.G. Smith

FROM anterior cerebral

FROM middle cerebral

FROM posterior communicating

FROM anterior choroidal

Figure 16-9. Lateral aspect of the internal capsule, showing its blood supply. The two concentric broken lines indicate the position of the borders of the lentiform nucleas and the globus pallidus, respectively.

the inferior colliculus to supply the portion of the tegmentum that is not supplied by the paramedian vessels.

Anterior Choroidal Artery

The name of this artery does not do justice to its distribution (Figs. 16-9, 16-10, and 16-11). It supplies part of the choroid plexus of the lateral ventricle, but its important distribution is to the optic, pyramidal, and pallidothalamic pathways.

The artery accompanies the optic tract. It comes from the internal carotid artery at the lateral side of the optic chiasma and clings to the optic tract to reach the lateral side of the lateral geniculate body, where it enters the choroid plexus of the inferior horn. Its branches to the optic pathway are a series of collateral branches that are distributed to the optic tract, the lateral part of the lateral geniculate body, and, by penetrating this, the optic radiation in the sublenticular part of the internal capsule. Its branches to the pyramidal pathway are another set of collateral branches that are distributed to the posterior limb of the internal capsule immediately above the basis pedunculi. (That part of the posterior limb is applied to the globus pallidus.) Those nutrient vessels, like the teeth of a comb, enter the lower border of the posterior limb chiefly along the lateral border of the optic tract, but some pierce it.

Its branches to the pallidosubthalamic pathway accompany the branches to the posterior

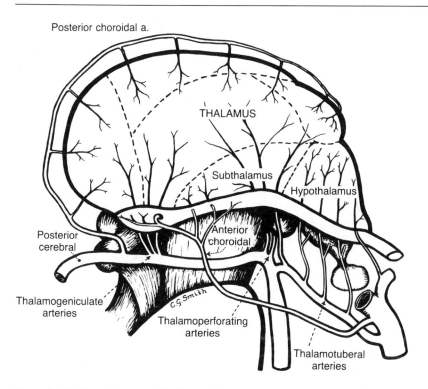

Posterior choroidal a.

THALAMUS

Subthalamus

Hypothalamus

Posterior cerebral

Anterior choroidal

Thalamogeniculate arteries

C.G.Smith

Thalamoperforating arteries

Thalamotuberal arteries

Figure 16-10. Lateral aspect of the diencephalon and the midbrain, showing the blood supply of the subthalamus, the hypothalamus, the lateral and medial geniculate bodies, and the thalamus.

limb. Of those, the lateral ones supply the globus pallidus; the medial ones penetrate the junction of basis pedunculi and posterior limb to reach the subthalamic nucleus.

Developmentally, the anterior choroidal artery is a fourth cerebral artery for the supply of the posterior part of the olfactory pathway to the cerebral cortex. Hence it has branches that arborize on the surface of the uncus and enter the hippocampal sulcus to help the posterior cerebral artery supply the hippocampal formation.

Pontine Branches of the Basilar Artery

The pontine branches of the basilar artery are a series of vessels that supply the pons through its ventral and lateral surfaces. About four to six of them enter the pons close to the midline on each side. Those paramedian vessels, like those of the midbrain, are long and supply a paramedian region that contains (1) a portion of the motor pathway and (2) a nucleus of the somatic motor column, namely, the abducens nucleus. Another four to six pontine vessels course laterally onto the brachium pontis. They give off nutrient vessels that penetrate and supply the lateral portion of the basilar part of the pons and the tegmentum as deep as the fourth ventricle. Their distribution will be discussed later in dealing with the blood supply of the pons segment.

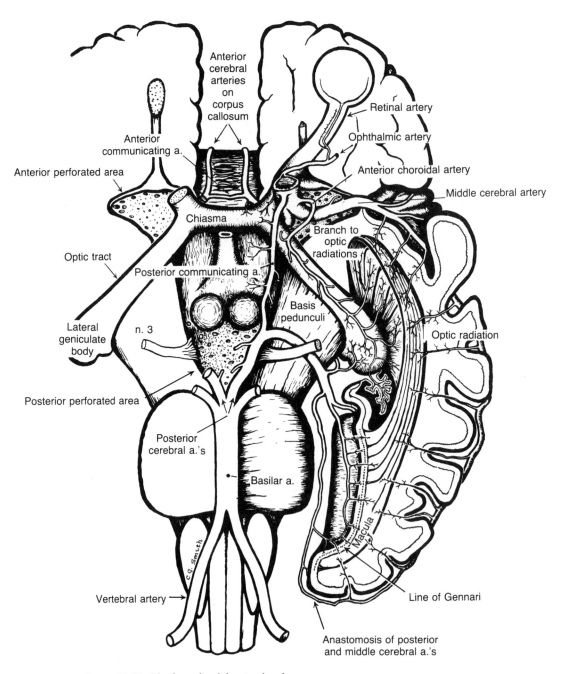

Figure 16-11. Blood supply of the visual pathway.

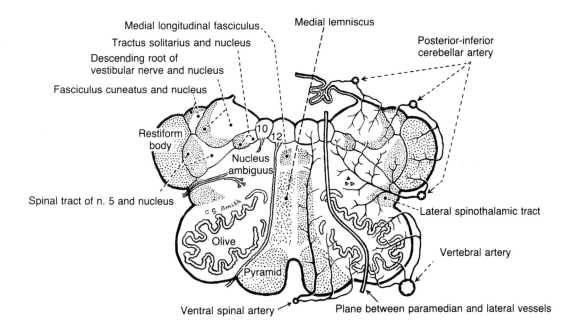

Medial longitudinal fasciculus
Tractus solitarius and nucleus
Descending root of vestibular nerve and nucleus
Fasciculus cuneatus and nucleus
Medial lemniscus
Posterior-inferior cerebellar artery
Restiform body
Nucleus ambiguus
Spinal tract of n. 5 and nucleus
C. G. Smith
Olive
Lateral spinothalamic tract
Vertebral artery
Pyramid
Ventral spinal artery
Plane between paramedian and lateral vessels

Figure 16-12. Cross section of the medulla, showing its blood supply.

Anterior Spinal Artery

The anterior spinal artery leaves the medial side of the vertebral artery near its upper end and courses medially to unite with its fellow of the opposite side and descend in the midline onto the the spinal cord (Figs. 16-2, 16-12).

Dorsal Spinal Artery

The dorsal spinal artery is smaller than the anterior spinal artery and comes off the lateral side of the vertebral artery at the caudal end of the medulla (Fig. 16-12). It courses dorsally onto the fasciculus cuneatus, where it divides into a short, ascending and a long, descending branch. The descending branch has a zigzag course on the dorsal surface of the spinal cord. Its branches anastomose freely with its fellow of the opposite side and also with branches of the anterior spinal artery (Fig. 16-13).

Blood Supply of the Internal Capsule

The blood supply of the internal capsule is illustrated in Figure 16-9. To understand the distribution of vessels to the internal capsule, it is necessary to keep in mind that the lateral surface of the anterior limb and of the posterior limb faces not only laterally but also inferiorly. Hence in a coronal section of the hemisphere, the inferior border of the internal capsule will be nearer the midline than the superior border. Since nutrient vessels

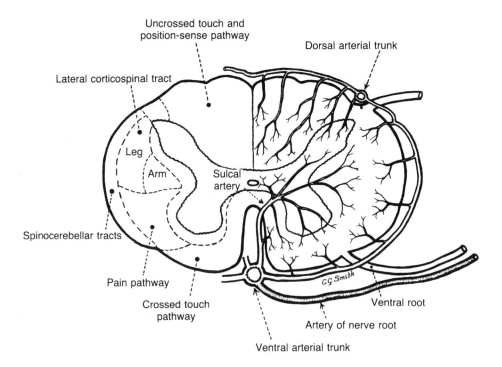

Uncrossed touch and
position-sense pathway

Dorsal arterial trunk

Lateral corticospinal tract

Leg

Arm

Sulcal
artery

Spinocerebellar tracts

Pain pathway

Crossed touch
pathway

Ventral root

Artery of nerve root

Ventral arterial trunk

C.G. Smith

Figure 16-13. Cross section of the spinal cord, showing the course and distribution of its nutrient vessels.

ascend almost vertically through perforations on the inferior surface of the brain, it follows that the superior lateral part and the inferior medial part of the capsule will be supplied by different nutrient arteries. Let us consider the blood supply of each of the parts of the internal capsule in turn.

Anterior Limb

This part of the capsule is supplied by the striate branches of the anterior cerebral and the middle cerebral arteries. The anterior cerebral artery supplies its inferior medial part and the middle cerebral artery supplies its superior lateral part. Those nutrient vessels reach their destination through the anterior perforated area.

Genu

The genu is also supplied by striate branches of the middle and anterior cerebral arteries and in the same way as the anterior limb. However, it has an additional blood supply from branches to the diencephalon. Those branches come from the posterior communicating artery or, occasionally, directly from the internal carotid artery. They enter the base of the brain just lateral to the mammillary body and course along the medial side of the genu, supplying it and the adjacent part of the diencephalon as far as the anterior nucleus of the thalamus.

Posterior Limb

The posterior limb receives striate branches from the middle cerebral artery and from the anterior choroidal arteries. The branches from the middle cerebral artery enter the external capsule through perforations in the lateral part of the perforated area. They fan out in that lamina and branch and turn into the putamen of the lenticular nucleus to reach the portion of the posterior limb that extends above the globus pallidus. The branches from the anterior choroidal artery enter the brain through the optic tract or along its borders as it lies on the basis pedunculi. Some of those branches pass directly into the posterior limb; others reach it after passing through the globus pallidus.

Sublenticular Limb

The sublenticular part of the internal capsule is supplied by the anterior choroidal artery. Its branches penetrate the lateral border of the optic tract and the lateral part of the lateral geniculate body and pass directly into the optic radiations (Fig. 16-11).

Blood Supply of the Diencephalon

Nutrient vessels of the diencephalon are restricted to its pia-covered surfaces, that is, to its superior and inferior surfaces (Fig. 16-10). The nutrient vessels of the superior surface come from the posterior choroidal branches of the posterior cerebral artery. They are uniformly distributed and enter the diencephalon at right angles to the surface. They reach a third of the distance to the inferior surface.

The nutrient vessels of the inferior surface come directly from large basal arteries. They are not uniformly distributed, because those that should enter where the midbrain is attached are displaced, some forward and some backward. Those displaced vessels have an arched course to reach their destination in the part of the diencephalon directly above the attachment of the midbrain.

The chief source of nutrient vessels to the inferior part of the diencephalon is an arterial trunk that consists of of posterior communicating and the posterior cerebral arteries. That trunk extends from the optic chiasma around the side of the basis pedunculi to the pulvinar. Its nutrient branches are in three groups: two of these—the thalamotuberal and the thalamoperforating—enter the diencephalon in front of the attachment of the midbrain; the third group—the thalamogeniculate vessels—enters the diencephalon behind the attachment of the midbrain.

The thalamotuberal vessels leave the posterior communicating artery as it lies alongside the hypothalamus. They enter the tuberal region of the hypothalamus and penetrate into the overlying nuclei of the thalamus (hence their name). They supply all but the anterior end of the hypothalamus, which receives fine vessels from the internal carotid and the anterior cerebral arteries.

The thalamoperforating vessels are so named because they reach the thalamus through the posterior perforated area. They are long stout vessels that leave the posterior communicating artery and the stem of the posterior cerebral artery and enter the subthalamus lateral to the mammillary body and also immediately behind it. They diverge in the subthalamus and reach into the nuclei of the overlying thalamus. Those vessels supply all the subthalamus except its most lateral part, which receives nutrient vessels from the anterior choroidal artery. The latter pierce the fibers of the basis pedunculi just deep to the optic tract.

The thalamogeniculate vessels are so named because they enter the thalamus through the geniculate bodies. They diverge as they enter the diencephalon and help to supply the thalamic nuclei above the attachment of the midbrain. In passing through the geniculate bodies, these vessels supply them, except for the lateral half of the lateral geniculate body, which is supplied by the anterior choroidal artery.

The thalamogeniculate vessels are the ones that help to supply the nucleus ventralis posterior, which is the relay station for the general sensory pathway. Occlusion of those vessels will therefore be followed by some loss of sensation on the opposite side of the body. The condition is characterized usually by spontaneous, excruciating pain referred to the side of the body where the interrupted pathway begins.

Blood Supply of the Pons Segment

The pons segment is described as having a ventral paramedian set and a lateral set of nutrient vessels. The paramedian set enters the pons close to its origin from the basilar artery. Of those vessels, the ones leaving the middle part of the basilar artery have to penetrate the thickest part of the pons and manage to reach only into the marginal part of the tegmentum. Toward the upper and the lower borders of the pons, the thickness of the basilar portion gets progressively smaller and the corresponding upper and lower perforating nutrient vessels are able to penetrate deeper into the tegmentum. Those upper and lower paramedian vessels not only penetrate progressively deeper into the tegmentum as the pons gets less massive, they also alter their course to arch toward each other in the sagittal plane and supply the intervening portion of the tegmentum.

The lateral part of the tegmentum is only partially covered by the pons and by its lateral extension, the brachium pontis. In the interval between the brachium pontis below, and the midbrain above, the nutrient vessels can enter the tegmentum directly from the superior cerebellar artery and course medially to penetrate as far as the paramedian region. Where the pons covers the lateral part of the tegmentum, it is supplied like the paramedian portion of the tegmentum by nutrient vessels that arch into it from above and below, that is, from the vicinity of the midbrain and from the vicinity of the medulla. Those reaching it from above are branches of the superior cerebellar artery and branches of the lateral pontine vessels. Those reaching it from below are branches of the anterior-inferior cerebellar artery and branches of the lateral pontine vessels.

Blood Supply of the Medulla

The nutrient vessels of the medulla fall into two groups: paramedian and lateral (Fig. 16-12). The paramedian vessels enter the medulla through its ventral surface, that is, medial to the olive. They are long vessels that penetrate the pyramid, then the medial lemniscus, and end in the motor nuclei in the floor of the fourth ventricle. Near the pons, those vessels come from the vertebral artery, but caudal to the origin of the ventral spinal artery, they come from the latter vessel.

The nutrient vessels of the lateral and dorsal portions of the medulla are all short vessels except for those that enter the medulla in the depression lateral to the olive.

Some of those long vessels penetrate to the medial lemniscus; others extend dorsally to supply the sensory nuclei in the floor of the fourth ventricle. The source of those vessels shifts from one artery to another throughout the length of the medulla. Near the upper pole of the olive, they come from the anterior-inferior cerebellar artery; below that level, they come from the vertebral and the posterior-inferior cerebellar arteries. Where the posterior- and the anterior-inferior cerebellar arteries fail to contribute their quota of nutrient vessels, the vertebral artery makes up the deficit.

The short nutrient vessels of the dorsal aspect of the medulla oblongata supply the nucleus gracilis, the nucleus cuneatus, the caudal part of the vestibular nuclei, and the restiform body (Fig. 16-13). Those vessels come from the posterior spinal and the posterior-inferior cerebellar arteries. Near the pons where the inferior velum makes up the whole of the dorsal surface of the medulla the restiform body is supplied by nutrient vessels that enter its ventral lateral border.

Blood Supply of the Spinal Cord

The spinal cord receives its blood through the branches of three longitudinal arterial trunks (Fig. 16-13). Each of those trunks extends from the brain to the filum terminale. One is a median vessel located in front of the ventral median fissure. The other two, one on the right side of the spinal cord, the other on the left, follow a zigzag course in the vicinity of the dorsolateral sulcus. The two dorsal trunks communicate with each other through numerous anastomotic channels. Each of those trunks begins on the medulla as a branch of the vertebral artery. As they descend, they receive feeder vessels from some of the arteries that reach the spinal cord along the nerve roots.

The feeder vessels for the ventral or anterior arterial trunk reach it along four to six of the ventral roots. Of those vessels some come in on the right side; others, on the left. Similarly, each of the dorsolateral trunks receives only two or three feeder vessels. The feeder vessels are not uniformly spaced along the length of the spinal cord, nor is the pattern consistent from one specimen to another. Nevertheless, anatomical studies and studies of pathological material indicate that the arterial trunks of the spinal cord receive most of their blood through vessels that reach the cervical and lumbar segments. The available data suggest that blood flows caudally, in the upper part of the trunks, to about the fourth thoracic segment and ascends in the lower part of the spinal cord to the same segment. Hence the fourth thoracic segment is prone to suffer most when the amount of blood reaching the spinal cord is reduced through injury or disease. Such a reduction in the flow of blood to the spinal cord could follow an injury to a nerve root if it happened to be conveying a large feeder vessel.

The Nutrient Vessels of the Spinal Cord

The largest nutrient arteries of the spinal cord are the sulcal vessels (Fig. 16-13). Those vessels arise from the ventral spinal arterial trunk and pass back to the floor of the ventral median sulcus. There each sulcal vessel turns to one side or the other and enters the spinal cord to branch and supply all the gray matter except the dorsal one-third of the dorsal horn and all the fibers of the ventral and the lateral funiculus except for a thin, superficial layer. That artery, therefore, supplies both the lateral and the ventral corticospinal tracts. The rest of the fibers of the ventral and lateral funiculi are supplied by short, perforating branches from the pial network of vessels formed by branches of the ventral arterial trunk and the dorsolateral one.

The dorsal funiculus and the dorsal portion of the dorsal horn are supplied by nutrient vessels that penetrate the dorsal surface of the spinal cord from the pial network formed by the anastomosing branches of the right and left dorsolateral arterial trunks.

Review Questions (Answers Available on the Pages Cited)

1. What names are given to the portions of the arterial trunks that lie on the medulla, the pons, the midbrain, and the diencephalon (pp. 213–214 and Fig. 16-2)?
2. What are the two ways that blood can reach the left cerebral hemisphere from the right internal carotid artery (see Fig. 16-2)?
3. Describe the extent of the cortical distribution of the middle cerebral artery (p. 220).
4. Name the artery that supplies most of the midbrain, the diencephalon, and the portion of the cerebral cortex that includes the visual area (pp. 220–224).
5. Name the successive portions of the optic pathway supplied by the anterior choroidal artery (p. 224).
6. What is the blood supply of the pain pathway's thalamic relay station (p. 230)?
7. Explain why severing a dorsal or ventral root of a lumbar nerve may result in paralysis of both legs (p. 231).

17

The Autonomic Nervous System

Definition and Characteristics

The autonomic nervous system is a subdivision of the *motor* portion of the nervous system. It carries impulses to a special group of effectors, smooth muscles, heart muscle, and glands. Those effectors are found in viscera and also in nonvisceral structures, such as the skin.

The autonomic nervous system has two distinguishing features: (1) Its motor nerves to the viscera are paired, one acting as an excitor and one as an inhibitor. (2) Each of the "motor nerves" of this system is a chain of two nerve cells, with the cell body of the distal nerve cell in a peripheral nerve ganglion. To illustrate these two characteristics, let us consider the nerves to the heart (Fig. 17-1). The heart is a muscle and, therefore, it should be activated like the quadriceps femoris by one motor nerve. Instead, its activity is influenced by two nerves, one acting to increase the frequency of its contractions and the other, to decrease the frequency. Each of those two nerves has its own cell station (relay station) in the peripheral nervous system. They are autonomic ganglia and will be described later.

Sympathetic and Parasympathetic Divisions of the Autonomic Nervous System

The two motor nerves to each of the viscera come from widely separated parts of the central nervous system. One of the pair comes from a spinal cord segment between T1 and L2. The other comes from either the brain or the sacral part of the spinal cord. The nerves that emanate from the thoracic part of the spinal cord and from the first two

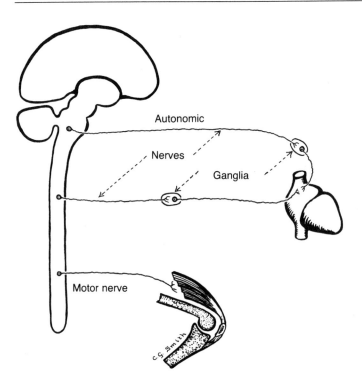

Figure 17-1. The difference between motor nerves to striated muscles and the autonomic nerves.

lumbar segments comprise the sympathetic division of the autonomic nervous system (Fig. 17-2). The nerves that emanate from the brain and sacral part of the spinal cord comprise the parasympathetic (*para*, "on either side") portion of the autonomic nervous system.

Sympathetic Division

The fibers of the sympathetic nerves leave the spinal cord in the ventral roots of nerves T1 to L2. They course distally into the anterior ramus to a point just lateral to the vertebral column. There they leave the anterior ramus and course medially in a branch, called the *white ramus communicans* (Fig. 17-3). The name of that branch is fitting because the fibers are myelinated and it connects a spinal nerve with the sympathetic trunk, which is described in the next section.

The white rami pass medially to the side of the vertebral column and there some of the nerve fibers of each ramus turn at right angles to ascend a certain distance toward the head, while others turn to descend a certain distance toward the coccyx. The longitudinally running fibers of the 14 nerves come together as they ascend or descend to form a cable-like bundle, called the *sympathetic nerve trunk*, which lies alongside the vertebral bodies. It extends all the way from the base of the skull to the tip of the coccyx (Fig. 17-4). It is through this nerve trunk that the sympathetic nerves are distributed to

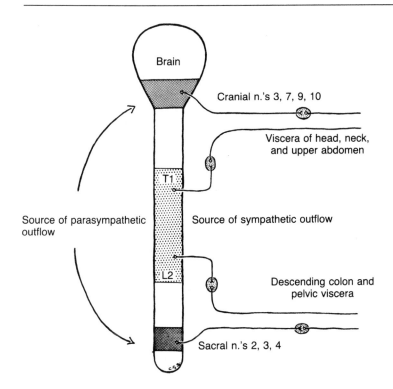

Brain

Cranial n.'s 3, 7, 9, 10

Viscera of head, neck,
and upper abdomen

T1

Source of parasympathetic
outflow

Source of sympathetic outflow

L2

Descending colon and
pelvic viscera

Sacral n.'s 2, 3, 4

Figure 17-2. Sympathetic and the parasympathetic portions of the autonomic nervous system.

the head and neck and to the pelvis and lower limb. The sympathetic trunk, therefore, is a device to ensure the distribution of impulses to smooth muscles and glands throughout the length of the body. Let us turn now to a description of the nerves that leave the sympathetic trunk to distribute these impulses.

Segmental Nerves
The sympathetic nerve fibers for each segment leave the lateral side of the sympathetic trunk in a thread-like nerve, called the *gray ramus communicans*. That nerve is gray because the nerve fibers are unmyelinated; they are coming from cells located within the trunk (described later). One of those nerves enters the anterior ramus of each of the spinal nerves (Fig. 17-5). By entering the spinal nerve, the sympathetic nerve fibers are able to reach all parts of the segment of the body. To reach the posterior part of the body, some fibers must pass toward the spinal cord for a short distance to find their way into the posterior ramus.

By comparing the drawings showing the gray and the white rami of the sympathetic trunk in Figures 17-4 and 17-5, it will be evident that the anterior rami of the spinal nerves T1 to L2 have both a white and gray ramus and that all the other nerves have only a gray ramus. The two rami of the second lumbar nerve and the single gray ramus of the third lumbar nerve are illustrated in Figure 17-6. Cutting a gray ramus would be one way of cutting all the sympathetic fibers to a body segment. This is sometimes necessary

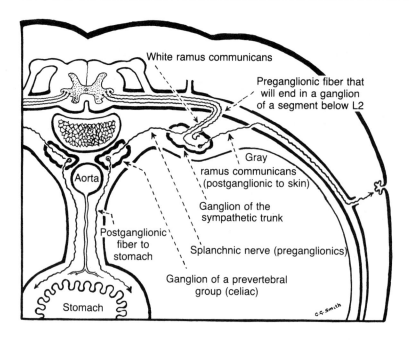

White ramus communicans

Preganglionic fiber that will end in a ganglion of a segment below L2

Gray ramus communicans (postganglionic to skin)

Ganglion of the sympathetic trunk

Aorta

Postganglionic fiber to stomach

Splanchnic nerve (preganglionics)

Ganglion of a prevertebral group (celiac)

Stomach

c.c. smith

Figure 17-3. Section of the upper abdomen, showing the sympathetic pathways to the skin and to the viscera below the diaphragm.

to alleviate an abnormal condition that is brought about by an overactive sympathetic nerve. An example of such an abnormal condition is impaired blood supply due to excessive vasoconstriction.

Visceral Nerves

The nerves that leave the sympathetic trunk for the viscera run from the medial side of the trunk (Fig. 17-7). They course toward the midline to reach the viscera of the neck, thorax, and abdomen. Those nerves are called the *carotid, cardiac, great splanchnic, small splanchnic, smallest splanchnic,* and *lumbar splanchnic nerves.* Some unnamed nerves leave the sacral part of the sympathetic trunk to go to the viscera of the pelvis. All those visceral nerves pass toward the front of the vertebral column, where they form networks, called *prevertebral plexuses.* The prevertebral plexus in the neck is called the *carotid plexus.* In the thorax, there is a cardiac, a pulmonary, and an esophageal subdivsion. In the abdomen, the prevertebral plexus extends from the level of the celiac artery to the second piece of the sacrum, where it forks into a right and a left portion. Each of those pelvic portions of the plexus forms a quadrilateral sheet that is interposed between the pelvic viscera and the vessels on the pelvic wall. The upper, median part of the plexus in the abdomen is divided for descriptive purposes into a celiac portion, located around the root of the celiac artery, an intermesenteric portion, located between the level of the origin of the superior mesenteric artery and that of the inferior mesenteric artery, and a caudal part, called the *superior hypogastric plexus.* The pelvic plexus—divided into a right

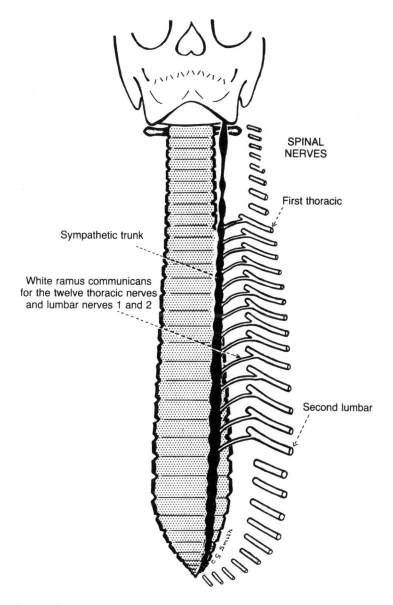

SPINAL
NERVES

First thoracic

Sympathetic trunk

White ramus communicans
for the twelve thoracic nerves
and lumbar nerves 1 and 2

Second lumbar

Figure 17-4. The sympathetic trunk and its afferent branches, the white rami communicantes.

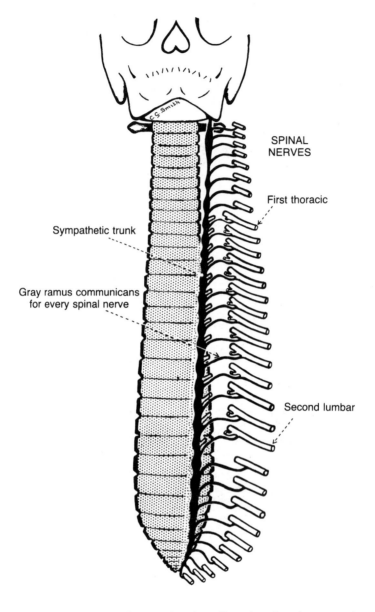

SPINAL
NERVES

First thoracic

Sympathetic trunk

Gray ramus communicans
for every spinal nerve

Second lumbar

Figure 17-5. The sympathetic trunk and its efferent branches, the gray rami communicantes.

RAMI COMMUNICANTES

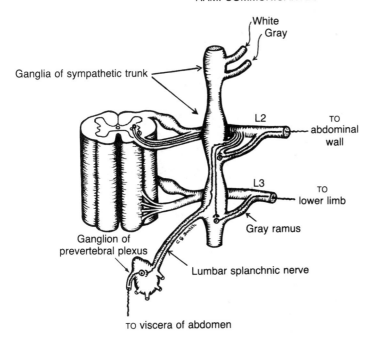

Figure 17-6. Three sympathetic pathways: (1) to the sweat glands of a segment supplied by a nerve that has a white ramus communicans (L2), (2) to the sweat glands of a segment supplied by a nerve that lacks a white ramus communicans (L3), and (3) a pathway to the abdominal viscera.

and a left portion—is the inferior hypogastric plexus. The nerve fibers leave each plexus and course along one of the visceral arteries to reach the organ they supply.

Ganglia of the Sympathetic Nerves
It was pointed out earlier that the motor nerves of the autonomic nervous system are peculiar in that they are a chain of two nerve cells. Hence somewhere along each sympathetic nerve there must be a collection of cell bodies—a relay station. Each of those cell masses is a sympathetic ganglion and it may be located in one of two places, either in the sympathetic trunk or in a prevertebral plexus.

The Ganglia of the Sympathetic Trunk. The ganglia of the sympathetic trunk form a longitudinal series of swellings—one in front of each spinal nerve. They develop as discrete ganglia (one for each segment), but later the cells of adjacent ganglia may move together and form one mass. Thus it happens that the ganglia of segments C1, C2, C3, and C4 form one long fusiform superior cervical ganglion; C5 and C6 form a single nodular middle cervical ganglion, and C7 and C8 form the inferior cervical ganglion. Usually the first thoracic ganglion and the inferior cervical ganglion unite to form a composite mass, called the *stellate ganglion.*

In the thoracic region, there are usually ten ganglia; in the lumbar region, four; and

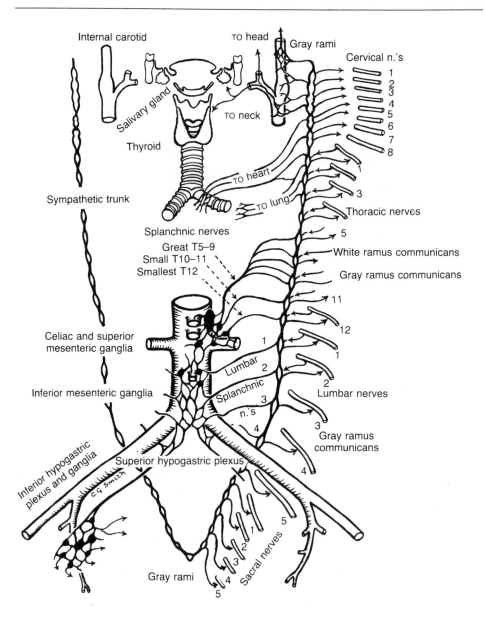

Figure 17-7. Visceral branches of the sympathetic trunk and the parts of the prevertebral plexus, which they help to form.

in the sacral region, three or four. The coccygeal ganglia of the right and left trunks may come together to form the ganglion impar ("unpaired").

Ganglia of the Prevertebral Plexuses. The ganglia of the prevertebral plexuses are found only below the level of the diaphragm. They are irregularly distributed within the abdominal plexuses, but they tend to cluster around the origin of the celiac, the superior mesenteric, and the inferior mesenteric arteries. In the pelvis, large ganglia exist in the inferior hypogastric plexus of each side.

Location of the Relay Stations of Each of the Segmental and Visceral Sympathetic Nerves
Each of the segmental nerves has its relay station in a ganglion in the sympathetic trunk at the level of the segment it supplies. Each of the visceral nerves to the structures in the head, neck, and thorax also has its relay station in a ganglion in the sympathetic trunk. The nerves that supply structures in the head have their relay station in the superior cervical ganglion. The visceral nerves to the heart have a relay station in one of the cervical ganglia or in one of the upper four thoracic ganglia. Cardiac nerves may have some relay stations in the cervical ganglia, because the tubular heart develops in part in the cervical region. The visceral nerves to the lungs have their relay stations in the upper four thoracic ganglia. The visceral nerves to the abdomen and pelvis have their relay stations in the ganglia of the prevertebral plexus at a level corresponding to the position of the viscus supplied. For example, those to the stomach have relay stations in ganglia in the celiac plexus, whereas those to the bladder and rectum have relay stations in the inferior hypogastric plexus.

Afferent Fibers in the Sympathetic Nerves
The nerves of the sympathetic nervous system are motor, but they also contain some sensory fibers. Those sensory nerve fibers come from sense organs in the viscera. They course toward the spinal cord through the splanchnic nerves as far as the sympathetic trunk and then course upward or downward as the case may be to reach the level of the spinal nerve, which conveys them to the central nervous system. There they leave the sympathetic trunk in a white ramus to enter the spinal nerve, course toward the spinal cord, and enter it through a dorsal root. The cell bodies of those visceral sensory fibers are in the dorsal root ganglion.

A knowledge of the segmental origin of the sensory nerve fibers of each of the viscera is of value in interpreting pain referred to the body wall from a diseased organ. Pain that emanates from the heart is felt in the chest in the distribution of nerves T1 to T5. Esophageal pain is referred to the distribution of nerves T5 and T6. Stomach pain is referred to segments T7, T8, and T9, chiefly in the epigastrium. Pain in the small intestine is referred to body segments T9 and T10. Appendix pain is referred to T10 in the umbilical region. Pain emanating from the ascending and the transverse colon is referred to segments T10, T11, and T12. The descending colon and part of the rectum receive pain fibers from segments L1 and L2; the kidney receives its fibers from segments T12, L1, and L2; the ureter, from L1 and L2.

The pain fibers from the bladder follow the parasympathetic nerves of segments S2, S3, and S4 to the spinal cord. The body of the uterus is supplied with pain fibers from T11, T12, L1, and L2, through the sympathetic nerves, but the cervix receives its pain fibers from the sacral segments 2, 3, and 4, through the parasympathetic nerves.

Parasympathetic Division of the Autonomic Nervous System

The nerve fibers of the parasympathetic division leave the central nervous system in cranial nerves 3, 7, 9, and 10, and in sacral nerves 2, 3, and 4. Those parasympathetic nerve fibers differ in their distribution from those of the sympathetic nervous system in that they go almost exclusively to the viscera. They lack a segmental distribution; hence there is no need for a parasympathetic trunk.

Each of the parasympathetic nerves leaves its parent cranial nerve 3, 7, 9, or 10 and its parent spinal nerve, that is, sacral nerve 2, 3, or 4, and proceeds on its own to the organ it is to supply. Some cranial nerves give off more than one parasympathetic nerve to supply more than one organ. The autonomic ganglia, that is, parasympathetic ganglia, on each of those nerves are close to, or are embedded in, the organ supplied. To describe the parasympathetic nervous system more fully, it is necessary to deal with it piecemeal, that is, one nerve at a time.

Parasympathetic Branch of Cranial Nerve 3

The parasympathetic branch of cranial nerve 3 arises from the inferior division of the third nerve at the apex of the orbit and supplies the smooth muscles in the eye. The relay station is in the ciliary ganglion. That ganglion is about the size of a pin's head and is flattened against the optic nerve by the lateral rectus. The postganglionic fibers (fibers of cells in the ganglion) leave the ganglion as a tuft of thread-like nerves, called the *short ciliary nerves*. They pierce the sclera around the optic nerve and course forward deep to the sclera to reach the ciliary muscle (accommodation) and also the sphincter of the pupil (light reflex).

Parasympathetic Branches of Cranial Nerve 7

Greater Superficial Petrosal Nerve. This supplies the glands of the nose, orbit, and palate. It leaves the seventh nerve in the petrous bone and, traveling medially, it gradually rises through the floor of the middle cranial fossa. It is so named because it is the larger of two nerves on the superior surface of the petrous bone. The lesser superficial petrosal nerve is a parasympathetic nerve from cranial nerve 9.

The greater superficial petrosal nerve leaves the middle cranial fossa by descending in the foramen lacerum until it reaches the opening of the pterygoid canal. There it is joined by its fellow sympathetic nerve, called the *deep petrosal nerve*, which has come up from the superior cervical ganglion alongside the internal carotid artery. The composite nerve, called the *nerve of the pterygoid canal*, enters its canal and is conducted to the pterygopalatine fossa, where it ends in its relay station, the sphenopalatine ganglion. The postganglionic nerve fibers join the maxillary nerve and are distributed with its branches to the nose, orbit, and palate.

Chorda Tympani. This nerve, the nerve to the submandibular and the sublingual salivary glands, leaves the seventh nerve in the petrous bone just above the stylomastoid foramen. It courses medially across the eardrum and thus acquires its name. At the anterior (medial) border of the eardrum, it passes inferiorly to emerge from the skull through the petro-tympanic fissure and then passes forward as it descends to join the lingual nerve. It follows the lingual nerve to the side of the tongue, where it leaves it, to end in its relay station, the submandibular ganglion. The postganglionic fibers are grouped into filaments that are distributed to the closely associated submandibular and sublingual glands.

Parasympathetic Branch of Cranial Nerve 9

The parasympathetic branch of cranial nerve 9 is the tympanic branch of the ninth nerve. It leaves the ninth nerve as it passes through the jugular foramen, penetrates the base of the skull to reach the medial wall of the middle ear (tympanum), and continues on through the roof of the middle ear to course alongside the greater superficial nerve. There it is called the *lesser superficial petrosal nerve*. It travels medially to the mandibular foramen, where it descends to its relay station, the otic ganglion, located just below the foramen at the medial side of the mandibular nerve. The postganglionic fibers join the mandibular nerve and are distributed with its auriculotemporal branch to the parotid gland.

Parasympathetic Branches of the Vagus Nerve

Most of the fibers of the vagus are parasympathetic. They leave the nerve in branches that come off in the neck, thorax, and abdomen.

Cardiac Nerves. The cardiac nerves leave the vagus partly in the neck and partly in the thorax. They course to the base of the heart, where they enter the prevertebral plexus, formed by the cardiac branches of the sympathetic trunk, and accompany the sympathetic fibers to the heart. The relay stations, that is, cell clusters for the parasympathetic fibers, are either in the plexus or on the surface of the heart.

Pulmonary Nerves. The parasympathetic nerves to the lungs leave the vagus as it passes behind the root of the lung. They help form the pulmonary plexus, which was described earlier as a sympathetic prevertebral plexus. The relay stations of those parasympathetic fibers are clusters of cells in that plexus or in the substance of the lung. The postganglionic fibers follow the bronchial tree to the smooth muscles and glands in its wall.

Esophageal Branches. The esophageal branches leave the vagus nerve as it courses alongside the esophagus. The relay stations are in the wall of the esophagus.

Branches to the Abdominal Viscera. Some branches to the stomach reach its anterior surface from the plexus formed by the right and left vagus nerves on the esophagus. They supply the stomach and the first part of the duodenum and the liver as well. Others follow the left gastric artery to the upper end of the prevertebral plexus, where the parasympathetic fibers are distributed with their fellow sympathetic fibers. Their destinations are the parts of the alimentary tract as far as the left colic flexure, liver, pancreas, and kidney. The relay stations of those parasympathetic nerves are embedded in the viscera. In the alimentary tract, the cell bodies of those ganglia are located between the layers of circular and longitudinal muscle, and also in the submucosa.

Parasympathetic Branches of Sacral Nerves 2, 3, and 4. These parasympathetic nerves leave the anterior rami of sacral nerves 2, 3, and 4 to supply pelvic viscera and are called the *pelvic splanchnics*. They pass forward on the lateral side of the rectum and bladder into the pelvic part of the sympathetic prevertebral plexus. The parasympathetic fibers are distributed to the pelvic viscera and the descending colon along with the sympathetic fibers. To reach the descending colon, they ascend in the prevertebral plexus to the level of origin of the inferior mesenteric artery, which conducts them to their destination.

Afferent Fibers in the Parasympathetic Nerves

The parasympathetic nerves are visceral efferent, that is, motor to smooth muscle and glands. Nevertheless, the viscera they supply contain sense organs, and sensory fibers course back to the central nervous system in those nerves. Most of the sensory fibers are a variety of special sensory fiber; they come from stretch receptors in the lung, chemoreceptors in taste buds, and chemoreceptors in the carotid body. All the sensory fibers, including some pain fibers, have their cell bodies in the sensory ganglion of the nerve that supplies the organ with parasympathetic fibers, that is, in the sensory ganglia of cranial nerves 7, 9, and 10 and in the dorsal root ganglia of sacral nerves 2, 3, and 4.

Review Questions (Answers Available on the Pages Cited)

1. In general terms, what are the effectors that are controlled by the autonomic nervous system (p. 233)?
2. How do the "motor" nerves of the autonomic nervous system differ from the motor nerves of skeletal (striated) muscles (p. 233)?
3. Locate the preganglionic cell bodies of the sympathetic and the parasympathetic portions of the autonomic nervous system (p. 233).
4. Explain why the spinal nerves of segments T1 to L2 have two connections with the sympathetic trunk and all the other nerves have only one (pp. 233 and 234).
5. What is the general distribution of all the nerves leaving (a) the medial border of the sympathetic trunk; (b) the lateral border (pp. 235 and 236)?
6. Where are the cell bodies of the fibers of the gray rami communicantes (pp. 235 and 241)?
7. Where are the cell bodies of the postganglionic fibers that supply (a) the heart and (b) the stomach (p. 241)?
8. Locate the cell bodies of the postganglionic fibers that supply the dilator muscle of the pupil (p. 241).
9. Do the pain fibers that supply the heart pass through the sympathetic trunk (p. 241)? Trace them in Figure 17-7.
10. What is the general rule regarding the location of parasympathetic postganglionic cell bodies (pp. 239 and 242)?

18

A Guide to the Dissection of the Brain

The brain you will dissect was removed from the cranial cavity by opening the subdural space and cutting (1) the vertebral and carotid arteries, (2) the veins draining into the venous sinuses of the dura, and (3) the cranial nerves. That leaves the vessels on the brain for study and the arachnoid intact except ventrally, where the arachnoid is usually torn in the process of removing the soft unfixed brain.

To render the brain suitable for dissection, it is hardened in 10% formaldehyde for at least 1 month, and then removed and kept in a plastic bag with a little water to avoid drying.

For the dissection of the brain, you will require a set of instruments that includes a probe with a fine, angled tip, a medium-sized scissors, a knife with a long thin blade to section the brain, and two forceps, one blunt and one fine.

Ventral Arterial Trunks of the Brain

Clean and examine the arteries at the base of the brain as you follow the description on pages 213–215. The following comments will answer some of your questions as you proceed.

(1) There is no marking on the brain to locate the junction of the brain and the spinal cord. (2) You will open the basilar artery at a later stage to look for the median septum. (3) Free the third nerve of arachnoid carefully to avoid pulling it away. (4) The fourth nerve arises from the back of the midbrain and courses ventrally between the posterior cerebral and the superior cerebellar arteries. Look for it coming through the arachnoid,

if this membrane is intact, and then free it of arachnoid and pia as far dorsally as its exit from the brain. (5) It is advisable to cut the strong strands of pia-arachnoid and the veins within them, which extend in the midline from the dorsal surface of the cerebellum toward the cerebral hemispheres. Tension on those strands might evulse the pineal gland, located at the upper end of the midbrain. (6) The anterior perforated area must *not* be cleaned now. (7) The lamina terminalis is a thin membrane that is attached to the upper border of the optic chiasma. It will be put on the stretch and made evident by tilting the optic nerves and the chiasma ventrally. (8) The middle cerebral artery is to be iden-tified but not traced to see the insula.

Cerebellar and Anterior Spinal Arteries

Clean and trace the arteries as you read the description of each in the text. As previously stated, the comments for each artery that follow are intended to explain certain new terms you will encounter.

Superior Cerebellar Artery (p. 216). (1) The isthmus region of the brain stem is the junction of the pons segment and the midbrain. (2) The tegmentum is the central "core" of those two segments. (3) The medial lemniscus, lateral lemniscus, and brachium con-junctivum are fiber bundles that are on the surface of the isthmus region and are shown in Figure 6-1. (4) The cortical branches course on the surface of the cerebellum to reach the posterior border of the tentorial surface, where they end on a part of the cerebellum, called the *inferior semilunar lobule*.

Anterior-Inferior Cerebellar Artery (p. 217). (1) This artery and the posterior-inferior artery together supply the inferior surface of the cerebellum, and if one is small the other will be large. (2) The flocculus is a bud-like tuft of folded cerebellar cortex about the size of a grapefruit seed (Figs. 10-8A and 16-4). (3) To see the opening at the end of the sleeve-like structure formed by the inferior velum, carefully remove the arachnoid caudal to the flocculus. The granular material projecting from its open lateral end is choroid plexus (Figs. 1-12 and 16-4). (4) The rootlets of the ninth nerve are adherent to the ventral aspect of this sleeve.

Posterior-Inferior Cerebellar Artery (pp. 217–219). (1) The origin and course of this artery are inconstant. The description in the text traces the artery as it appears when it has its longest course on the surface of the medulla. It may be much shorter if it arises closer to the pons and does not meander. Observe how the course of the artery in your dissection differs from the textbook description, and look for the compensatory branches to the medulla that come from the vertebral and the anterior-inferior cerebellar arteries because of this variation. (2) The olive, restiform body, and cuneate tubercle are labeled in Figure 16-5. (3) The cut nerves 9, 10, and 11 form a linear series of rootlets that become finer and more widely spaced toward the spinal cord. There is no grouping of rootlets according to the nerve they are to form. (4) To see the median aperture (foramen of Magendie), gently separate the cerebellum from the dorsal surface of the medulla and break the fine threads of pia-arachnoid that obscure it. Observe that the inferior velum is adherent in the midline to the overhanging cerebellum. It will be necessary to free it from the cerebellum in order to follow the artery. (5) The obex is the caudal angle of the median aperture. Label it in Figure 1-12.

Anterior (Ventral) Spinal Artery (p. 227). This artery may arise from the vertebral artery close to the spinal cord, leaving the supply of the pyramid to the vertebral artery (see Fig. 16-12).

Cerebellum

Remove all the arteries from the hindbrain as follows. Cut each cerebellar artery, right and left, at its origin and peel it away, taking note of the fine nutrient branches to the brain stem. Cut the right and left posterior cerebral arteries at their origin from the basilar artery and then as you strip the basilar and the two vertebral arteries off from the hindbrain, look for the fine nutrient branches they give off to supply the pons and the medulla (see p. 230 and Figure 16-12). Also look for the small dorsal spinal artery (p. 227) which arises either from the vertebral or the posterior inferior cerebellar artery. Now cut across the basilar artery and look for the remains of a median septum (p. 214).

Having cleaned the cerebellum, you will find it easier to examine if the brain stem is cut across at the level of the midbrain. The section should pass through the interpeduncular fossa just caudal to the attachment of the third nerve and through the middle of the inferior colliculi (see Figs. 6-1 and 16-2). Draw a line around the midbrain with a colored pencil to mark the plane of the section and make the cut as clean as possible. The detached upper part of the midbrain and the forebrain will be studied later and should be placed in a container at once to protect it from drying.

The Surfaces of the Cerebellum and Its Lobules. Remove all remaining pia-arachnoid from the surface of the cerebellum and open its deep sulci. Follow the description of its surfaces on page 124.

To make it easier to examine and identify the subdivisions (lobules) of the cerebellum, which are demarcated by deep sulci that extend across it from one side to the other, it is advisable to cut the cerebellum and the portion of the brain stem to which it is attached into right and left halves. Unfortunately, the cerebellum and with it the brain stem are usually distorted. Hence to ensure a median section, the lobules must be cut one at a time and special care must be taken to cut precisely along the lines marking the median plane of the brain stem. Proceed as follows.

Refer to Figures 10-5 and 10-6, locate the midline of each subdivision of the vermis, and cut across it in the midsagittal plane to a depth of about 1 cm. Then, after cutting all the lobules in the median plane, deepen the cut carefully in the sagittal plane until it enters the fourth ventricle and thus complete the separation of the right and left halves of the cerebellum. Next, using scissors, cut the inferior velum and the superior velum (lingula) (Figs. 10-5B and 10-7).

To cut the brain stem into right and left halves, make use of (1) the median sulcus in the floor of the fourth ventricle and the median sulcus on the dorsal surface of the medulla, (2) the features of the cross section of the midbrain, and (3) the sulcus between the pyramids on the ventral surface of the medulla. You will now be able to follow the description of the subdivisions of the cerebellum in Chapter 10 (pp. 125–126).

You will not be able to see the stalk of the flocculus until the other lobules are removed in the course of the dissection to follow.

Removal of the Lobules of the Cerebellum. Follow the directions as they are given and remove the lobules from the right half of the cerebellum—the side illustrated in the text. If this is done with sufficient care you will avoid breaking the attenuated portion at the junction of the vermis and the hemisphere. This will make it easier to assemble them on a tray, as was done in preparing Figure 10-5B.

Begin by pinching across the attachment of the culmen to the core of the vermis and then, working laterally, progressively detach the quadrangular lobule from the core of the hemisphere. Next, detach the central lobule in the same way. Leave in place the lingula and the superior velum to which it adheres. Significant branches of the superior cerebellar artery enter the core of the cerebellum lateral to the lingula.

Because the vermis portion of three cerebellar lobules, namely, the declive, the folium, and the tuber, are all attached to one branch-like extension of the core of white matter (Fig. 10-3A), it is easier to remove the folium and the superior semilunar lobule before removing the declive and the simple lobule. Note that in each case you are to work laterally from the midline. Thick bundles of fibers from the brachium pontis enter the lateral part of each subdivision and those must be broken to avoid inadvertently stripping fibers off the surface of the pons.

Turn to Figure 10-6 and observe that the tuber is a composite structure formed by the vermal parts of two lobules that separate in the hemisphere to form the inferior semilunar lobule and the gracilis lobule. Remove the tuber and the inferior semilunar and gracilis lobules in one piece. As you do this, see and break the connection of the gracilis lobule with the pyramis. Next remove the pyramis and the biventral lobule. The subdivisions— uvula, tonsil, and paraflocculus (all parts of one lobule)—can now be cleaned and examined. Gently elevate the tonsil to see its bed, formed by the inferior velum, and its attenuated connection with the uvula and the paraflocculus, and then, being careful to leave the nodule in place, remove the uvula, tonsil and paraflocculus, if possible, in one piece.

To remove the flocculonodular lobe and the inferior velum (Fig. 10-7B), begin by peeling the flocculus away from the brachium pontis. The inferior velum is attached to the stalk of the flocculus and will come away with it. Now, working toward the midline, peel the stalk of the flocculus away from the core. You will have to break (pinch across) a bundle of vestibular fibers that enters the stalk from the floor of the fourth ventricle. Observe the hairpin bend in the stalk, where it forms part of the hollow in which the tonsil is lodged. Complete the detachment of the flocculonodular lobe and, with it, the inferior velum, by freeing the nodule. Then float the lobe and the velum on a few drops of water on your tray. Read the description of the flocculonodular lobe on page 126. Then lay out the detached lobules of the right half of the cerebellum, as was done to prepare the drawing for Figure 10-6.

Dissection of the Core of the Cerebellum (pp. 127–128). Steps in the dissection are illustrated in diagrams A and B of Figures 10-8 and 10-9. Tease away some superficial fibers of the core to obtain the preparation shown in Figure 10-8B. The next step is to remove the outer part of the core that is formed by the fibers of the brachium pontis. Pass the tip of a probe upward across the deep aspect of the brachium pontis, starting at its posterior border, where the eighth nerve has its nucleus: the cochlear nucleus (see Fig. 10-9A). Cut down on the probe, that is, across the brachium pontis, and then remove the cut fibers from the core of the cerebellum, peeling them away a few at a time. When you have removed all of them, you will have exposed the restiform body, that is, the bundle of fibers that contains the spinocerebellar tracts, the olivocerebellar fibers, and vestibulocerebellar fibers. The fibers of that composite bundle sweep medially to form the second fiber layer of the core. Deep to these outer two layers of the core, which are made up of afferent fibers of the cerebellum, we find the central nuclei and two bundles of fibers with cell bodies in these nuclei that are carrying impulses out of the cerebellum. These two efferent bundles are (1) the brachium conjunctivum emerging from the central nuclei of the cerebellar hemisphere and (2) the fastigiobulbar tract that emerges from the central nucleus of the vermis, the fastigial nucleus. Use Figure 10-9B as your guide and cut across and remove successive small bundles of fibers of the restiform body until you uncover the wrinkled surface of dentate nucleus. You will then see a small bundle of fibers that emerges from the core of the vermis and passes laterally across the brachium conjunctivum in front of the dentate nucleus to descend into the brain stem on the medial side of the afferent fibers of the restiform body. The brachium conjunctivum is coursing toward the midbrain, and en route it forms the wall of the fourth ventricle and lies just lateral to the superior velum (Fig. 5-2). The fastigial nucleus and the two medial nuclei of the cerebellar hemisphere are not demonstrable by dissection.

Medulla

External Features (Chapter 4, pp. 43–47). All the pia mater must be removed to be able to define the external features of the medulla. Cut a thin slice off from the caudal end of the medulla to freshen the cut surface and then insinuate the tip of a probe between the pia and the lateral funiculus; working from here, where the pia mater is relatively thick, strip it all away. In doing this, most of the nerves will be torn away (Fig. 18-1), but this is a necessary sacrifice. Identify the clava, the swollen upper end of the fasciculus gracilis (see Figs. 4-3 and 4-6). The cuneate tubercle, the swelling at the upper end of the cuneate fasciculus, is not well defined. This is partly because a thin layer of fibers extends from it on the surface to join the restiform body. These are the dorsal external arcuate fibers (Fig. 4-3). They are a part of a pathway from the upper limb that corresponds to the dorsal spinocerebellar tract. The accessory cuneate nucleus is located in the cuneate tubercle.

The three features of the lateral surface of the medulla are illustrated in Figure 4-3. On the cut surface at the caudal end of the medulla, locate the spinal tract of the fifth nerve at the tip of the posterior horn. Having located it in the cross section, follow the poorly defined bundle upward on the lateral surface, where it becomes much wider before passing deep to the restiform body. The gray color of the spinal tract of the fifth nerve gives this feature its name, that is, the tuberculum cinereum, but unfortunately the gray color is lost in formalin-fixed brains. Some anomalous fibers may cross the lateral aspect of the olive. Some of these are fibers that are leaving the pyramid and turning dorsally to end in cells that failed to migrate from the site of origin of the pontine nucleus.

Pons Segment

External Features (Chapter 5, pp. 53–54). Remove all the pia mater, particularly in the isthmus region. Refer to Figures 5-8 and 5-13 and identify all the external features. Note, there is no demarcation sulcus between the lateral and medial lemnisci. They come to

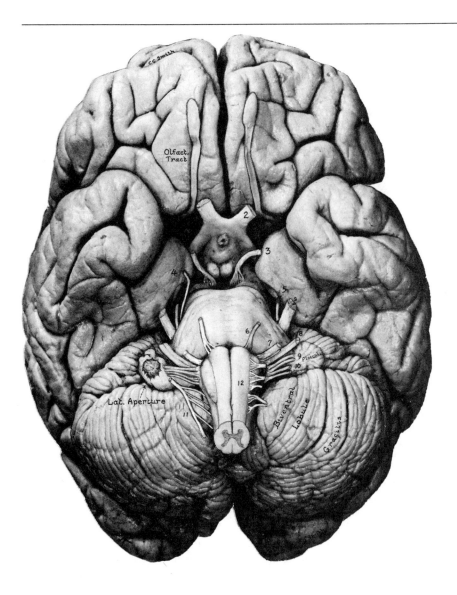

Figure 18-1. Ventral aspect of the brain.

the surface at the upper border of the brachium pontis as one wide ribbon of fibers. Turn to Figures 6-3 and 6-4 and locate on the cross section of the midbrain (1) the basis pedunculi, (2) the medial lemniscus, (3) the brachium of the inferior colliculus, which is conveying the auditory impulses that were brought to the inferior colliculus by the lateral lemniscus, (4) the section of the brachium conjunctivum. The study of the midbrain will be completed after making a midsagittal section of its upper portion.

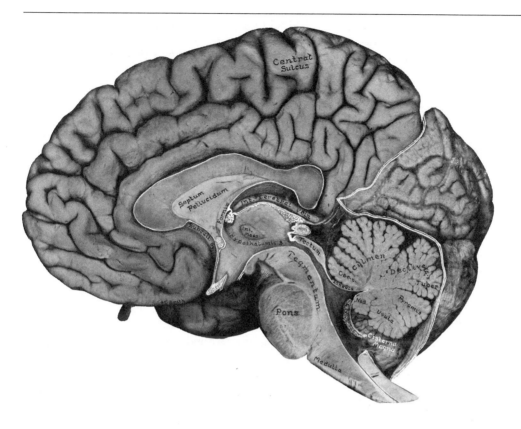

Figure 18-2. Midsagittal section of the brain.

A Midsagittal Section of the Midbrain and Forebrain

To obtain the preparation illustrated in Figure 16-6, the structures shown in Figures 7-9 and 18-2 must be divided. Clear away the pia-arachnoid that obscures the features of the midline region. A useful guide to the midline is the pineal gland. It extends backward, dorsal to the midbrain, and is easily torn away because it is embedded in dense connective tissue. Work with special care, therefore, to expose it. Next, clean the right and left mammillary bodies, one on each side of the midline ventrally, but do not remove the fine vessels that enter the brain stem just behind them (Fig. 16-11). Then remove the pia-arachnoid from the optic chiasma and the anterior cerebral arteries just in front of it. Separate the hemispheres to see the short anterior communicating artery (Fig. 16-2), and slide the handle of a scalpel into the median cleft between them to separate the right and left anterior cerebral arteries as they sweep around the corpus callosum located in the floor of this cleft (Fig. 16-11). Note, only as an anomaly does one artery send branches to both hemispheres.

With scissors, cut the anterior communicating artery and the optic chiasma precisely in the midline. This will cut the anterior part of the floor of the third ventricle. Now, with a knife, extend the cut in the floor of the ventricle, backward, to pass between the mammillary bodies and then, referring to the cross section of the midbrain, split the midbrain into right and left halves, being sure that the cut does not deviate from the axis of the aqueduct as you extend it forward to split the pineal gland into right and left halves.

If you consult Figure 7-9, you can see that the only structures as yet uncut are (1) the membranous roof of the third ventricle, (2) the fibers of the hippocampal commissure, connecting the right and left fornices, (3) the anterior commissure, and (4) the corpus callosum. The septum pellucidum is only a thin membrane in the midsagittal plane. To cut these structures and thus complete the midsagittal section, slide the blade of a long knife into the cleft between the right and left halves of the brain stem, being sure it is between the parts of the divided pineal gland, and then turn the brain over, dorsal surface up, so you can look into the cleft between the hemispheres and proceed to guide the cutting edge toward the midline of the corpus callosum. Cut with a sawing action and a minimum of pressure until the knife emerges between the hemispheres.

Midbrain and Diencephalon

The external features of the midbrain and forebrain are to be studied on the left side (Fig. 18-3) in preparation for the detailed study of all the arteries on the right portion. Pick up the stem of the left posterior cerebral artery and pull out the nutrient branches that enter the posterior perforated area medial to the basis pedunculi (see Fig. 16-11). Cut the posterior communicating artery and then gently pull the posterior cerebral artery out of the cleft between the parahippocampal gyrus (labeled in Fig. 12-3) and the midbrain. As you do this, you will see it gives some branches to the diencephalon and some to the inner aspect of the parahippocampal gyrus (Fig. 16-6). Cut these where they enter the brain and strip away the large branches that lie on the inferior surface of the temporal lobe. Near the back of the midbrain, the artery enters the calcarine sulcus and its terminal branches follow the calcarine and parietooccipital sulci (labeled in Fig. 12-4). Open these sulci and remove the vessels and all the pia mater. Now remove all the vessels and supporting tissue from the transverse fissure (Fig. 11-3C).

Having cleaned the left half of the diencephalon and the portion of the midbrain attached to it, fit together the upper and lower portions of the left half of the midbrain and identify its external features using Fig. 6-1. Then refer to Figure 7-4 and examine the inferior surface of the diencephalon. The features of the superior surface of the diencephalon are illustrated in Figure 7-3 and can be seen by elevating the roof of the transverse fissure.

Cavity of the Brain Stem

Third Ventricle (pp. 81–84). Use Figure 7-9 and identify each of the features of the floor, the anterior wall, the roof, and the lateral wall that are labeled there. Refer to the description on pages 81–84 for help.

Cerebral Aqueduct (p. 68). This canal extends from the level of the posterior commissure in the third ventricle to the upper end of the superior velum, in the roof of the fourth ventricle.

Fourth Ventricle. The fourth ventricle is a cleft-like space with a ventral and a dorsal

Figure 18-3. *Ventral aspect of the brain stem.*

wall. Its lower end is at the middle of the medulla, where it narrows to form a canal that continues into the spinal cord. Its upper end extends to the midbrain, where it also narrows to form a canal, that is, the cerebral aqueduct. It has its greatest width just caudal to the stalk of the cerebellum, where it has a tubular extension to each side, called a *lateral recess*.

The dorsal wall, or roof, is formed by the cerebellum and the superior velum and the inferior velum (Fig. 10-3A). The superior velum is invaded by the lingula (Fig. 10-6). The inferior velum contains a right and left choroid plexus (see Fig. 1-12). The inferior velum forms the roof of the lateral recess and extends beyond the lateral border of the medulla as a sleeve-like structure having the lateral aperture (the foramen of Luschka) at its lateral extremity (Figs. 4-5 and 18-4).

The ventral wall or floor of the fourth ventricle is covered with a thick layer of gray matter. It contains nuclei of cranial nerves. Refer to Figure 8-3 and identify the features of the floor that are labeled there. The nuclei that lie under these features are labeled in the cross sections in Figures 8-3 and 8-4.

Arteries of the Right Half of the Forebrain

Anterior Choroidal Artery (p. 224). Study the right anterior choroidal artery making the observations listed here and then remove it. Refer to Figures 16-2, 16-9, and 16-11. (1) The artery follows the optic tract and gives off branches that penetrate it or the basis pedunculi. (2) It reaches the lateral geniculate body and supplies its lateral part. (3) It sends branches to the medial part of the temporal pole, a region called the *uncus* (see Fig. 12-5). (4) Its choroidal branches enter the cleft between the hemisphere and the diencephalon. As you remove the anterior choroidal artery, cut the branches that enter the hemisphere to avoid pulling the choroid plexus out of the lateral ventricle.

Anterior Cerebral Artery (p. 219). Clean and examine the right anterior cerebral artery making the observations listed here and then remove it (see Figure 16-6). Observe (1) Heubner's artery. This is the common stem for a tuft of fine branches (the medial striate arteries) that penetrate the medial part of the anterior perforated area. Observe (2) the relationship of the anterior communicating artery to the optic chiasma (Fig. 16-11). (3) Note the relationship of the anterior cerebral artery to the corpus callosum. (4) Determine the extent of its distribution on the medial surface in relation to the parietooccipital sulcus. (5) Find the extent of its supply to the lateral surface, where it shares in the supply of the motor area. (6) Note its branches to the olfactory pathway and the orbital cortex.

Middle Cerebral Artery (p. 220). Clean the right middle cerebral artery to make the following observations and then remove it. (1) Elevate the artery from the perforated area to see the fine lateral striate arteries that penetrate the lateral part of the anterior perforated area. Occlusion of these vessels results in hemiplegia. The motor pathways they supply will be revealed in the course of the dissection. (2) Open the lateral sulcus as in Figure 16-7 to see how the cortical branches fan out on the insula, the floor of this sulcus, and then, leaving the floor, cling to the portions of the hemisphere that overlap the insula to reach and emerge from the lateral sulcus. These hairpin bends make the vessels difficult to follow in x-ray films. (3) Estimate the fraction of the length of the precentral gyrus (motor area) that is supplied by the middle cerebral artery.

Posterior Cerebral Artery (p. 222). The branches of this artery supplying the surface of

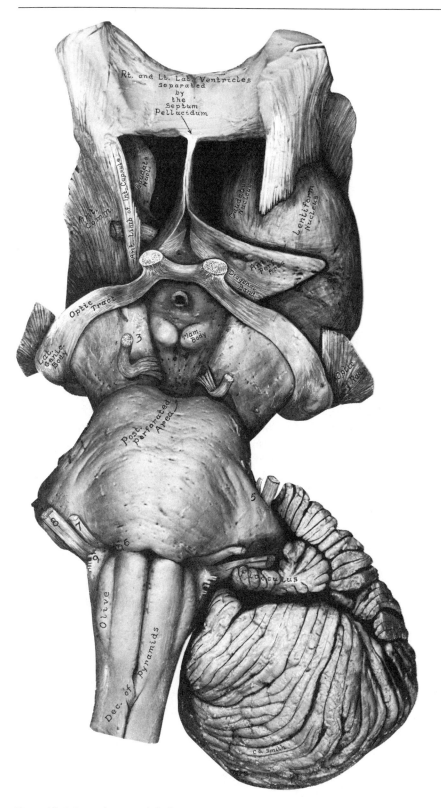

Figure 18-4. Lateral aspect of the brain stem.

the hemisphere were examined on the left side in the course of its removal to see the external features of the diencephalon and the midbrain. The branches to the midbrain and the diencephalon will be traced on the right side after the hemisphere has been dissected.

Cerebral Hemisphere

Insight into the form and structure of the cerebral hemisphere and its connections with the brain stem and with its fellow of the opposite side can be obtained from the story of its development (see pp. 139–144).

Sulci, Gyri, and the Cortical Areas. Remove all the vessels and pia-arachnoid that remain on the surface of the right hemisphere except in the region immediately adjacent to the diencephalon. This will leave the trunk of the posterior cerebral artery in place as it crosses the midbrain and will ensure that the choroid plexus of the third ventricle and that of the lateral ventricle are not disturbed.

Identify the sulci and gyri as you encounter them in the description in Chapter 12, pages 153–158. The sulci and gyri are used to locate the areas of cortex that can be demarcated functionally and histologically (pp. 158–164). Of these, the sensory and motor areas are outlined with dotted lines in Figure 12-3. You will find it helpful to color them. The cortex of the visual area can be recognized in an unstained section because the myelinated fibers of the optic pathway are crowded together where they terminate in the cortex and form a white line, the line of Gennari (Chapter 11, p. 150). Cut about half an inch off the occipital pole and look for this line in the cortex in the upper and lower walls of the calcarine sulcus.

Dissection of the Hemisphere. The first long bundle of fibers to be sought in the dissection of the hemisphere is made up of association fibers and is called the *superior longitudinal fasciculus* (Chapter 13, p. 170, Fig. 13-3). It is well defined as it courses deep to the inferior parietal lobule; hence uncover this part of it first. Using the *handle* of a knife, scrape the cortex off the walls and floor of the intraparietal sulcus and the inferior part of the postcentral sulcus. The bundle we are seeking has a diameter of 1.5 cm and is covered by a thin layer of short association fibers (Chapter 13, p. 169). Strip away small bundles of these fibers that connect adjacent gyri until you can see the long fibers of the superior longitudinal fasciculus. Having located the bundle at this site, strip away some of its superficial fibers in a posterior direction, and in so doing open into cleavage planes that permit you to shell out major portions of the cortex and white matter of the parietal and temporal lobes that lie superficial to the posterior part of the bundle. Now use Figure 13-3 as a guide and complete the exposure of this bundle. You will encounter bundles of projection fibers that penetrate the bundle at right angles in the region of the postcentral and the precentral gyri. These may frustrate the attempt to demonstrate the anterior part of the superior longitudinal fasciculus. Lift up and then pinch off enough of those portions of the parietal and frontal lobes that overlap the insula in order to demonstrate the relationship of the fasciculus to the insula. Trace the borders of the insula—that is, the superior, the anterior-inferior, and the posterior-inferior. The two inferior borders meet at the edge of the anterior perforated area. Identify the anterior transverse temporal gyrus, which is covered by the cortex of the auditory area. It is on the lower lip of the lateral sulcus and extends from the posterior superior angle of the insula to the middle of the superior temporal gyrus (Chapter 12, p. 160 and Figure 13-3).

Inferior Longitudinal Fasciculus (Chapter 13, p. 170). To expose this bundle, it is necessary to remove the superior longitudinal fasciculus and the cortex of the insula with its bed of short association fibers. Lift up small bundles of the superior longitudinal fasciculus at the posterior superior angle of the insula and peel them away, noting how they fan out posteriorly in the occipital and temporal lobes and anteriorly into the frontal lobe. In the process of removing all these fibers you will remove almost all of the lower lip of the lateral sulcus and will break off the auditory fibers that enter the anterior transverse temporal gyrus. To remove the insula, find a cleavage plane in the white matter about 2 mm deep to the upper border of the cortex of the insula to permit you to lever away the insula in one piece. This will expose a mound-like eminence covered by the claustrum, a very thin layer of gray matter that only acquires appreciable thickness inferiorly (see Fig. 13-4).

Remove this thin layer of gray matter to expose the thin layer of fibers, called the *external capsule*. Tease away the fibers of this layer, noting their course and thus uncover the underlying large lens-shaped lentiform nucleus. When you have completed the removal of the external capsule, you will have exposed the compact cord-like portion of the inferior longitudinal fasciculus, which has the diameter of a lead pencil, as it crosses the inferior border of the lentiform nucleus. Peel away enough of the fibers of this bundle in an anterior and posterior direction to obtain the demonstration of the bundle illustrated in Figure 13-4.

Corona Radiata (Chapter 13, pp. 172–173, Fig. 13-8). The corona radiata is a thick fan-shaped layer of projection fibers that extend radially from the edge of the lentiform nucleus. It has been uncovered already except where the fibers of the inferior longitudinal fasciculus are superficial to it. Unfortunately, these association fibers have the same general direction as the underlying projection fibers and are not easily distinguished from them. It is possible, however, to selectively remove the association fibers if they are picked up where they cross the lentiform nucleus and then peeled away from the corona radiata.

When all the association fibers have been removed, you will be able to see that the projection fibers that emerge from below the lentiform nucleus course toward the temporal pole before making a hairpin turn to course toward the occipital pole (Fig. 13-8B). Some of these are fibers of the optic pathway. You will also see the lateral striate arteries entering the lateral part of the lentiform nucleus through the lateral part of the anterior perforated area (Fig. 13-12B).

Cingulum (Chapter 13, pp. 169–170). This is a bundle of long association fibers in the core of the cingulate gyrus. Expose it first above the middle of the corpus callosum by scraping away the cortex of this gyrus. Then using Figure 13-2 as a guide, expose that portion of the cingulum that lies above and extends in front of the corpus callosum. Cut across the cingulum near the splenium of the corpus callosum and peel away the anterior part of the bundle. This will remove large portions of cortex and white matter and expose the upper surface of the corpus callosum and the forceps minor (see Fig. 13-6A). Do not attempt to expose the forceps major or the tapetum of the corpus callosum.

Lateral Ventricle (Chapter 13, pp. 180–182). The lateral ventricle is a key to the understanding of the structure of the hemisphere. It is to be opened from end to end along a line that will permit the separation of what developmentally were its medial and lateral walls. The curved cut will begin anteriorly and follow the outermost border of its lateral projection (see the central drawing in Fig. 13-14).

Insert the tip of a probe into the interventricular foramen, directing it forward and laterally as far as it will go within the anterior horn. Cut down onto the probe severing the fornix and the septum pellucidum in the medial wall of the lateral ventricle, and then extend the cut through the portion of the corpus callosum that forms its roof (see diagram 1 in Fig. 13-14). Look into the cavity you have opened and, under direct inspection to avoid lacerating the caudate nucleus, shove the tip of the probe obliquely upward and laterally through the white matter above the caudate nucleus until, having penetrated the corona radiata, it emerges on the lateral surface. Cut down on the probe through the marginal part of the hemisphere to extend the cut that began at the interventricular foramen. Separate the margins of the cut and, carefully avoiding the surface of the caudate, slip the blunt blade of the scissors into the ventricle, directing it backward, and let the other blade be applied to the lateral aspect of the corona radiata. Now, keeping the blade that is in the ventricle pressed *upward and laterally*, cut obliquely across the portion of the corona radiata between the blades. Look into the ventricle and see the choroid plexus and the fornix as well as the caudate nucleus. Extend the cut backward along the superior border of the posterior horn of the ventricle to its posterior end. Then cut around the tip of its blind end and continue forward along the inferior border of the posterior horn and part of the inferior horn. Gently separate the walls of the lateral ventricle and obverve how the choroid plexus and the fornix curve around the posterior end of the diencephalon to disappear in the inferior horn. Identify the hippocampal eminence (Figs. 13-8B and 13-15). There may be an adhesion between it and the opposing wall of the ventricle. Free it with your finger and then extend the cut forward in the wall of the inferior horn along the lateral border of the hippocampal eminence, stopping short of its anterior end.

Before proceeding, check the description of the wall of the lateral ventricle (Chapter 13, pp. 180–182), observing the features mentioned. As you do this, you will observe that a part of the superior surface of the diencephalon appears to form part of the floor of the body of the ventricle. Actually, the membranous medial wall of the ventricle, which in the embryo is free as far laterally as the groove between diencephalon and caudate nucleus, in the mature brain is adhering to the lateral part of the superior surface of the diencephalon and therefore is still interposed between the lumen of the ventricle and the diencephalon.

The next step in the dissection is to free the medial wall of the lateral ventricle so it can be removed. Slip a fingertip into the inferior horn and, easing it toward the temporal pole, use it as a wedge to open up a cleavage plane between the amygdaloid nucleus and the anterior end of the hippocampal eminence (see the dotted line in Fig. 13-15). This cleavage will reach the external surface of the temporal pole and thus break the connection between the medial and lateral walls at the anterior end of the inferior horn. Carefully break the paper-thin choroid membrane along the edge of the fornix to leave the choroid plexus on the brain stem. Cut any branches of the posterior cerebral artery to the medial part of the hemisphere, leaving the artery on the brain stem, and you will find you can remove the medial wall of the lateral ventricle. It can be fitted back into place to study the relationship of the amygdaloid nucleus to the uncus and to the wall of the ventricle.

Turn to Fig. 16-8 and use it as a guide to locate and trace the branches of the posterior cerebral artery to the brain stem, then clean the diencephalon by removing all the vessels, the choroid plexus of the third and the lateral ventricles and pia mater.

Hippocampal Formation (Chapter 14, p. 150). The hippocampal formation is a composite structure consisting of two strips of archicortex named the *hippocampus* and the *dentate gyrus*, respectively. The cortex known as the hippocampus is located in both walls of the hippocampal sulcus; the cortex known as the dentate gyrus extends along the floor of the hippocampal sulcus and onto the back of the splenium of the corpus callosum. Its free border, seen by looking into the sulcus, has tooth-like elevations; hence its name (Fig. 13-7). Observe how the deep hippocampal sulcus bulges into the inferior horn of the lateral ventricle to form the hippocampal eminence. To obtain a section of the hippocampal formation, cut across the middle of the floor of the inferior horn as was done to obtain the preparation shown in Figure 13-7. You will now be able to follow the description of the projection fibers of the archicortex in Chapter 13, p. 173. Trace in your dissection the pathway for impulses leaving the hippocampal formation for (1) the hippocampal formation of the opposite side and (2) the mammillary body on the same side.

Corpus Striatum and Internal Capsule. Examine the corpus striatum as you follow the description on pages 174–180. Identify the head of the caudate nucleus bulging into the anterior horn and then follow its tail-like extension to the amygdaloid nucleus (Fig. 13-12B) at the tip of the inferior horn (Fig. 13-8C). The amygdaloid nucleus forms part of the wall of the ventricle and part of the external surface that is known as the *uncus*. Replace the detached part of the temporal pole to appreciate this. The lateral surface of the lentiform nucleus has been exposed by removing the claustrum and the external capsule (Fig. 18-4). Part of its inferior surface is free and forms the anterior perforated area. Complete the examination of the present stage of the dissection by locating two fiber bundles that connect the amygdaloid nucleus with the hypothalamus. The one is the stria terminalis, which courses with a large vein just deep to the ependyma in a groove at the medial border of the caudate nucleus. Follow this band (which partly hides the vein) from the amygdaloid nucleus to the region of the interventricular foramen, where it and the fornix enter the diencephalon together. It is shown but not labeled in the horizontal section of Figure 13-12. The second bundle connecting the amygdaloid nucleus and the hypothalamus is the diagonal band. It forms a white band, about 4 mm wide, at the posterior border of the anterior perforated area. It is easier to recognize in a fresh brain, where the differentiation between white and gray matter is greater. It is labeled in Figure 13-12C.

To see the medial portion of the lentiform nucleus, called the *globus pallidus*, use Figure 13-12A as a guide, and make a clean cut with a long thin blade through the diencephalon and corpus striatum in a horizontal plane at the level of the interventricular foramen. This section will also show all the features of the internal capsule and the diencephalon that are labeled in Figure 13-12A. To show the continuity of the lentiform and caudate nuclei below the anterior limb of the internal capsule (as in Fig. 13-2B), carefully remove the white matter of the orbital surface of the hemisphere just in front of the anterior perforated area. To reveal the union of lentiform and amygdaloid nuclei, strip away the fibers of the anterior commissure as they emerge as a compact bundle from the lateral surface of the lentiform nucleus close to the anterior perforated area (see Fig. 13-8A). In doing this you get a better exposure of the beginning of the optic radiation (Fig. 13-8B). This completes the examination of the corpus striatum. You may now demonstrate how the fibers of the posterior limb of the internal capsule descend to form the basis pedunculi (crus cerebri) (Fig. 13-8C). To do this, remove the lentiform nucleus, the tail of the caudate nucleus, the amygdaloid nucleus, and the optic tract.

Exposure, Within the Diencephalon, of the Fornix and the Mammillothalamic Tract (Fig. 7-11B). The mammillothalamic tract extends from the mammillary body to the anterior tubercle of the thalamus and is close to the wall of the third ventricle. Carefully remove the rubbery ependyma above the mammillary body and then gently scrape away a thin layer of gray matter until you see the small compact bundle passing dorsally. You can then expose the fornix in the same way, but begin to expose it in the region of the interventricular foramen and follow it from there to the mammillary body.

Examination of the Undissected Portions of the Brain

The undissected portions of the brain can be used for review. You may wish to cut the left half of the forebrain to see the features illustrated in the sections drawn in Figures 7-8, 13-1, and 13-12C. Sections of the brain stem at the levels chosen for Figures 4-8, 4-9, 4-10, and 5-5, even though they are not stained, will show many features of the internal structure of the hindbrain.

Index

Uncinate fasciculus, 128, 131, 137, 170, 187
Uncus, 158, 161
Utricle, 62
Uvula, 133, 187, 248

Vagal trigone, 108
Vagus nerve, 47, 48, 49, 51, 91, 103, 243
  branchial motor, 109, 110, 111
  preganglionic motor, 107, 108–109
  sensory, 111, 113, 114, 191, 198
Vasopressin, 92
Velum
  inferior, 5, 46–49, 126
  superior, 54
Ventricular system
  development of, 4–5
  fourth, 5, 47, 51, 54, 57, 252
  lateral, 5, 141–142, 180–182, 223, 257–258
  third, 5, 75, 223, 252–254
Ventromedial hypothalamic nuclei, 93
Vermis, 123, 125, 133

Vestibular pathways, 62–63
  cerebellar, 134
  nerve, 62–63, 111, 114–117
  nucleus, 72, 114–117, 231
Vestibulocochlear nerve, 56, 59–61, 103, 111, 217
Vestibulospinal tract, 63
Visceral fibers
  motor, 101, 102–103
  sensory, 103, 201–203
Visceral nerves, 236–239
Visual pathways. *See* Optic pathways

White commissure, 29
White matter, 17
  cerebellar, 123–124
  definition of, 15
  hemisphere, 167–173, 180
  spinal cord, 29–30
White ramus communicans, 12, 234, 241
Willed responses, 16

Zona incerta, 86, 120